THE SLIDE RULE

A TutorText

THE

PUBLISHED BY

DOUBLEDAY & COMPANY, INC., GARDEN CITY, N.Y.

1962

SLIDE RULE

by Robert Saffold
and Ann Smalley

PREPARED UNDER THE DIRECTION OF
EDUCATIONAL SCIENCE DIVISION
U. S. Industries, Inc.

Library of Congress Catalog Card Number 61-18016

Printed in the United States of America

First Edition

System disclosed herein is the subject of a pending patent application.

Contents

Introduction

The slide rule is a handy calculating device which can be used to solve a variety of problems with speed and accuracy. A knowledge of the slide rule can be of great benefit to students, technicians, engineers, scientists, statisticians, and businessmen.

With the slide rule, a problem such as $\frac{(.0036 \times .392)^2}{.029 \times 1.06}$ can be solved in a few moments. Inches can be converted to centimeters, or francs to dollars, with ease.

There's nothing magical about the slide rule, although it may seem so to the uninitiated. Its operation is based upon a few simple mathematical facts of life which will be explained here in some detail.

There are many kinds of slide rules with different scales, ranging in form from the familiar straight rule to round and even cylindrical rules. All work on the same basic principle. If you understand one kind, you'll be able to transfer your knowledge to others without much trouble.

You should have a slide rule handy while reading this TutorText* course. The type of slide rule used for illustrations is the Mannheim Polyphase, marketed under several trade names, such as Maniphase, Multiplex, Polyphase, etc. A rule costing only a few dollars is quite adequate for most purposes.

The emphasis in this course is on understanding the slide rule rather than on merely performing operations with certain scales. When you understand *why* the slide rule works, the *how* will become evident, even in new situations.

The first two chapters will develop the principle behind the most commonly used scales of the slide rule. Ninety per cent of the work done by slide rules is performed entirely on these scales. Later chapters will treat the various arithmetical, algebraic, and trigonometric operations made simpler by the use of other scales.

We have assumed that the reader has only an elementary knowledge of simple arithmetic, algebra, and plane geometry. All con-

*TM

clusions will be made on the basis of material that we advance in this book. The more informed reader will find his knowledge helpful, but we will not take it for granted. We have made every effort to be complete yet readable for both the student and the casual reader.

The TutorText book is an automatic teaching machine in book form. You will find it necessary to work your way through this book by choosing answers to multiple-choice questions. Should an answer choice be wrong, you will be given additional information to enable you to make the correct choice.

We are deeply indebted to Norman A. Crowder, technical director of the Educational Science Division, U. S. Industries, Inc., for developing this automatic tutoring system, and for giving us the opportunity to prepare this book.

Robert Saffold
Ann Smalley

NOTE TO THE READER

This is not an ordinary book. The pages are numbered in the usual way, but they are not read consecutively. You must follow the directions which you find at the bottom of each page.

You will find that reading this book is very much like having an individual tutor. The book will continually ask you questions, and correct errors as well as give you information.

Your progress through this course will depend entirely on your ability to choose right answers instead of wrong ones—and on your endurance. The course is divided into chapters, and several short learning sessions produce better results than a few long ones.

Follow the instructions and you will find it is impossible to get to the final page without mastering the fundamentals of the slide rule.

CHAPTER 1

Scales and Powers

What is a slide rule? It is nothing more than a set of scales, some of which can be moved relative to others, with a movable hairline indicator that simplifies setting and reading the scales. Yet, by using these scales properly, you can carry out many kinds of calculations with speed and accuracy.

To use the slide rule effectively, you should know how the scales are derived and what the numbers on them really represent. The first two lessons are devoted to teaching you these matters.

Two simple facts provide the basis for the slide rule:

1. Quantities can be represented by distances along a scale.
2. Two scales can be used to add and subtract quantities represented by distances on the scales.

Suppose you had two six-inch rulers. You could let a distance of 1 inch on the rulers represent the quantity 2. Every half inch would represent 1, a three-inch distance would represent 6, and so on.

If you placed the two six-inch rulers end to end, you would be, in effect, adding the quantities represented by them. What quantity would be represented by the sum of the two six-inch distances?

Please choose the correct answer and then turn to the page indicated after your answer.

The quantity represented would be 12. **page 6**

The quantity represented would be 24. **page 11**

You did not follow instructions.

This course in the use of the slide rule is not put together like an ordinary book. You do not turn directly from page 1 to page 2 to page 3, and so on. This TutorText course will make no sense if you try to follow that procedure.

Each page that you read will tell you what page to turn to next. Now there was no way you could have arrived at this page if you had followed instructions.

Please return to page 1 and select the correct page to read next.

[*from page 15*]

YOUR ANSWER: 10^5 is the proper notation for 100,000.

Very good.

$$10 \times 10 \times 10 \times 10 \times 10 = 100{,}000$$

Ten is a factor 5 times, so the notation is 10^5; it is read, *10 to the fifth power.*

Every number made up of a 1 followed by zeros is a power of 10:

1,000
10,000
100,000
. . . and on and on.

A power of 10 can always be factored in this fashion:

$$10{,}000 = 10 \times 10 \times 10 \times 10 = 10^4$$

The number of times 10 is used as a factor determines the power of 10. Ten is a factor of 10,000 four times, so we write 10,000 as 10^4.

There's a shorter way of arriving at this brief notation. Instead of factoring the number, it is enough simply to count the number of zeros in it. For example, there are six zeros following the 1 in 1,000,000, so it is written 10^6.

The advantages of this notation become even more clear when you look at a number such as one quadrillion:

1,000,000,000,000,000

If you ever save this many pennies you will find it an advantage to be able to total them as 10^{15}.

But you're here to learn to multiply, using the slide rule. So here's a problem. Solve it the easiest way you know.

$$1{,}000{,}000 \times 100{,}000{,}000 = ?$$

The answer to this multiplication is:

100,000,000,000. **page 7**

100,000,000,000,000. **page 12**

[*from page 11*]

YOUR ANSWER: The setting represents 1 + 5 = 6.

You are quite right in supposing that the drawing shows a setting that is equivalent to 1 + 5 = 6. But you were asked to think about the calculation in terms of subtraction. Your answer indicates addition.

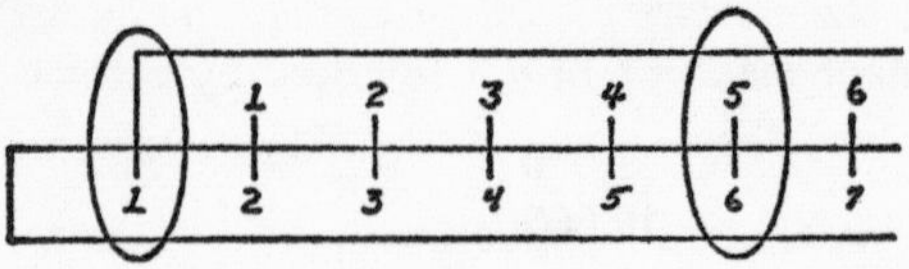

Using the same quantities you used in your answer, but thinking of them in terms of subtraction, you can read the scales as follows:

The drawing shows the setting of 6 on the lower scale. Opposite 6 on the top scale is the number we wish to subtract, 5. And now moving left to the end of the top rule we can read off the answer on the bottom scale, 1.

Do you see how the operations of addition and subtraction differ?

To add, we set the left end of the top scale opposite one of the numbers on the bottom scale. Then we find the other number on the top scale and read the answer directly below this number. To one distance, we add another in the same direction.

To subtract, we adjust the scales until the lesser number located on the top scale is opposite the greater number on the bottom scale. We then read downward along the top scale to the left end and find the corresponding number on the bottom scale, which is our answer. To the distance representing the original number we apply a distance in the opposite direction.

In each case, the lower ruler gives us the starting figure and the answer. The upper ruler is used to extend the starting figure, upward (toward higher numbers) in adding, downward (toward lower numbers) in subtraction.

Please return to page 11 and look at the problem again.

[*from page 12*]

YOUR ANSWER: Yes, we've simply added the exponents of the powers of 10.

You are correct. The values of exponents can be represented by distances, and added or subtracted with the aid of two rulers. And when we add and subtract the exponents we are really multiplying and dividing the powers of 10. Be sure you understand that the two equations below represent the same process with the same quantities.

$$1{,}000{,}000 \times 100{,}000{,}000 = 100{,}000{,}000{,}000{,}000$$

and

$$10^6 \times 10^8 = 10^{6+8} = 10^{14}$$

This manipulation with powers of 10 is fundamental to an understanding of how a slide rule works.

We have shown powers of 10 with exponents. There is another notation in wide use, called the common logarithm.

A logarithm can indicate *any* number merely by showing the power to which 10 must be raised to create the number.

Confusing? Perhaps it is at first, but it's very simple once you get the idea. We're introducing a kind of code for writing ordinary numbers such as 100, 23.6, or 0.00729. It's a logical and orderly code. Our base of operations is the number 10. When we want to express the number 100, we say that the logarithm of 100 is 2. This means simply that we can get the number 100 by using our base 10 as a factor *twice*. (We'll get to the logarithms of numbers that are not whole-number powers of 10 in due time—numbers such as 23.6 and 0.00729, for example. For the time being, though, we'll keep on using whole-number powers of 10 in our explanations.)

$10 \times 10 = 100$. Thus the logarithm of 100 is 2. $10 \times 10 \times 10 = 1{,}000$, so the logarithm of 1,000 is 3. The logarithm of 10,000 is 4.

Now think about this question carefully: *Why* does the logarithm of 10,000 equal 4?

Because there are four zeros in the number 10,000. **page 9**

Because $10 \times 10 \times 10 \times 10 = 10{,}000$. **page 16**

[*from page 1*]

YOUR ANSWER: If a half-inch distance on a ruler represents the quantity 1, then two six-inch rulers placed end to end represent the quantity 12.

No, you have chosen the wrong answer.

These are the points we want to make:

1. Distances can be used to represent quantities. If one-half inch represents the quantity 1, then 3 inches stand for 6, a six-inch length stands for 12, and so on.
2. Distances can be added by means of scales. And since this is so, the quantities represented by the distances can likewise be added.

We have two six-inch rulers, each representing the quantity 12. By placing the rulers end to end, we add the two distances—and add the two quantities at the same time.

What quantity is represented by the total length of the two rulers? Please go back to page 1 to choose the correct answer.

[*from page 3*]

YOUR ANSWER: 1,000,000 × 100,000,000 = 100,000,000,000.

No, you lost some zeros somewhere.

You may recall that you can multiply a number by a power of ten just by adding the appropriate number of zeros.

To multiply by 10, add one zero.

To multiply by 100, add 2 zeros.

To multiply by 1,000, add 3 zeros.

To multiply by 10,000, add 4 zeros, and so on.

35 × 10 = 350.

35 × 100 = 3,500.

35 × 1,000 = 35,000.

35 × 10,000 = 350,000.

And so on.

Now to our problem;

1,000,000 × 100,000,000 = ?

We write the first numeral without commas, and then count and see that there are eight zeros in the second numeral and merely add on eight more zeros like this.

$$\underbrace{1000000}_{\text{(the first number)}}\underbrace{00000000}_{\text{(eight more zeros)}}$$

Put the commas where they should be, and then return to page 3 to choose the right answer.

[*from page 15*]

YOUR ANSWER: A notation for 100,000 is 10^6.

Sorry, but no.

Remember: the exponent of 10 in a power of 10, such as 10^6, indicates how many times 10 must be used as a factor to obtain the product.

Let's break this down a little:

$$\underset{\text{power of 10}}{10^6} = \underset{\text{10 used as a factor 6 times}}{10 \times 10 \times 10 \times 10 \times 10 \times 10} = \underset{\text{multiple}}{1{,}000{,}000}$$

On the left, then, we have 10 raised to the sixth power—that is to say 10 used as a factor in multiplication 6 times.

In the same way, if we have 10^4 (10 raised to the fourth power) it is 10 multiplied by itself repeatedly until 10 has been used as a factor 4 times.

$$10^4 = 10 \times 10 \times 10 \times 10 = 10{,}000$$

There's something that will help you with powers of 10. Notice that the exponent in each power of 10 tells you how many zeros follow the 1 when the number is written out. To go back to 10^6, it represents 1,000,000 (1 followed by six zeros); 10^4 represents 10,000 (1 followed by four zeros).

What number do you think 10^3 represents? And how would you express one billion as a power of 10? Think about these before you go to the next paragraph.

Did you figure that 10^3 is a 1 followed by 3 zeros, or 1,000? And did you decide that one billion is 1,000,000,000 which is 1 followed by nine zeros and may be written as 10^9?

If you didn't get those answers, go back over this page again. After doing so, you should be in good shape to decide how to write 100,000 in powers of 10 so that you can answer the question on page 15.

[*from page 5*]

YOUR ANSWER: The logarithm of 10,000 is 4 because there are four zeros in the number 10,000.

You may think we're being unnecessarily difficult, but we can't accept this answer.

It is essential that you understand what a logarithm is. Your answer is wrong because it doesn't strike at the heart of the matter. It is true that there are four zeros in the numeral 10,000. But 10,000 can also be written as 10^4. There aren't four zeros in 10^4 but the logarithm still is 4. Don't confuse the way of writing a number with the number itself.

In defining logarithms, we start with a given *base*. Our base is 10.

When we use the base 10 as a factor twice in a multiplication, the product is 100. That is, $10 \times 10 = 10^2 = 100$. Because our base 10 is used twice, we say that the logarithm of 100 is 2.

When our base is used as a factor three times, the logarithm is three. Thus, since $10 \times 10 \times 10 = 1{,}000$, the logarithm of 1,000 is 3.

It is true that with a number such as 10,000.0, the logarithm of the number is equal to the number of zeros to the left of the decimal point. But this is incidental; it's not a definition of the logarithm of the number.

By definition, a logarithm of a number is the exponent indicating the power to which the base 10 must be used as a factor to produce the number.

Please return to page 5 and pick the better answer.

[*from page 16*]

YOUR ANSWER: If $10^3 \times 10^5 = 10^8$, then $\log 10^3 + \log 10^5 = \log 10^8$.

Good. An example of such a multiplication might be:

$$1{,}000 \times 100 \times 10{,}000 = ?$$

First, we determine the logarithm of each factor.

$$\log 1{,}000 = 3$$

$$\log 100 = 2$$

$$\log 10{,}000 = 4$$

Using the form above, log 1,000 + log 100 + log 10,000 = ?, we get

$$3 + 2 + 4 = 9;$$

9 is the logarithm of 10^9, or 1,000,000,000, which is our answer.

The answer could have been found by adding the logarithms on the rulers, of course, but not in one step. The first setting would be log 1,000 + log 100, or 3 + 2:

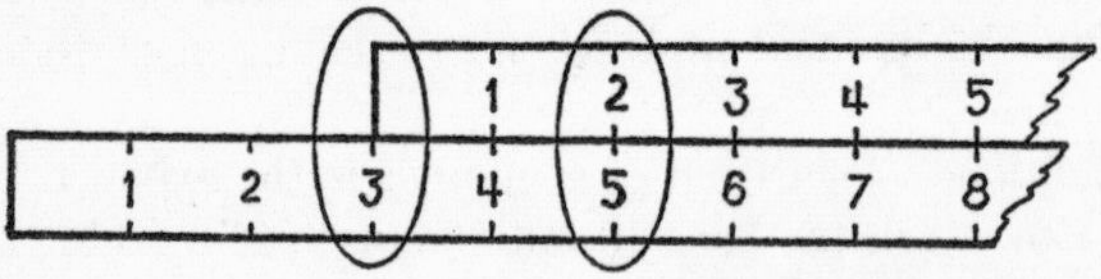

Read 5 on the lower scale. Then add log 10,000, or 4, to the first answer, 5.

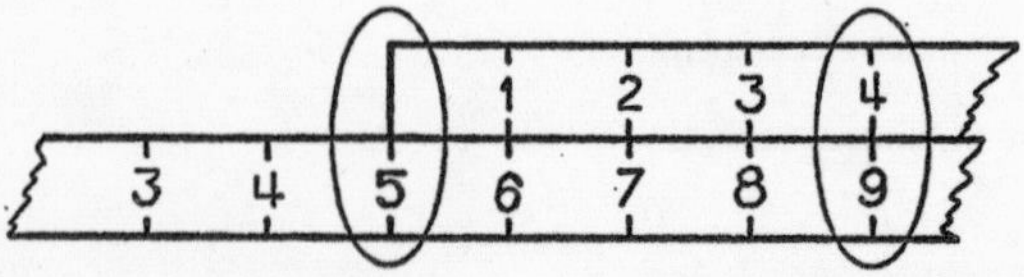

The final answer, 9, again is read on the lower scale. Two factors can be handled in one step, or setting, but each additional factor requires another setting.

So much for multiplication of powers of ten. Let's see whether logarithms are useful in division. Try this problem, using the best method you know. 100,000 divided by 1,000 is:

100. **page 14**

1,000. **page 20**

YOUR ANSWER: If a half-inch distance on a ruler represents the quantity 1, then two six-inch rulers placed end to end represent the quantity 24.

Correct. Quantities can be represented by distances; distances can be added and subtracted by means of scales; therefore, quantities can be added and subtracted by means of scales.

It would be a simple matter to mark a ruler directly with the quantities represented. A pair of rulers with such markings can be placed edge to edge to form an elementary slide rule—one that will only add and subtract. Here is the way they would be set for the computation $4 + 2 = 6$.

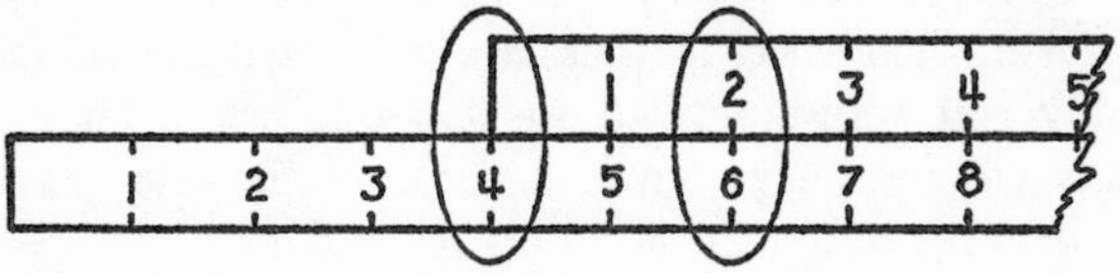

The rules are placed side by side so that the distance corresponding to 2 on the top scale is placed at the end of the distance corresponding to 4 on the bottom scale. The answer, 6, appears on the lower scale opposite the 2 of the top scale. This means that 4 inches, extended by 2 inches, equals 6 inches.

How about subtraction? What do you think this setting represents in terms of subtraction?

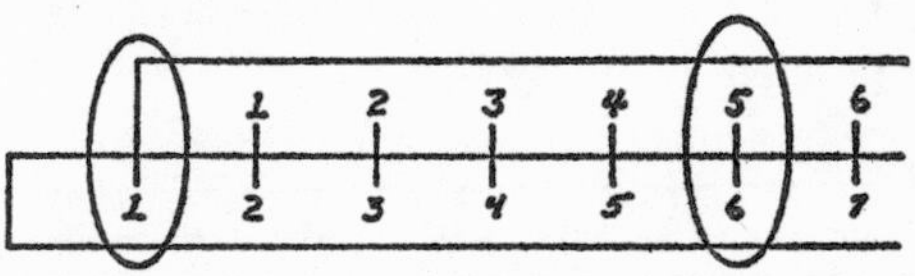

The setting represents $1 + 5 = 6$. **page 4**

The setting represents $6 - 5 = 1$. **page 15**

I don't understand this. **page 19**

[*from page 3*]

YOUR ANSWER: 1,000,000 × 100,000,000 = 100,000,000,000,000.

Yes, and how did you find the answer?

With numbers that are not powers of 10, the usual procedure is this:

$$\begin{array}{r} 143 \\ 93 \\ \hline 429 \\ 1287 \\ \hline 13299 \end{array}$$

With the numbers 1,000,000 and 100,000,000 this is inconvenient and unnecessary. There is an easier approach. There will be as many zeros in the answer as there are in the terms combined.

Probably you were taught to use that rule, way back when. And most likely you were never given a reason for the rule. Like so many mathematical operations, it is simply learned.

Consider our problem again:

$$1{,}000{,}000 \times 100{,}000{,}000 = 100{,}000{,}000{,}000{,}000$$

Using the notation you've just learned, this could be written as

$$10^6 \times 10^8 = 10^{14}$$

As you can see, the exponents of the factors have been added to obtain the exponent of the product.

You know how to add with a pair of rulers. Does this setting represent the problem correctly?

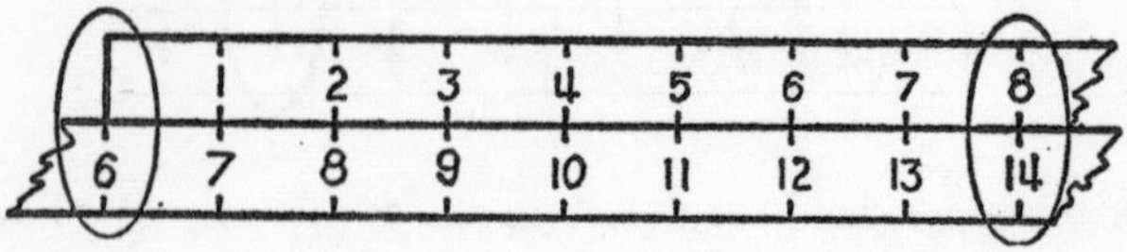

Yes, we have simply added the exponents of the powers of 10. **page 5**

No, this violates the rules we've learned. **page 17**

[*from page 16*]

YOUR ANSWER: If $10^3 \times 10^5 = 10^8$, then $\log 10^3 \times \log 10^5 = \log 10^8$ expresses the same fact.

No, you missed the point.

The *logarithm* (often abbreviated *log*) of a number is the exponent indicating the power to which the base 10 must be raised to equal the number. For example, the logarithm of 1,000 is 3, because $10^3 = 10 \times 10 \times 10 = 1{,}000$. The logarithm of 10,000 is 4, because $10^4 = 10 \times 10 \times 10 \times 10 = 10{,}000$ and so on.

Now, we found that $10^6 \times 10^8 = 10^{14}$. That is, the exponent of the product was equal to the sum of the exponents of the factors—$14 = 6 + 8$.

But we also know that 6 is the *logarithm* of 10^6, 8 is the *logarithm* of 10^8, and 14 is the *logarithm* of 10^{14}. So if we write

$$\log 10^6 + \log 10^8 = \log 10^{14}$$

this expression may be taken to represent the multiplication

$$10^6 \times 10^8 = 10^{14}$$

Similarly, the expression

$$10^3 \times 10^5 = 10^8$$

means that

the exponent of 10^3, plus

the exponent of 10^5, equals

the exponent of 10^8,

and this may also be written

$$\log 10^3 + \log 10^5 = \log 10^8$$

because *the logarithm of the product equals the sum of the logarithms of the factors.*

Study this page carefully. When you feel sure of yourself, return to page 16 and choose the correct answer.

[*from page 10*]

YOUR ANSWER: 100,000 divided by 1,000 is 100.

Good. Did you use a short cut in arriving at this answer?

As with multiplication, there are short cuts for division by powers of 10. To divide any number by a whole-number power of 10, simply move the decimal point to the left as many places as there are zeros in the divisor:

$$10{,}000 \div 10 = 1{,}000.0$$

$$35{,}902 \div 100 = 359.02$$

$$1{,}000{,}000 \div 1{,}000 = 1{,}000.000$$

To divide 100,000 by 1,000, then, simply move the decimal point of 100,000 three places to the left: 100.000.

Another method is to write the problem in fraction form and reduce to lowest terms as follows:

$$\frac{100{,}\not{0}\not{0}\not{0}}{1{,}\not{0}\not{0}\not{0}} = 100$$

As you may have guessed by now, the same problem can be solved by the use of logarithms. Suppose we rewrite the problem:

$$\frac{10^5}{10^3} = 10^2$$

Here, the exponent of the denominator has been subtracted from the exponent of the numerator to give the exponent of the quotient. Written in terms of logarithms: $\log 10^5 - \log 10^3 = \log 10^2$.

When dividing powers of 10, the logarithm of the quotient (the answer) *is found by subtracting the logarithm of the divisor* (the number that does the dividing) *from the logarithm of the dividend* (the number being divided).

What is the logarithm of $\frac{100}{100}$?

$\log \frac{100}{100} = 1.$ **page 18**

$\log \frac{100}{100} = 0.$ **page 23**

I don't understand. **page 29**

[*from page 11*]

YOUR ANSWER: The setting represents $6 - 5 = 1$.

Good.

When we place the rulers side by side in this manner, the distance corresponding to 6 on the bottom is "shortened" by 5 on the top scale. We have used the rulers to figure that 6 shortened by 5 equals 1 on the bottom scale.

So two rulers can be used to add and subtract numbers. But what has this to do with the slide rule?

As a matter of fact, the main function of a slide rule is to add and subtract in exactly the fashion you have observed.

But you probably know that the scales on a slide rule can be used to multiply and divide. Let's see how this is done.

We'll have to dig a little bit into mathematics to see how we can multiply by adding and divide by subtracting. The number 10 will be the most important to us, so let's investigate some of its properties.

It will be no news to you that $10 \times 10 = 100$. From this we can say that 10 appears twice as a factor of 100. This may also be expressed as

$$10^2 = 10 \times 10 = 100.$$

10^2 may be read *10 squared,* or *10 to the second power.* The small numeral 2 is called an exponent. When we write numerals with exponents, their meaning is shown by the following examples:

$$10^2 = 10 \times 10 = 100$$

$$10^3 = 10 \times 10 \times 10 = 1{,}000$$

$$5^2 = 5 \times 5 = 25$$

$$2^4 = 2 \times 2 \times 2 \times 2 = 16$$

Similarly, 1,000,000 may be written as 10^6; this time, the exponent is 6. This means that the number 10 is used as a factor six times, thus:

$$10^6 = 10 \times 10 \times 10 \times 10 \times 10 \times 10 = 1{,}000{,}000.$$

So when 10 is used as a factor six times, the product is one million. Suppose you try one. What is a correct notation for 100,000?

10^5. **page 3** 10^6. **page 8** I don't understand. **page 21**

[*from page 5*]

YOUR ANSWER: The logarithm of 10,000 is 4 because $10 \times 10 \times 10 \times 10 = 10{,}000$.

You are correct. A common logarithm shows the number of times the base 10 must be used as a factor to yield a certain product. Because $10 \times 10 = 100$, the logarithm of 100 is 2. Because $10 \times 10 \times 10 \times 10 \times 10 = 100{,}000$, the logarithm of 100,000 is 5.

The word logarithm is often shortened to *log*. Instead of writing *the logarithm of 100 is 2* we simply write *log 100 = 2*. Of course, since $100 = 10^2$, we may also write $\log 10^2 = 2$. Note that the logarithm of a power of 10 is simply its exponent.

We have pointed out that $10^6 \times 10^8 = 10^{14}$, and observed that for simplified computation we merely added exponents, $6 + 8 = 14$. Since

$$\log 10^6 = 6$$

$$\log 10^8 = 8$$

$$\log 10^{14} = 14$$

we can write

$$\log 10^6 + \log 10^8 = \log 10^{14}.$$

Now look at this statement:

$$10^3 \times 10^5 = 10^8.$$

Which of the statements below expresses the same fact?

$\log 10^3 + \log 10^5 = \log 10^8$. **page 10**

$\log 10^3 \times \log 10^5 = \log 10^8$. **page 13**

I don't understand. **page 22**

[*from page 12*]

YOUR ANSWER: This violates the rules we've learned.

You'd better take another look. Here is the problem again:

$$1{,}000{,}000 \times 100{,}000{,}000 = 100{,}000{,}000{,}000{,}000$$

Using the powers of 10 notation,

$$1{,}000{,}000 = 10^6$$

$$100{,}000{,}000 = 10^8, \quad \text{and}$$

$$100{,}000{,}000{,}000{,}000 = 10^{14}$$

So we can write the problem this way:

$$10^6 \times 10^8 = 10^{14}$$

Since $6 + 8 = 14$, it's clear that the exponents of the factors have been added to give the power of ten of the product.

Now, look at the ruler setting again:

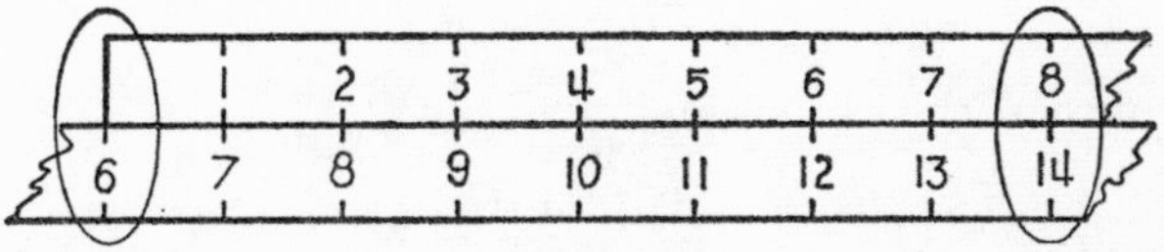

The end of the top scale is over the 6 of the bottom scale; counting over to 8 on the top scale, and reading the number directly below it on the bottom scale, we see that this scale setting represents the addition of 6 and 8. In other words, it represents the addition of the exponents of the factors 10^6 and 10^8.

Return to page 12 and answer the question correctly.

[*from page 14*]

YOUR ANSWER: 1 is the logarithm of $\frac{100}{100}$.

No, it isn't.

$$\frac{100}{100} = 1,$$

because any number (except 0) divided by itself is 1. But you were asked to find the *logarithm* of the answer, not the answer itself.

We have seen that when we are dividing one power of 10 by another, the logarithm of the answer is equal to the logarithm of the dividend (the number to be divided) minus the logarithm of the divisor (the number that does the dividing). For example:

$$\frac{10{,}000{,}000}{1{,}000} = \frac{10^7}{10^4} = 10^3$$

and

$$\log 10^7 - \log 10^3 = \log 10^4$$

or

$$7 - 3 = 4$$

In this particular problem,

$$\frac{100}{100} = \frac{10^2}{10^2} = ?$$

and

$$\log 10^2 - \log 10^2 = \log 10^?$$

or

$$2 - 2 = ?$$

Return to page 14 and select the correct answer.

[*from page 11*]

YOUR ANSWER: I don't understand.

We'll assume to begin with that it is the actual operation that isn't clear. Let's look again at the first diagram from page 11.

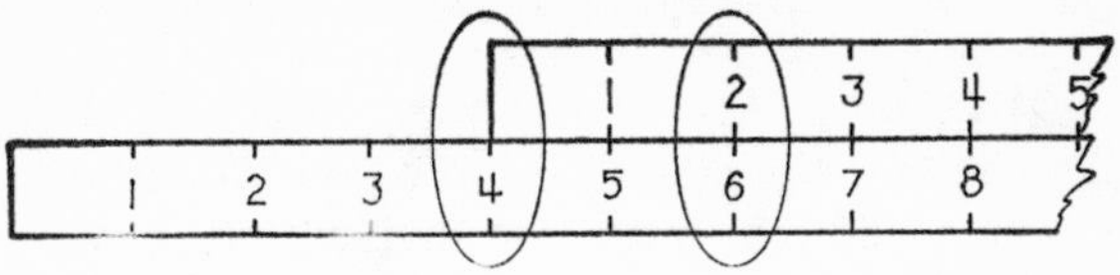

We have taken a number, 4, as a starting point on the lower ruler. Then using the upper ruler, we have added 2 by *extending* along the upper ruler to that number. Transferring to the lower ruler again, we get the answer that 4 extended by 2 equals 6. Or, in figures:

$$4 + 2 = 6.$$

Now let's think about that same setting of the rulers in terms of subtraction. We'll start with 6 on the lower scale and, by *shortening* it by 2 on the upper ruler, read off the answer 4 on the lower ruler. Thus we can use the rulers to figure that 6 shortened by 2 equals 4 or,

$$6 - 2 = 4.$$

Do you see the difference in the two operations?

To add, we extend from the original number on the first scale by working upward through the values on the second scale. To one distance we add another in the same direction.

To subtract, we shorten the original number on the first scale by working downward through the values on the second scale. To the distance representing the original number we apply a distance in the opposite direction.

And now, if your "I don't understand" meant that you didn't see why we were doing this, we can only say, "Patience. This simple business of moving scales back and forth relative to each other and reading from one to another is all there is to using a slide rule."

Please return to page 11 and try again.

[*from page 10*]

YOUR ANSWER: 100,000 divided by 1,000 is 1,000.

You can do better than this. By long division:

$$\begin{array}{r} 100 \\ 1{,}000\overline{)100{,}000} \\ \underline{1000} \\ 000 \end{array}$$

Besides, you should remember that division by a power of ten can be accomplished by moving the decimal point to the left the correct number of places.

To divide by 10, which has one zero, move the decimal point one place to the left.
To divide by 100, which has two zeros, move the decimal point two places to the left.
To divide by 1,000, which has three zeros, move the decimal point three places to the left.

And so on.

So to divide 100,000 by 1,000, all you need to do is move the decimal point of 100,000 three places to the left:

100.000.

Return to page 10 and choose the right answer.

[*from page 15*]

YOUR ANSWER: I don't understand.

Let's begin by making sure you know what a factor is. The factors of a number are those numbers that, when multiplied together, give the original number as a product. For example, 7 and 3 are factors of 21, because $3 \times 7 = 21$; and 2 and 5 are factors of 10, because $2 \times 5 = 10$.

A number can appear more than once as a factor of another number. Ten appears as a factor *twice* in the expression $10 \times 10 = 100$, so we say that $100 = 10^2$ (read *10 squared*, or *10 raised to the second power*). The exponent 2 indicates the number of times that 10 is used as a factor.

In the expression

$$10 \times 10 \times 10 = 1{,}000,$$

10 is used as a factor *three* times, so we say that $1{,}000 = 10^3$ (read *10 cubed*, or *10 raised to the third power*).

Going on in the same vein:

$$10 \times 10 \times 10 \times 10 = 10{,}000, \text{ so } 10{,}000 = 10^4$$

$$10 \times 10 \times 10 \times 10 \times 10 = 100{,}000, \text{ so } 100{,}000 = 10^5$$

$$10 \times 10 \times 10 \times 10 \times 10 \times 10 = 1{,}000{,}000, \text{ so } 1{,}000{,}000 = 10^6$$

Similarly, 10^7 means the product arrived at when 10 is used as a factor 7 times, 10^8 means the product obtained when 10 is used as a factor 8 times, and so on indefinitely.

Before you return to page 15 to pick the correct answer, be sure you understand what an exponent signifies.

[*from page 16*]

YOUR ANSWER: I don't understand.

Let's work it out together.

The *logarithm* (often abbreviated *log*) of a number is the power to which the base 10 must be raised to equal the number. For example, the logarithm of 1,000 is 3, because $10^3 = 10 \times 10 \times 10 =$ 1,000. The logarithm of 10,000 is 4, because $10^4 = 10 \times 10 \times 10 \times 10 =$ 10,000, and so on.

Now, we found that $10^6 \times 10^8 = 10^{14}$. That is, the exponent of the product was equal to the sum of the exponents of the factors—$6 + 8 = 14$.

But we also know that 6 is the logarithm of 10^6, 8 is the logarithm of 10^8, and 14 is the logarithm of 10^{14}. So if we write

$$\log 10^6 + \log 10^8 = \log 10^{14}$$

this expression may be taken to represent the multiplication

$$10^6 \times 10^8 = 10^{14}$$

Similarly, the expression

$$10^3 \times 10^5 = 10^8$$

means that

the exponent of 10^3, plus

the exponent of 10^5, equals

the exponent of 10^8,

and this may also be written

$$\log 10^3 + \log 10^5 = \log 10^8$$

because *the logarithm of the product equals the sum of the logarithms of the factors.*

Study this page carefully. When you feel sure of yourself, return to page 16 and choose the correct answer.

[*from page 14*]

YOUR ANSWER: The logarithm of $\frac{100}{100}$ is 0.

Correct. You know that log 100 is 2 so the division of 100 by 100 can be thought of as $\log 10^2 - \log 10^2 = 0 = \log 10^0$.

Now, if we divide 100 by itself we get an answer of 1. Working in the logarithms for the powers of 10, we can say that $\log 1 = \log 10^0 = 0$.

Let's stop and pick up some loose ends.

Anything that can be represented by numbers—eggs, logarithms, or anything else—can be represented as distance on a ruler.

Two such rulers, properly marked, can be used to add or subtract the quantities represented.

To multiply powers of 10, it is often convenient to use logarithms.

The logarithm of a power of 10 is the number of times 10 is used as a factor to get the power. For instance, 10 is a factor of 10,000 four times:

$$10 \times 10 \times 10 \times 10 = 10{,}000 = 10^4$$

therefore

$$\log 10{,}000 = \log 10^4 = 4$$

In multiplying powers of 10 using logarithms, the logarithm of the answer is simply the sum of the logarithms of the factors. If $A \times B = C$, and A, B, and C are powers of 10,

$$\log C = \log A + \log B$$

In dividing powers of 10 using logarithms, the logarithm of the answer is the difference between the logarithms of the dividend and divisor. If $\frac{A}{B} = C$, and A, B, and C are powers of 10 as before:

$$\log C = \log A - \log B$$

Let's have a closer look at this matter of division. Could we write $\frac{A}{B} = C$ as $A \times \frac{1}{B} = C$?

Yes, they are equivalent expressions. **page 27**

No, multiplication just isn't the same as division. **page 31**

[*from page 27*]

YOUR ANSWER: $\log \frac{1}{10{,}000} = -4.$

Yes. Negative logarithms may seem to be simply an added complication, but they'll be very handy for dealing with fractions.

To keep our notation straight, we'll write $\frac{1}{100}$ as 10^{-2}. This extends our collection of logarithms quite a bit. Here are a few:

$$\log \frac{1}{1{,}000} = \log \frac{1}{10^3} = \log 10^{-3} = -3 \qquad \log 1 = \log 10^0 = 0$$

$$\log \frac{1}{100} = \log \frac{1}{10^2} = \log 10^{-2} = -2 \qquad \log 10 = \log 10^1 = 1$$

$$\log \frac{1}{10} = \log \frac{1}{10^1} = \log 10^{-1} = -1 \qquad \log 100 = \log 10^2 = 2$$

The list, of course, can go as far as you wish in either direction. For the most part, it won't matter whether you elect to use the form $\frac{A}{B} = C$, or $A \times \frac{1}{B} = C$. This will be especially true for problems such as: $\frac{100 \times 1{,}000{,}000 \times 1}{1{,}000 \times 10} = C$. The logarithm of the answer may be written as: $\log C = (2 + 6 + 0) - (3 + 1) = 4$. The same problem can be written as: $100 \times 1{,}000{,}000 \times 1 \times \frac{1}{1{,}000} \times \frac{1}{10} = C$.

In this case, $\log C = 2 + 6 + 0 - 3 - 1 = 4$. Consider the inverse of the problem. $\frac{1{,}000 \times 10}{100 \times 1{,}000{,}000 \times 1} = C$

What will the expression for the logarithm of the answer look like?

$\text{Log } C = (3 + 1) - (2 + 6 + 0) = -(4)$. **page 28**

$\text{Log } C = 3 + 1 - 2 - 6 - 0 = -4$. **page 32**

Either is correct. **page 35**

YOUR ANSWER: The second step is to place 2 on the top scale over 4 on the bottom scale.

That's right.

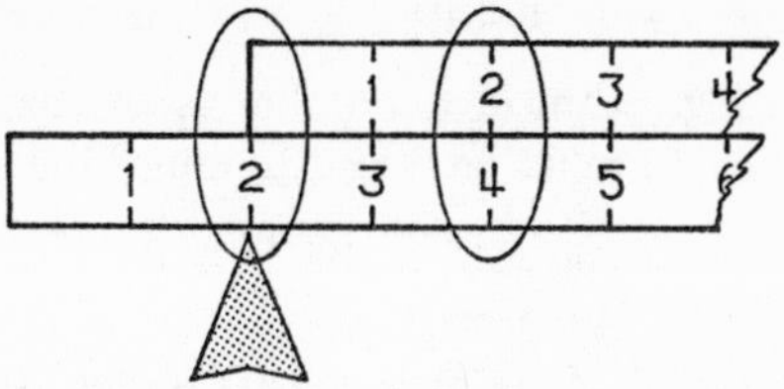

So far we've accounted for $3 + 1 - 2$. The answer, 2, is read on the lower scale opposite the end of the upper scale.

The next step is to consider -6. Here is the correct setting:

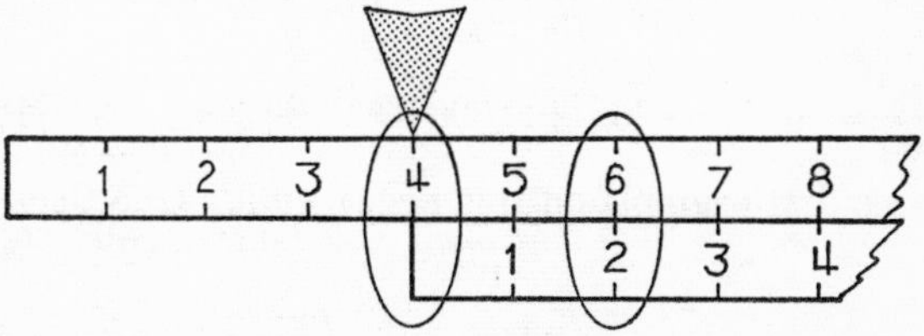

This time, the top scale extends out to the left, and the answer, -4, is opposite the end of the bottom scale. In general, when the answer is to be found on the top scale, it will be negative.

Consider this problem:

$$10^3 \times 10^7 \times 10^{-9} \times 10^6 \times 10^{-1} = ?$$

How many steps will be necessary?

Four. **page 33**

Five. **page 37**

[*from page 33*]

YOUR ANSWER: The first group contains an error.

No, all the problems in the first group are correct. Here they are, with explanations:

$$\log 10^{-5} = -5$$

Of course. The logarithm of a number is the exponent indicating the power to which 10 must be raised to equal the number.

$$\log (10^3 \times 10^{-3}) = 0$$

Yes, because

$$\begin{aligned} \log (10^3 \times 10^{-3}) &= \log 10^3 + \log 10^{-3} \\ &= 3 + (-3) \\ &= 0 \end{aligned}$$

$$\frac{1}{100{,}000} = 10^{-5}$$

$\log \frac{1}{100{,}000} = \log 1 - \log 100{,}000 = 0 - 5 = -5.$ But $-5 = \log 10^{-5}$ (see first example on this page), so it's true that

$$\frac{1}{100{,}000} = 10^{-5}.$$

$$\log (10 \times 10 \times 10 \times 10) = 4$$

Right—$\log (10 \times 10 \times 10 \times 10) = \log 10^4 = 4$.

Return to page 33 and try again.

[*from page 23*]

YOUR ANSWER: Yes, $\frac{A}{B} = C$, and $A \times \frac{1}{B} = C$ are equivalent expressions.

Yes. $\frac{1}{B}$ is the *reciprocal* of B. *Division by a number is the same as multiplication by the reciprocal of the same number.*

Suppose we have a division, such as $\frac{100}{10{,}000}$, in which the divisor is larger than the dividend. How do we solve this problem by means of logarithms? Well, if we follow the rule for division, we must subtract the log of the divisor from the log of the dividend to get:

$$\log \frac{100}{10{,}000} = \log \frac{1}{100} = \log 1 - \log 100 = 0 - 2 = -2$$

Thus, we see that $\log \frac{1}{100} = -2$, and we have "discovered" negative logarithms. The logarithm of 100 is 2 and the log of $\frac{1}{100}$ is -2.

On this basis, what would be the logarithm of $\frac{1}{10{,}000}$?

$\log \frac{1}{10{,}000} = -4.$ **page 24**

$\log \frac{1}{10{,}000} = 4.$ **page 34**

$\log \frac{1}{10{,}000} = \frac{1}{4}.$ **page 38**

[*from page 24*]

YOUR ANSWER: Log $C = (3 + 1) - (2 + 6 + 0) = -(4)$.

This is one possible expression. If

$$C = \frac{1{,}000 \times 10}{100 \times 1{,}000{,}000 \times 1}$$

then

$$\begin{aligned}
\log C &= \log (1{,}000 \times 10) - \log (100 \times 1{,}000{,}000 \times 1) \\
&= (\log 1{,}000 + \log 10) - (\log 100 + \log 1{,}000{,}000 + \log 1) \\
&= (3 + 1) - (2 + 6 + 0) \\
&= (4) - (8) \\
&= -(4)
\end{aligned}$$

However, the original expression can be rewritten in the form

$$C = 1{,}000 \times 10 \times \frac{1}{100} \times \frac{1}{1{,}000{,}000} \times \frac{1}{1}$$

And in this case, log C is given by the expression

$$\log C = \log 1{,}000 + \log 10 + \log \frac{1}{100} + \log \frac{1}{1{,}000{,}000} + \log \frac{1}{1}.$$

Determine these logarithms, and return to page 24 to choose the right answer.

[*from page 14*]

YOUR ANSWER: I don't understand.

Well, let's retrace our steps.
Specifically, we found that

$$\frac{100{,}000}{1{,}000} = 100$$

Then we rewrote the problem in terms of powers of 10:

$$\frac{10^5}{10^3} = 10^2,$$

where the exponent of the result is equal to the exponent of the dividend (the number to be divided) minus the exponent of the divisor (the number that does the dividing). But this is the same as saying that the *logarithm* of the result is equal to the *logarithm* of the dividend minus the *logarithm* of the divisor:

$$\log 10^5 - \log 10^3 = 5 - 3 = 2 = \log 10^2$$

So we made the following generalization:

When dividing powers of 10, the logarithm of the answer is found by subtracting the logarithm of the dividend from the logarithm of the divisor.

In this case, we want to divide 100 by 100, using logarithms:

$$\frac{100 \longrightarrow \text{dividend (number to be divided)}}{100 \longrightarrow \text{divisor (number that does the dividing).}}$$

Our general rule tells us that the logarithm of the result will be equal to the logarithm of 100 minus the logarithm of 100. Log 100 = 2, because $10^2 = 100$. Therefore, log result = log 100 − log 100 = 2 − 2 = ?

Complete the problem, and return to page 14 to select the correct answer.

[*from page 35*]

YOUR ANSWER: The next step is to place 1 on the top scale over 4 on the bottom scale.

No, that's the *result* we get when we add 3 and 1, in the first step of the problem:

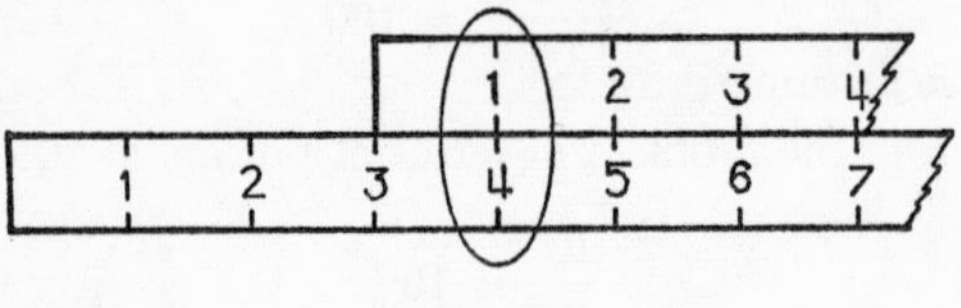

Now, however, we want to *subtract* 2 from 4, the answer we got when we added 3 and 1. This isn't difficult if we just remember what we would do to *add* 2 to some other number, such as 3: we would place the end of the top scale over the 3 of the bottom scale. Then we would count over to 2 on the top scale, and the answer, 5, would appear directly below on the bottom scale:

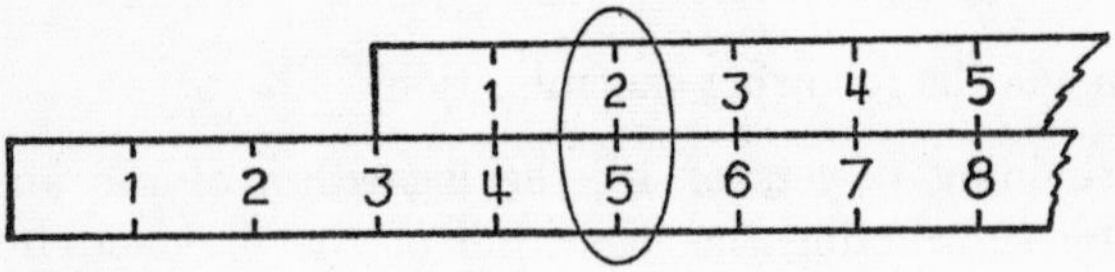

Now, to subtract 2 from 4, we just reverse this process. We place the 2 of the top scale directly over the 4 of the bottom scale. Our answer then appears on the bottom scale, directly beneath the end of the top scale:

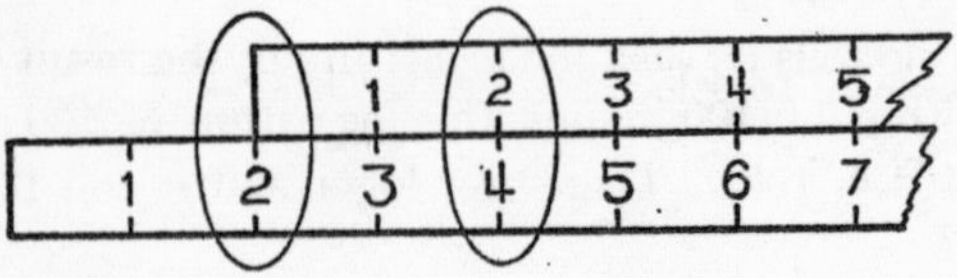

When you're sure that you understand what's happening here, return to page 35 to choose the right answer.

[from page 23]

YOUR ANSWER: No, multiplication just isn't the same as division.

No, but saying that $\frac{A}{B} = C$ and $A \times \frac{1}{B} = C$ are equivalent expressions is not the same as saying that multiplication and division are the same.

Consider this arithmetic example:

$$\begin{aligned} 5 \times \frac{1}{3} &= \frac{5}{1} \times \frac{1}{3} \\ &= \frac{5 \times 1}{1 \times 3} \\ &= \frac{5}{3} \end{aligned}$$

Applying these principles to the given expressions, we see that

$$\begin{aligned} A \times \frac{1}{B} &= \frac{A}{1} \times \frac{1}{B} \\ &= \frac{A \times 1}{1 \times B} \\ &= \frac{A}{B} \end{aligned}$$

So, since $A \times \frac{1}{B}$ and $\frac{A}{B}$ are equal, the expressions $A \times \frac{1}{B} = C$ and $\frac{A}{B} = C$ are equivalent.

Return to page 23 to select the right answer.

[*from page 24*]

YOUR ANSWER: Log $C = 3 + 1 - 2 - 6 - 0 = -4$.

Yes, because if

$$C = \frac{1{,}000 \times 10}{100 \times 1{,}000{,}000 \times 1}$$

then we can write

$$C = 1{,}000 \times 10 \times \frac{1}{100} \times \frac{1}{1{,}000{,}000} \times \frac{1}{1}.$$

And the logarithm of this expression is given by

$$\begin{aligned}\log C &= \log 1{,}000 + \log 10 + \log \frac{1}{100} + \log \frac{1}{1{,}000{,}000} + \log \frac{1}{1}.\\ &= 3 + 1 + (-2) + (-6) + 0\\ &= 3 + 1 - 2 - 6 + 0\\ &= -4\end{aligned}$$

But look at the original expression again:

$$C = \frac{1{,}000 \times 10}{100 \times 1{,}000{,}000 \times 1}$$

The logarithm of this expression, as it stands, is the logarithm of the dividend minus the logarithm of the divisor:

$$\begin{aligned}\log C &= \log (1{,}000 \times 10) - \log (100 \times 1{,}000{,}000 \times 1)\\ &= (\log 1{,}000 + \log 10) - (\log 100 + \log 1{,}000{,}000 + \log 1)\end{aligned}$$

Complete the problem, and return to page 24 to choose the right answer.

YOUR ANSWER: Four steps are necessary to find the logarithm of the answer to: $10^3 \times 10^7 \times 10^{-9} \times 10^6 \times 10^{-1}$

Fine. Let's run over them one by one. The expression for the log of the answer will be: $3 + 7 - 9 + 6 - 1$. Now add 7 to 3:

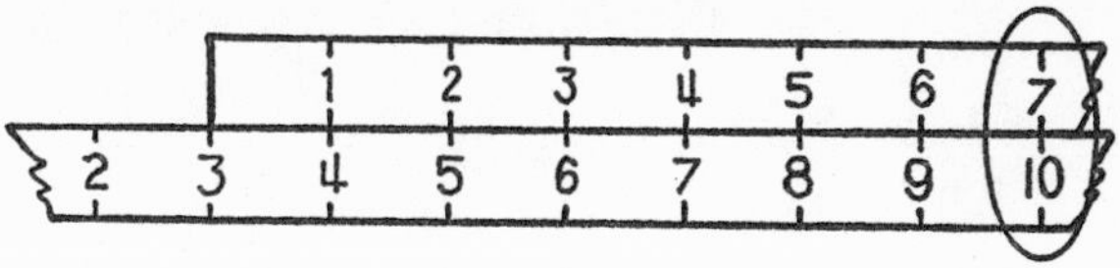

The answer, 10, appears on the lower scale. Next to subtract 9:

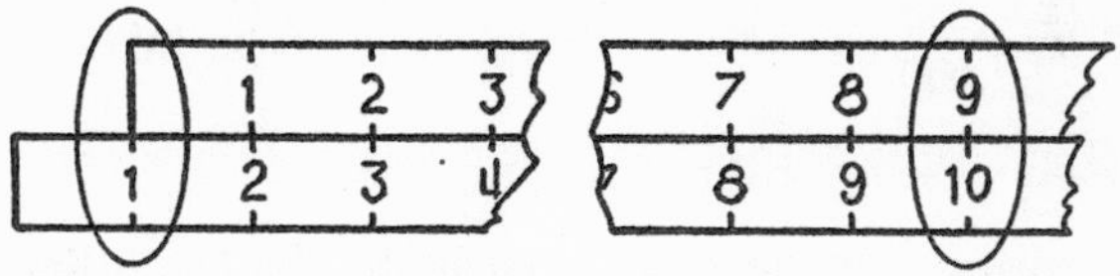

This gives 1, again read on the lower scale. Adding 6:

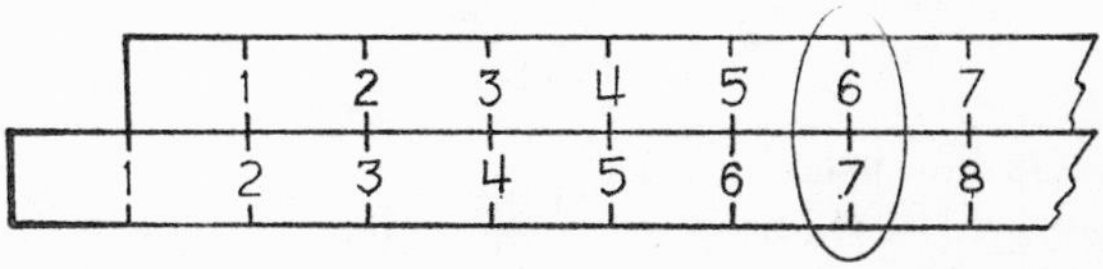

This is 7, still on the lower scale. Last of all subtract 1:

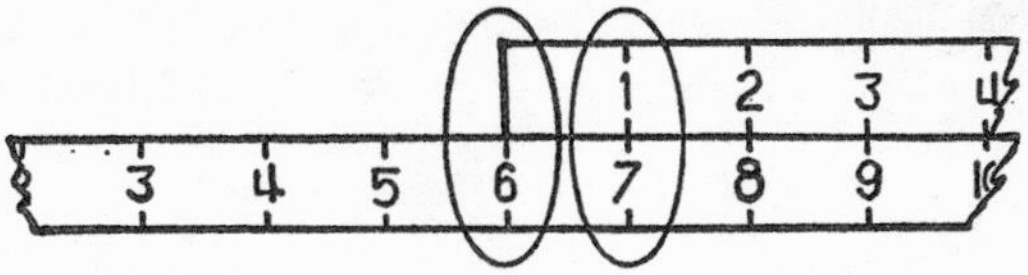

The log of the answer is 6. The answer then is 10^6.
Which series of problems contains an error?

$\log 10^{-5} = -5$	$10^{-4} \times 10^{-3} = 10^{-7}$	$100{,}000{,}000{,}000 = 10^{11}$
$\log (10^3 \times 10^{-3}) = 0$	$\log 1 = 0$	$\dfrac{10^8 \times 10^2 \times 10^9 \times 10^0}{10^{15} \times 10^3 \times 10^5} = 10^{-4}$
$\dfrac{1}{100{,}000} = 10^{-5}$	$\dfrac{1{,}000 \times 100}{1{,}000{,}000} = \dfrac{10^3 \times 10^2}{10^6}$	$\log (10^{-9} \times 10^3) = 10^{-6}$
$\log (10 \times 10 \times 10 \times 10) = 4$	$\dfrac{10^8}{10^2} = 10^8 \times 10^{-2}$	$\log \dfrac{1}{10{,}000} = -4$
page 26	**page 36**	**page 39**

[*from page 27*]

YOUR ANSWER: $\log \dfrac{1}{10{,}000} = 4.$

The numerical value of your answer is correct, but the sign is wrong. We found that the logarithm of $\dfrac{1}{100}$ is -2, and we can observe that $\dfrac{1}{100} = \dfrac{1}{10^2}$. Does this tell you anything?

Let's go a little further. $\dfrac{1}{1{,}000}$ is equal to $\dfrac{1}{10^3}$, so it looks as if the logarithm of $\dfrac{1}{1{,}000}$ should be -3. We can check this by using the rule for finding the logarithm of a quotient:

The logarithm of a quotient is equal to the logarithm of the dividend minus the logarithm of the divisor, i.e.,

$$\log \frac{1}{1{,}000} = \log 1 - \log 1{,}000 = 0 - 3 = -3$$

So our assumption is correct: $\log \dfrac{1}{1{,}000} = \log \dfrac{1}{10^3} = -3.$

At this point, you should be able to choose the correct answer on page 27.

[from page 24]

YOUR ANSWER: Either is correct:

$$\log C = (3 + 1) - (2 + 6 + 0) = -4$$

$$\log C = 3 + 1 - 2 - 6 - 0 = -4$$

Very good.

The logarithm of 10^{-4} is -4. Because this problem was the reciprocal of the original problem its answer is the reciprocal of the original answer (which was 10^4).

In general, to express the reciprocal of a power of ten such as 10^4, write it with a negative exponent. Thus, $\frac{1}{10^4}$ is 10^{-4}.

Let's make sure that you understand how -4 can be the logarithm of 10^{-4}. Remembering that 10^{-4} can be written $\frac{1}{10{,}000}$, and that $\frac{1}{10{,}000}$ is merely a simple problem of the form $\frac{A}{B} = C$, the expression for the logarithm of $\frac{1}{10{,}000}$ will be of this form:

$$\log \frac{1}{10{,}000} = \log 1 - \log 10{,}000 = 0 - 4 = -4$$

Could the problem have been worked out on our simple slide rule?

Here it is again: $\frac{10^3 \times 10^1}{10^2 \times 10^6 \times 10^0} = 10^{-4}$

The expression for the logarithm of the answer was:

$$3 + 1 - 2 - 6 - 0 = \log (10^{-4})$$

Adding the first two numbers, 3 and 1, is no problem:

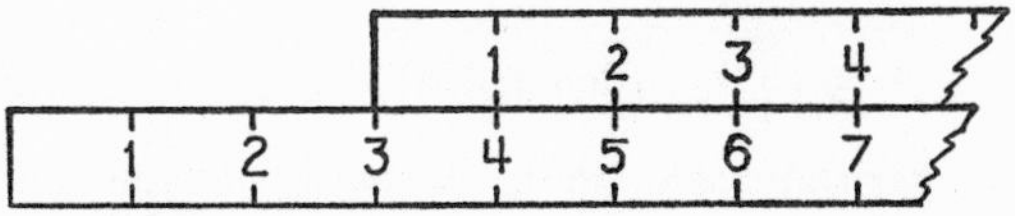

But what's the next step?

Put 2 on the top scale over 4 on the bottom scale. **page 25**

Put 1 on the top scale over 4 on the bottom scale. **page 30**

[*from page 33*]

YOUR ANSWER: The second series contains an error.

No, it doesn't. Look at the problems again:

$$10^{-4} \times 10^{-3} = 10^{-7}$$

The logarithm of a product is equal to the sum of the logarithms of the factors, so

$$\begin{aligned}\log (10^{-4} \times 10^{-3}) &= \log 10^{-4} + \log 10^{-3} \\ &= -4 + (-3) \\ &= -7\end{aligned}$$

Which means that $10^{-4} \times 10^{-3} = 10^{-7}$.

$$\log 1 = 0$$

Right. 1 is equivalent to any number (except 0) divided by itself.

$$\frac{1{,}000 \times 100}{1{,}000{,}000} = \frac{10^3 \times 10^2}{10^6}$$

Just count the zeros:

1,000 has 3 zeros, so $1{,}000 = 10^3$
100 has 2 zeros, so $100 = 10^2$
1,000,000 has 6 zeros, so $1{,}000{,}000 = 10^6$

$$\frac{10^8}{10^2} = 10^8 \times 10^{-2}$$

Checking the logarithms of the two expressions:

$$\log \frac{10^8}{10^2} = \log 10^8 - \log 10^2 = 8 - 2 = 6$$

$$\log (10^8 \times 10^{-2}) = \log 10^8 + \log 10^{-2} = 8 - 2 = 6$$

Since their logarithms are equal, the two expressions are equal.

Return to page 33 for another try.

YOUR ANSWER: Five steps will be necessary.

Well, let's check. Here's the problem again:

$$10^3 \times 10^7 \times 10^{-9} \times 10^6 \times 10^{-1} = ?$$

The first setting of the rules will be 3 + 7:

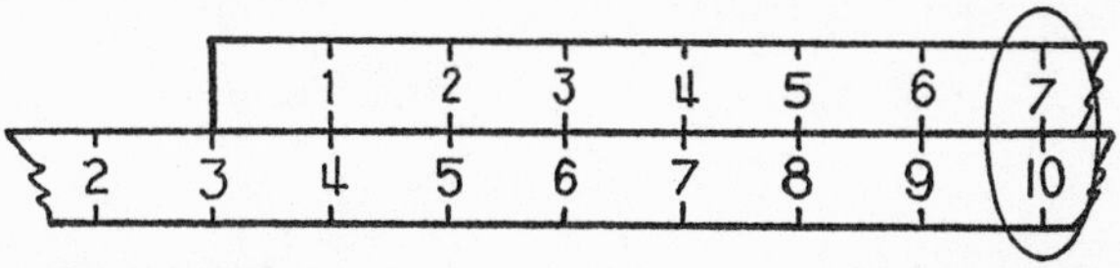

The answer is 10. So the second setting of the rules is 9 on the top rule over 10 on the bottom rule, to subtract 9 from 10:

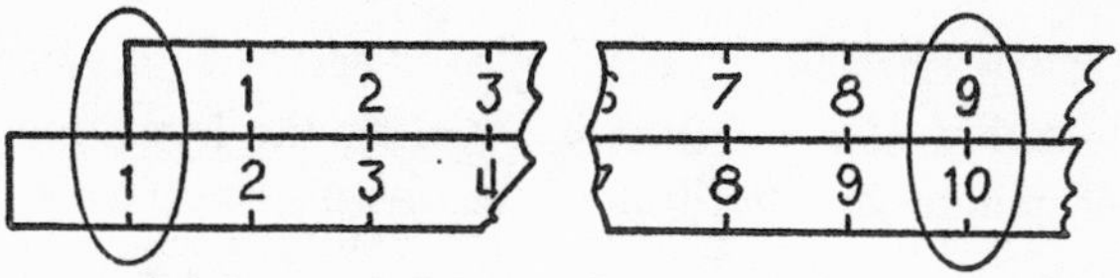

The answer is 1. The third step is 1 + 6:

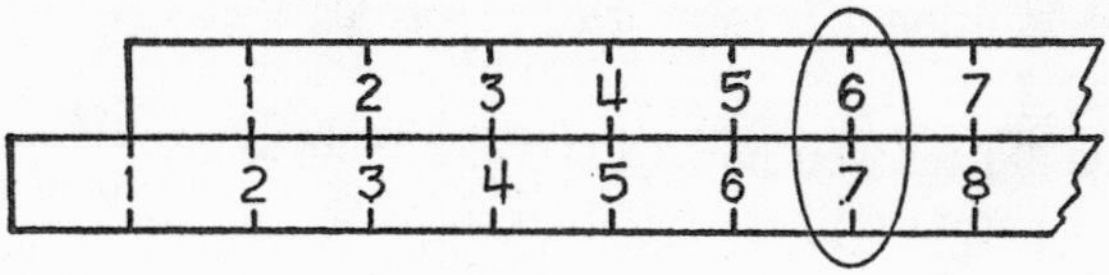

This gives us 7, and the final setting is 1 on the top rule over 7 on the bottom rule, to subtract 1 from 7:

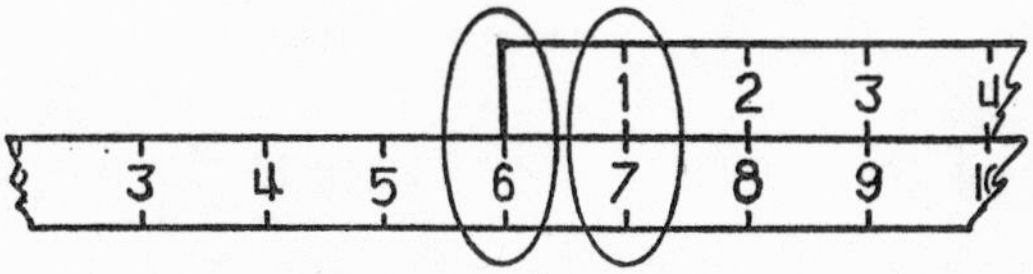

So our final result is 6.

Now, count the number of steps that were necessary, and then return to page 25 to answer the question correctly.

[*from page 27*]

YOUR ANSWER: $\log \frac{1}{10{,}000} = \frac{1}{4}$.

No. Either this is a careless error, or you missed the point. Let's review what we did.

We found that the logarithm of $\frac{1}{100}$ is -2, and we observed that $\frac{1}{100}$ is the same as $\frac{1}{10^2}$. Does this tell you anything?

Let's go a little further. $\frac{1}{1{,}000}$ is equal to $\frac{1}{10^3}$, so it looks as if the logarithm of $\frac{1}{1{,}000}$ should be -3. We can check this by using the rule for finding the logarithm of a quotient:

> The logarithm of a quotient is equal to the logarithm of the dividend minus the logarithm of the divisor, i.e.,
>
> $$\log \frac{1}{1{,}000} = \log 1 - \log 1{,}000 = 0 - 3 = -3$$

So our assumption is correct: $\log \frac{1}{1{,}000} = \log \frac{1}{10^3} = -3$.

This should tell you how to find the value of $\log \frac{1}{10{,}000}$. Return to page 27 and answer the question correctly.

[*from page 33*]

YOUR ANSWER: You have found an error in the third series:

$$100{,}000{,}000{,}000 = 10^{11}$$

$$\frac{10^8 \times 10^2 \times 10^9 \times 10^0}{10^{15} \times 10^3 \times 10^5} = 10^{-4}$$

$$\log (10^{-9} \times 10^3) = 10^{-6}$$

$$\log \frac{1}{10{,}000} = -4$$

You're right, but which one?

$$100{,}000{,}000{,}000 = 10^{11}$$

There's no error here. There are 11 zeros, so 10 has been used as a factor 11 times.

$$\frac{10^8 \times 10^2 \times 10^9 \times 10^0}{10^{15} \times 10^3 \times 10^5} = 10^{-4}$$

The log of 10^{-4} should result from this expression: $8 + 2 + 9 - 15 - 3 - 5 = -4$. It does, so this problem is o.k.

$$\log (10^{-9} \times 10^3) = 10^{-6}$$

Here's the trouble! $10^{-9} \times 10^3$ is 10^{-6}. But log $(10^{-9} \times 10^3)$ is -6.

$$\frac{10^8}{10^2} = 10^8 \times 10^{-2}$$

Of course this is correct. Dividing 10^8 by 10^2 is the same as multiplying 10^8 by the reciprocal of 10^2, or 10^{-2}.

In this first chapter you have built a foundation that should make the remainder of this book smooth sailing. As you've gathered, the slide rule works by adding and subtracting logarithms. There is really nothing mysterious about it at all.

Now please go on to Lesson 2, which begins on page 40.

CHAPTER 2

The C and D Scales

In the first lesson, you learned some basic facts about logarithms and how to use them. To review briefly:

Numbers such as 100, 1,000, and 1,000,000 are whole-number powers of 10; any of these can be obtained by multiplying 10 by itself an appropriate number of times. For example,

$$100 = 10 \times 10 = 10^2$$

$$1{,}000{,}000 = 10 \times 10 \times 10 \times 10 \times 10 \times 10 = 10^6$$

When a number is written as 10 with an exponent, the exponent shows how many times 10 must be used as a factor to obtain the number. For example, 3 in 10^3 means that $10 \times 10 \times 10 = 10^3$.

The common logarithm of a number is the exponent which indicates the power to which 10 must be raised to yield the number. For example, $\log 10{,}000 = 4$ because $10{,}000 = 10 \times 10 \times 10 \times 10 = 10^4$.

Numbers can be multiplied by using logarithms; the logarithm of the product is the sum of the logarithms of the factors. For example: $\log (A \times B) = \log A + \log B$.

The addition of logarithms can be carried out with scales. If the distance corresponding to $\log A$ is added to that corresponding to $\log B$, then the distance corresponding to the logarithm of their product, $\log (A \times B)$, is:

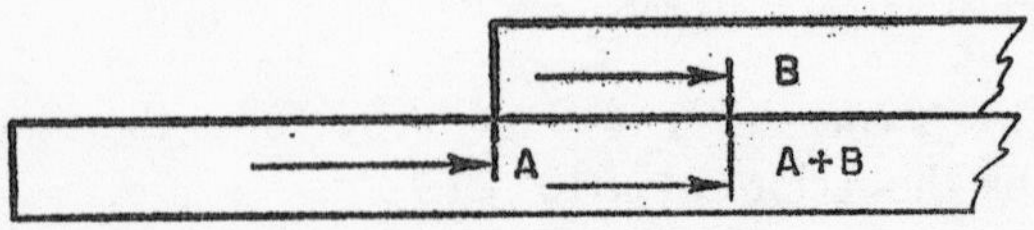

What about division by means of logarithms? Is this the proper setting for the log of $\frac{A}{B}$?

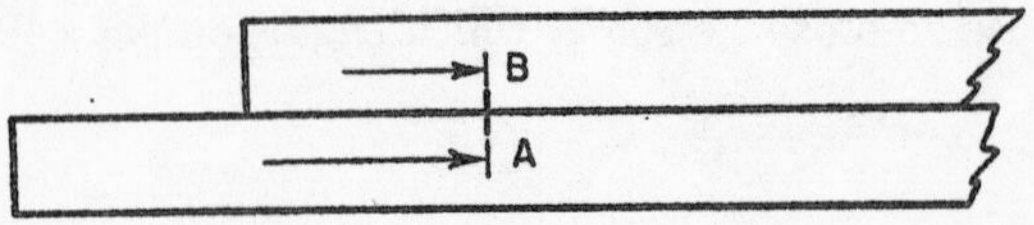

Yes. **page 45** No. **page 49**

[*from page 59*]

YOUR ANSWER: This setting represents the log of 8.

No, it doesn't. Look again:

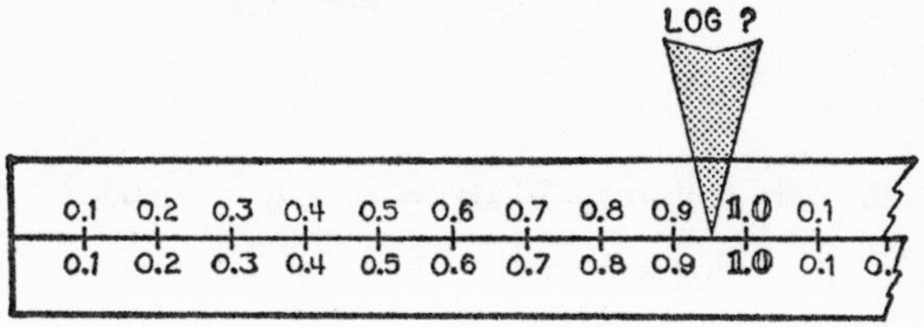

The point of the arrow lies approximately halfway between 0.9 and 1.0—let us say at 0.95.

Now consult the table of logarithms:

log 1 = 0.000	log 6 = 0.778
log 2 = 0.301	log 7 = 0.845
log 3 = 0.477	log 8 = 0.903
log 4 = 0.602	log 9 = 0.954
log 5 = 0.699	log 10 = 1.000

Which logarithm is closest to 0.95, the estimated position of the arrow in the drawing above? Certainly not the logarithm of 8, which is 0.903. But what about the logarithm of 9?

Now return to page 59 to select the correct answer.

[*from page 45*]

YOUR ANSWER: Yes, it is possible that log 2 is 0.2 and log 5 is 0.5.

No, it isn't. Look at it this way:

We have seen that the log of a product is equal to the sum of the logs of the factors:

$$\log (A \times B) = \log A + \log B.$$

Since 2 and 5 are factors of 10 (because $2 \times 5 = 10$), we know that

$$\log 2 + \log 5 = \log 10;$$

since $\log 10 = 1$,

$$\log 2 + \log 5 = 1.$$

But obviously,

$$0.2 + 0.5 \neq 1.$$

($\neq$ means *is not equal to*)

So we must conclude that 0.2 is not the log of 2, that 0.5 is not the log of 5, or that both are wrong.

Return to page 45 to answer the question correctly.

[*from page 58*]

YOUR ANSWER: The number 9 is 0.903 of the distance between 0 and 10.

Your answer is incorrect. And since we're making a big step here, it's important that you follow the argument.

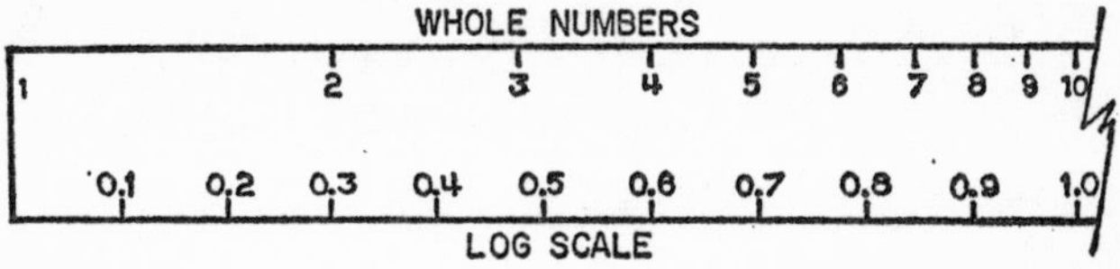

The large figures on the top of the scale are the whole numbers, or integers, 1 through 10.

The small figures on the bottom of the scale are the logarithms of these integers. As you know, the logarithms of the numbers 1 to 10 range from 0 to 1.0.

The logarithms on the bottom scale are evenly spaced. Thus the logarithm 0.5 is just halfway up the scale. The logarithm 0.75 is just three-quarters of the way up the scale.

The integers are not evenly spaced. Each integer is placed directly above its logarithm.

So the whole number which is 0.903 of the distance between 0 and 10 is the number whose logarithm is 0.903. This number, as you should know by now, is 8.

To understand the slide rule, it is absolutely imperative that you follow this idea of varying the intervals between integers according to the intervals between their logarithms. Go over this carefully until you are sure you understand; then return to page 58 and select the right answer.

[*from page 48*]

YOUR ANSWER: .301 is the log of 2. Yes.

Now let us consider the use of the table for a very simple multiplication problem. Use the table to check this example.

Number	Logarithm
1	0.000
2	0.301
3	0.477
4	0.602
5	0.699
6	0.778
7	0.845
8	0.903
9	0.954
10	1.000

$2 \times 5 = 10$, then $\log 2 + \log 5 = \log 10$, and $.301 + .699 = 1.000$.

Let's see whether our scales will work for this problem. To indicate .301 and .699 divide the intervals on the scales like this:

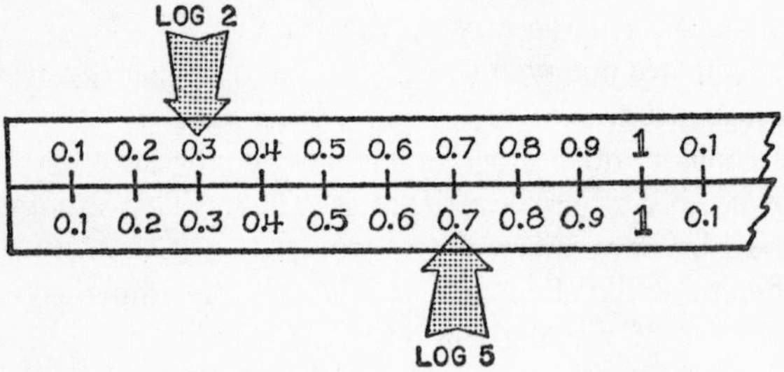

Adding the distances corresponding to the log of 2 and the log of 5 gives us this setting:

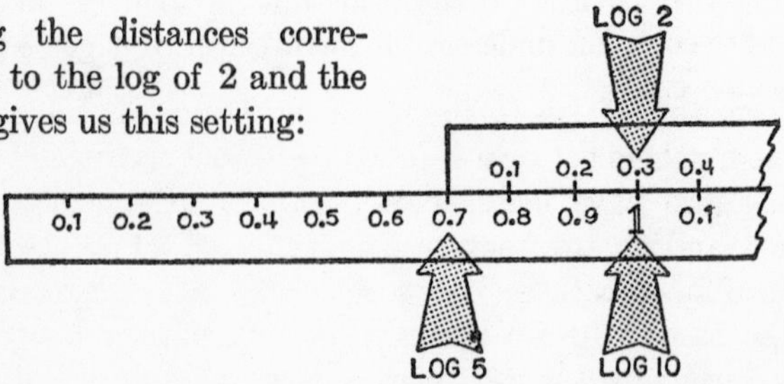

The answer 1, the log of 10, appears on the lower scale. Referring to the table above, what is the log of 4?

log 4 = 2.5. **page 53**

log 4 = .602. **page 59**

[*from page 40*]

YOUR ANSWER: Yes, the setting shown is $\log \frac{A}{B}$.

Correct. The log of $\frac{A}{B}$ is $\log A - \log B$, as shown.

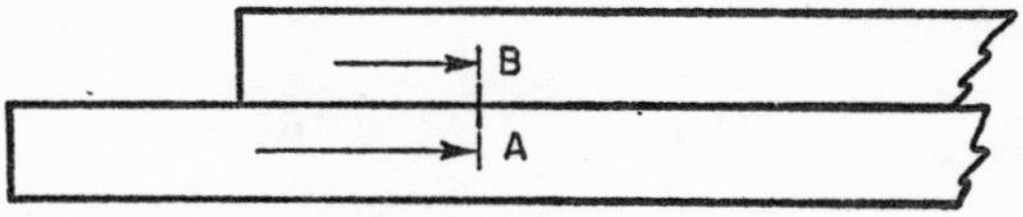

Most of the numbers you will handle are neither as large as 10^6, nor simple whole-number powers of 10. Since you can readily do such calculations mentally, scales are really not much help.

A more realistic problem concerns the amount of concrete required to pave a patio 6 feet 6 inches wide and 32 feet long. If the concrete must be 4 inches thick, the formula for the number of cubic yards of concrete required is given in this fashion:

$$\frac{6.5 \text{ feet} \times 32 \text{ feet} \times \frac{1}{3} \text{ feet}}{27 \text{ cubic feet}/1 \text{ cubic yard}} = 2.57 \text{ cubic yards}$$

If you were regularly estimating the cost of concrete work, the ability to find such answers rapidly and accurately could easily mean the difference between making money and losing it.

You know that common logarithms are simply exponents of the base 10. The logarithm of a number is the power to which 10 must be raised to produce the number.

number	logarithm
1	0
2	?
5	?
10	1

The logarithm of 1 is 0, and the logarithm of 10 is 1. Now what about the numbers between 1 and 10? Isn't it reasonable to suppose that they also have logarithms? The logarithms of the numbers between 1 and 10 are fractions between 0 and 1. In other words, for each number between 1 and 10, there is a fractional power to which the base of 10 can be raised to equal that number. (Notice that the term *raised* is used even though we are seeking a product that is smaller than the base of ten that we've more or less arbitrarily adopted.)

Is it possible that log 2 is simply 0.2, and log 5 is 0.5?

Yes. **page 42** No. **page 48** I don't know. **page 50**

[*from page 48*]

YOUR ANSWER: Log 2 = 1.5.

No. You must read the table from the left column to the right column. To find the logarithm of 2 in the table, look in the column headed "number" until you find "2". Then read to the right and you will find ".301".

Number	Logarithm
1	0.000
2	0.301
3	0.477
4	0.602
5	0.699
6	0.778
7	0.845
8	0.903
9	0.954
10	1.000

Return to page 48 and answer the question correctly.

[*from page 59*]

YOUR ANSWER: The arrow indicates the logarithm of 9.

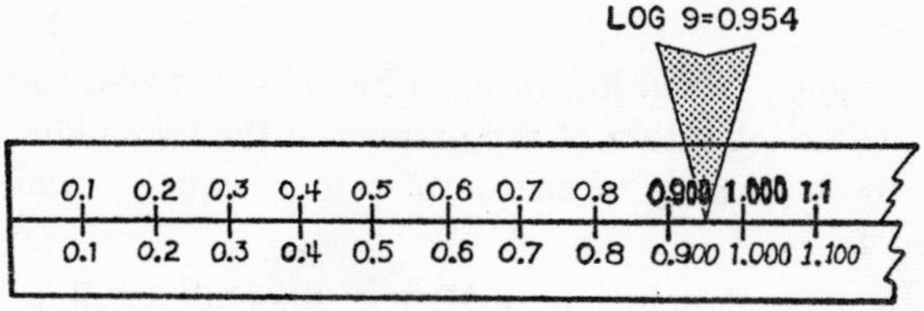

Very good. Of course, your answer is based on an estimate, since you can't really tell from the drawing whether the arrow is at 0.954 or, say, 0.950.

Nearly every answer you will read from the slide rule involves estimating of this sort. Here is another example:

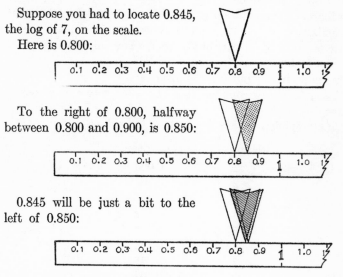

Suppose you had to locate 0.845, the log of 7, on the scale.

Here is 0.800:

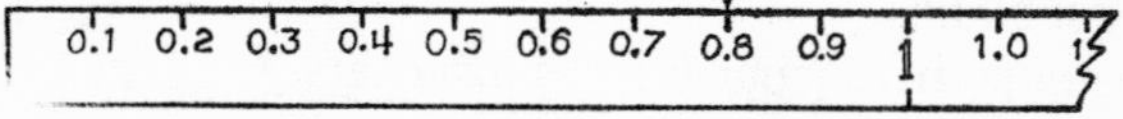

To the right of 0.800, halfway between 0.800 and 0.900, is 0.850:

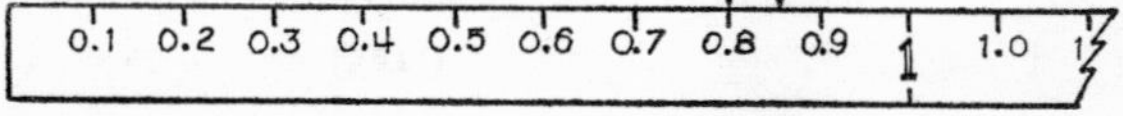

0.845 will be just a bit to the left of 0.850:

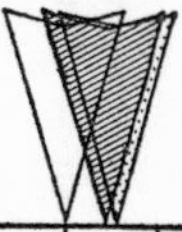

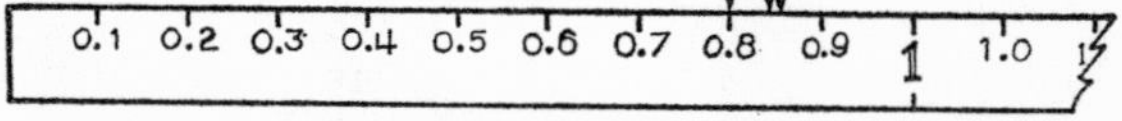

Read the settings indicated below. Choose the one that is in error and turn to the page indicated.

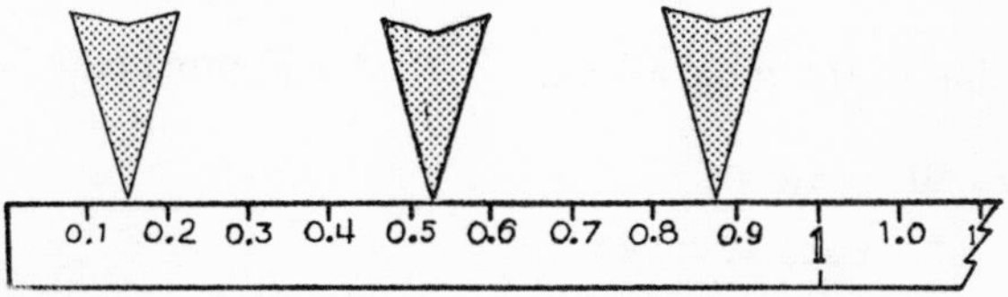

0.157. **page 52** 0.528. **page 54** 0.855. **page 58**

[*from page 45*]

YOUR ANSWER: No, it is not possible that log 2 is 0.2 and log 5 is 0.5.

You are right. When logarithms of any two numbers are added, their sum is the logarithm of the product of the two numbers. The logarithm of 2 plus the logarithm of 5 must equal 1, which is the logarithm of 10.

In mathematical notation, $2 \times 5 = 10$, and $\log 2 + \log 5 = \log 10$. However, the sum of the suggested logs does not equal log 10.

$$0.2 + 0.5 \neq 1$$

($\neq$ means *does not equal*)

So it's not quite this simple.

The process of computation of logarithms of numbers other than whole-number powers of 10 involves some aspects of mathematics which are not properly a part of this text. You will simply have to accept these facts:

(1) Every positive number has a logarithm.

(2) It is possible to compute these logarithms to a high degree of accuracy.

Here is a simplified section of a table of logarithms

Number	Logarithm
1	0.000
2	0.301
3	0.477
4	0.602
5	0.699
6	0.778
7	0.845
8	0.903
9	0.954
10	1.000

According to the table above, what is the approximate log of 2?

log 2 = .301. **page 44**

log 2 = 1.5. **page 46**

I don't understand. **page 55**

[*from page 40*]

YOUR ANSWER: No, this is not the proper setting for the log of $\frac{A}{B}$.

Yes, it is.

You have previously seen that the log of a quotient is equal to the log of the dividend (the number to be divided) minus the log of the divisor (the number that does the dividing). So

$$\log \frac{A}{B} = \log A - \log B$$

Now, using scales, we were told that the distance corresponding to log A is:

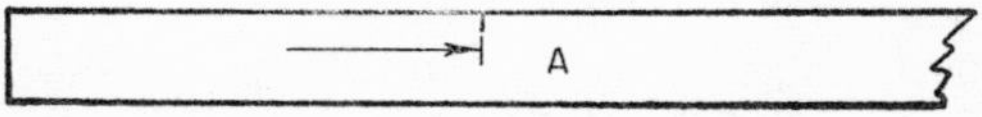

and that the distance corresponding to log B is:

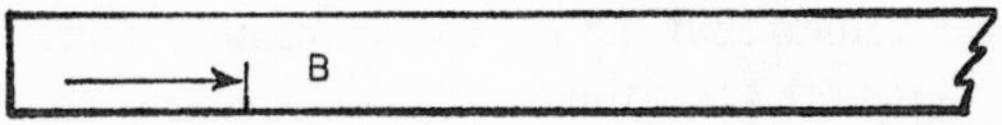

Then the distance corresponding to log $\frac{A}{B}$ is found by setting the scales so that they represent log A − log B:

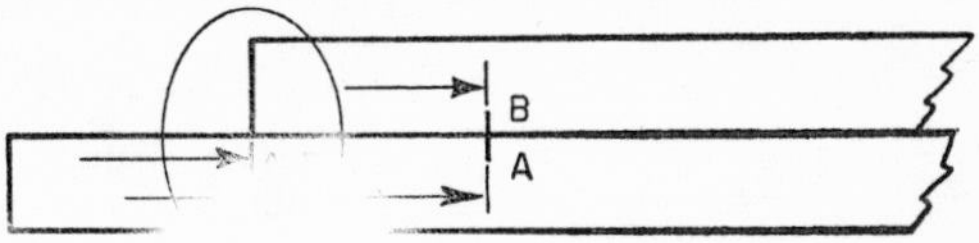

Study this until you're sure you understand it. Then return to page 40 to choose the right answer.

[*from page 45*]

YOUR ANSWER: I don't know.

The question was: Is it possible that log 2 is simply 0.2, and log 5 is 0.5?

There's a fairly straightforward way to check.

You have seen that the log of a product is equal to the sum of the logs in the factors:

$$\log (A \times B) = \log A + \log B$$

Since 2 and 5 are factors of 10 ($2 \times 5 = 10$), we know that

$$\log 2 + \log 5 = \log 10;$$

since $\log 10 = 1$,

$$\log 2 + \log 5 = 1$$

But obviously,

$$0.2 + 0.5 \neq 1$$

($\neq$ means *is not equal to*)

So we must conclude that 0.2 is not the log of 2, that 0.5 is not the log of 5, or that both are wrong.

Return to page 45 to answer the question correctly.

YOUR ANSWER: I don't understand.

You're probably confused because the arrow doesn't point directly to one of the numbers identified on the scale.

Here's the table of the first ten integers and their logs again:

log 1 = 0.000	log 6 = 0.778
log 2 = 0.301	log 7 = 0.845
log 3 = 0.477	log 8 = 0.903
log 4 = 0.602	log 9 = 0.954
log 5 = 0.699	log 10 = 1.000

Now, look at the setting below:

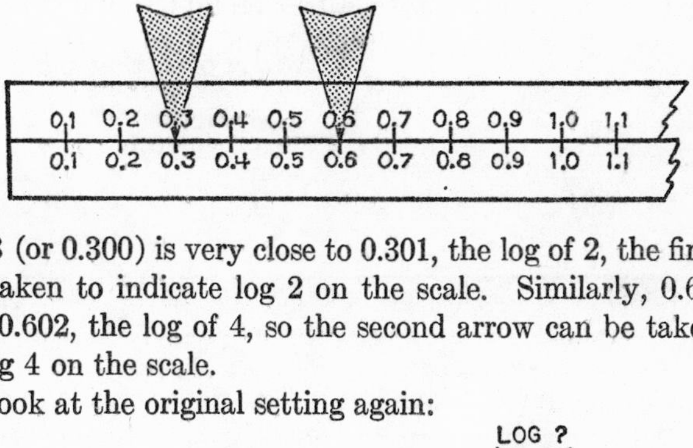

Since 0.3 (or 0.300) is very close to 0.301, the log of 2, the first arrow can be taken to indicate log 2 on the scale. Similarly, 0.6 is very close to 0.602, the log of 4, so the second arrow can be taken to indicate log 4 on the scale.

Now look at the original setting again:

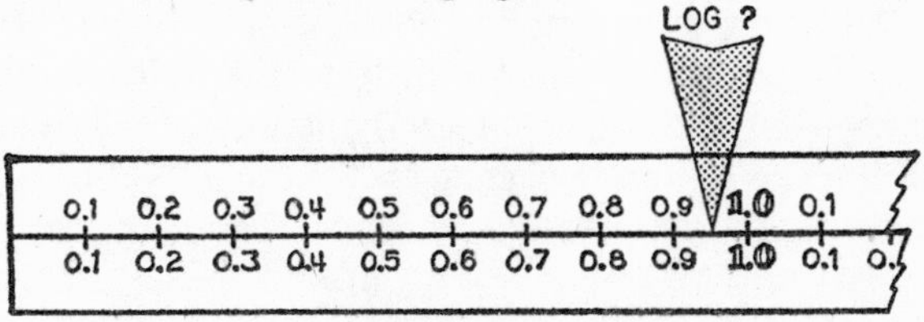

In this setting, the arrow lies approximately halfway between 0.9 (or 0.900) and 1.0 (or 1.000). According to our table, there are two numbers whose logarithms lie between 0.900 and 1.000—8 and 9. Decide which of the two logarithms the setting represents, and then return to page 59 for another try.

[*from page 47*]

YOUR ANSWER: The arrow indicating 0.157 is wrong.

No, it's all right. Look at an enlargement of that part of the diagram:

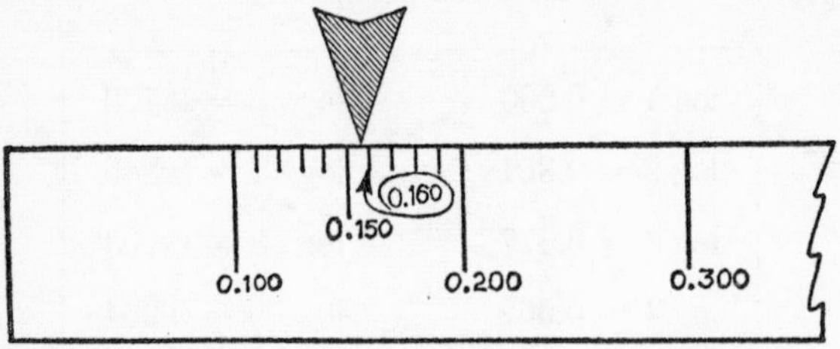

If we divide the distance between 0.1 (or 0.100) and 0.2 (0.200) into ten equal parts, then the halfway point between the two numbers is at 0.150. Moving $\frac{1}{10}$ of the distance more, we are at 0.160. The point representing 0.157 must lie between 0.150 and 0.160, and it must be closer to 0.160.

Now look at a reproduction of the original diagram:

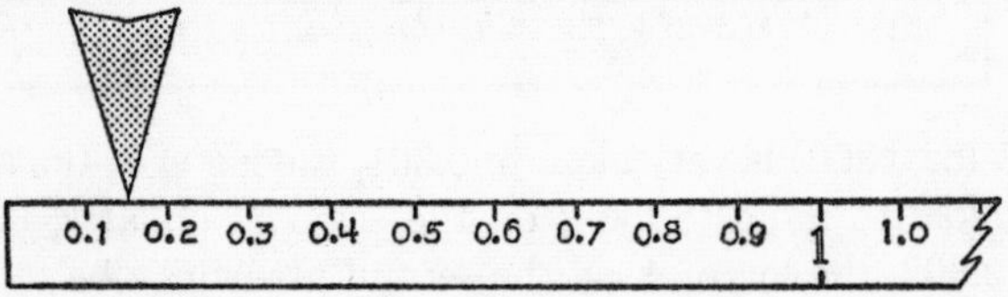

Since this diagram is so small, it is close to impossible to determine whether the arrow is in exactly the right spot to represent 0.157. However, it appears to be just a little to the right of the halfway point between 0.1 and 0.2, so, as nearly as we can tell, it's accurate.

Return to page 47 and try again.

[*from page 44*]

YOUR ANSWER: Log 4 = 2.5.

No. Evidently you're not getting the idea of reading the table. Here is the table again, with that portion that indicates the logarithm of 4 circled.

Number	Logarithm
1	0.000
2	0.301
3	0.477
4	0.602
5	0.699
6	0.778
7	0.845
8	0.903
9	0.954
10	1.000

You should understand this now, so return to page 44 and select the correct answer.

[*from page 47*]

YOUR ANSWER: The arrow indicating 0.528 is not accurate.

Sorry, but as nearly as we can tell on such a small scale, it is accurate.

If we divide the distance between 0.5 (or 0.500) and 0.6 (or 0.600) into ten equal parts, these divisions represent 0.510, 0.520, 0.530, and so on. Now, 0.528 must lie close to 0.530, between 0.520 and 0.530.

Look at this enlargement:

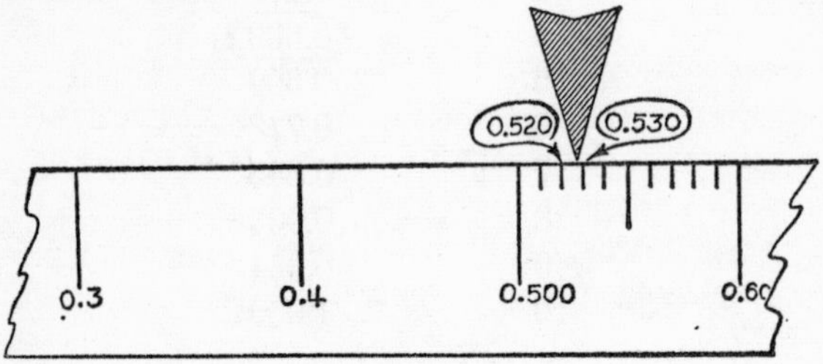

Now look at the original scale:

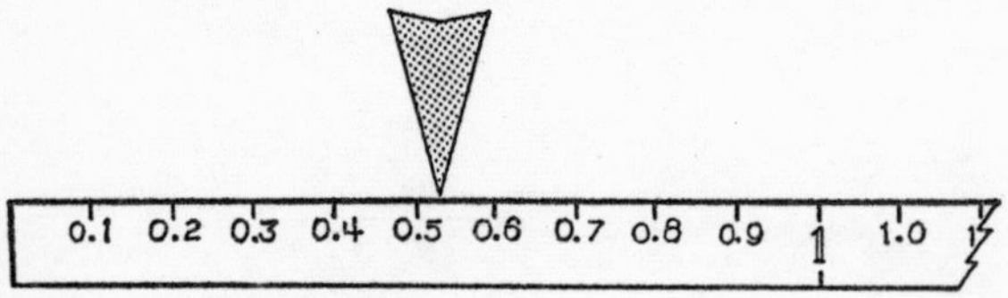

As closely as we can estimate, the arrow is accurately placed. Return to page 47 and try again.

[*from page 48*]

YOUR ANSWER: I don't understand.

Let's see if we can clear up the difficulty.

Each number has a logarithm, which is to say that since

$$\log 1 = 0$$

$$\log 10 = 1$$

$$\log 100 = 2$$

and so on,

then it is reasonable to assume that between log 1 and log 10 there are numbers corresponding to log 2, log 3, log 4. However, since it is not our purpose in this book to devote additional chapters on the development of mathematical processes necessary for the computation of log 2, log 3, log 4 and many others, we simply present here the results of such computation in a simplified table. To find the logarithm of 2 in this table, look in the column headed "number" until you find "2". Then read to the right and you will find ".301".

Number	Logarithm
1	0.000
2	0.301
3	0.477
4	0.602
5	0.699
6	0.778
7	0.845
8	0.903
9	0.954
10	1.000

Return to page 48 and answer the question correctly.

[*from page 58*]

YOUR ANSWER: 8.

You are correct. The logarithms on this scale are evenly spaced. The whole numbers are unevenly spaced because each one is placed directly over its own logarithm.

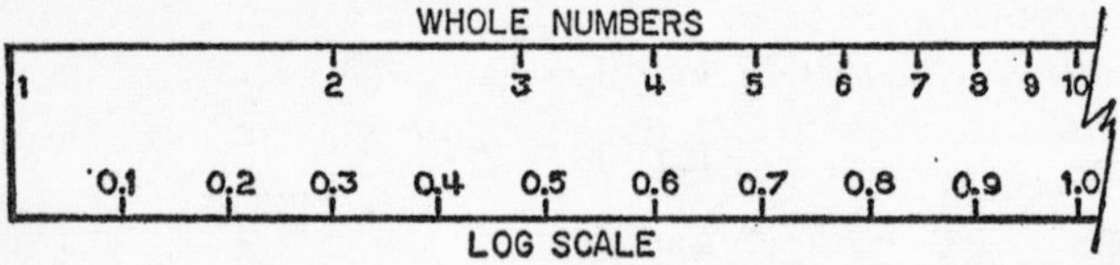

NOW! Get out your slide rule. Find the C and D scales. These scales are indicated with a letter C and a letter D at the left end of the scale. On all slide rules they will be identical and placed one above the other, with the C scale on top. Study the simplified illustration below and note that we have left out all of the smaller divisions on the C and D scales. Those shown below may be called the *major divisions.*

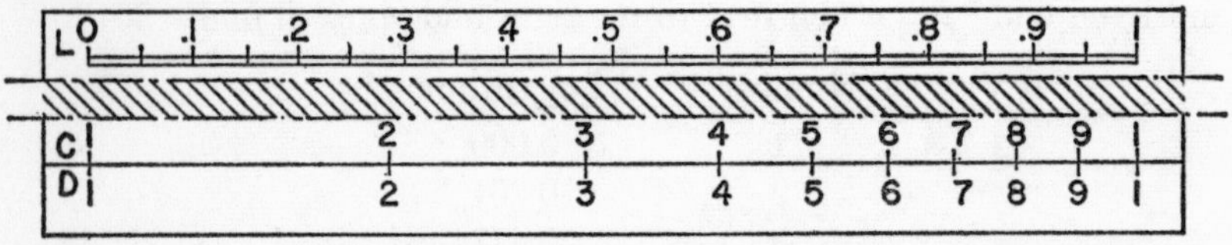

As we noted above, the numbers are not evenly spaced. These numbers are placed on the rule at intervals corresponding to their logarithms. For example since log 2 = .301, the number 2 is placed at a position corresponding to .301 or about 3/10 of the total length of the scale. If your slide rule has an L scale (do not confuse this with any LL scale) you will see that 2 on the D and C scales is very nearly opposite .3 (exactly opposite .301) on the L scale. This is because the L scale is evenly divided for the entire length of the scale, and the total length of the scale is considered as one unit.

Now study the figure below. What happens when we increase 2 units on the D scale by 3 units on the C scale?

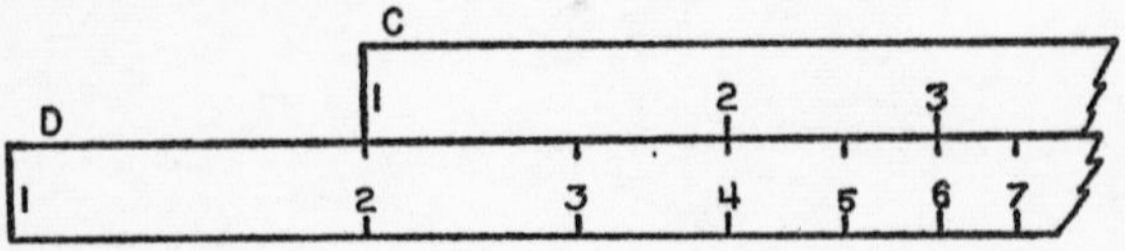

We see that $2 + 3 = 5$. **page 65**   We see that $2 \times 3 = 6$. **page 69**

[*from page 69*]

YOUR ANSWER: Any multiplication is a form of addition because 3×4 can be written as $4 + 4 + 4$.

True, but it does not describe the theory of slide rule operation.

The fact that 3×4 is the same as $4 + 4 + 4$ only means that it would be possible to take two ordinary rulers and perform any multiplication by extending one factor by itself again and again and again—if the rulers were long enough—just as we did earlier.

Thus we could multiply 2×3 in the following manner:

$$2 \times 3 = 2 + 2 + 2$$

STEP 1. $2 + 2 = 4$

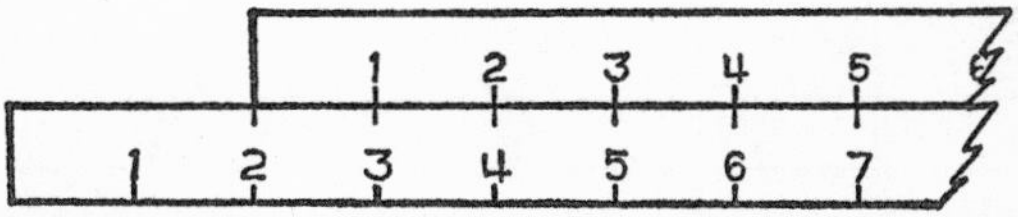

STEP. 2. $4 + 2 = 6$

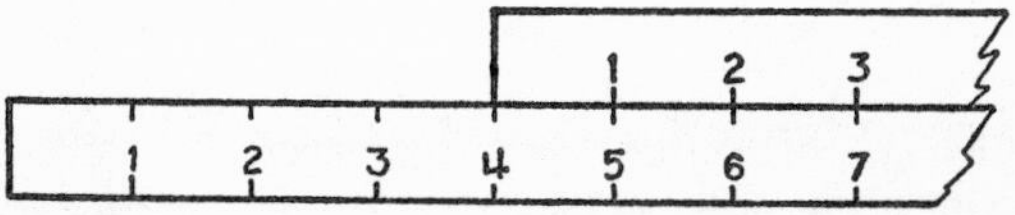

This would be a tiring and time-consuming task, especially if you had to perform some calculation such as 107×35.64. The idea of the slide rule is to simplify calculations, not to complicate them.

Your choice of this answer suggests that you may not yet understand the basic operation of the slide rule. For a review, return to page 40.

[*from page 47*]

YOUR ANSWER: 0.855 is not correct.

Right. The arrow more nearly points to 0.875.

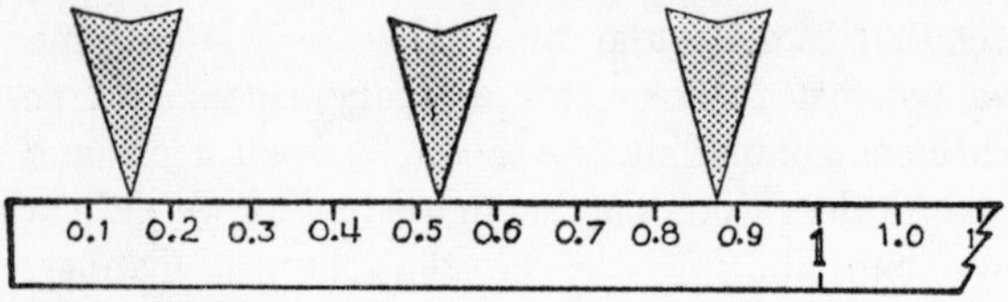

Now, here is the setting for 3 divided by 2.

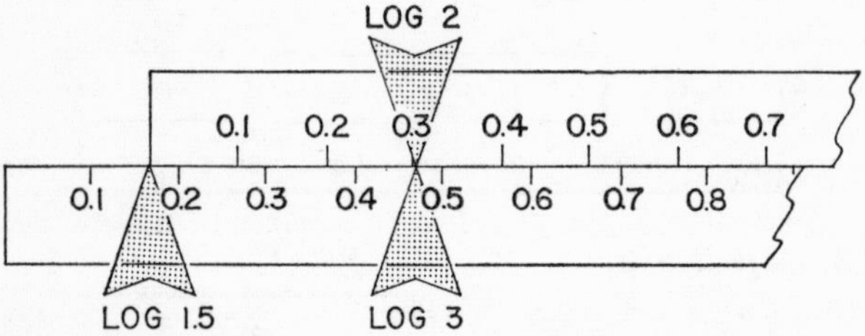

The result is $1\frac{1}{2}$, of course. But the answer isn't midway between 1 and 2 on the scale, because log 1.5 = 0.176, which is closer to log 2 (i.e., 0.301) than to log 1 (i.e., 0.000).

Now that we've some idea of how logs work, we are ready to take a giant step. Look at the scale below.

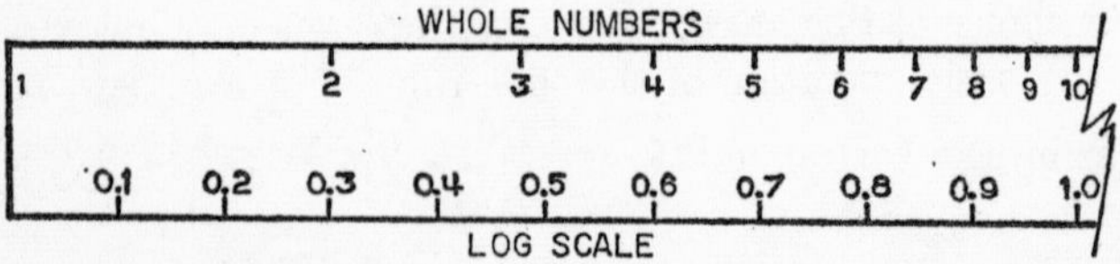

The numbers along the top of this scale are whole numbers, or integers. But the distances between them are not equal. Instead, the numbers are spaced to correspond to the values of their logarithms.

Since the log of 2 is 0.301, the figure 2 is placed not at a point $\frac{2}{10}$ of the way from the left end of the scale, but at a point just opposite 0.301 on the log scale. Similarly, the number 5 is not at the halfway point but opposite 0.699 on the log scale, since log 5 is 0.699.

What whole number is 0.903 of the distance between 0 and 10?

9. **page 43** 8. **page 56** I don't know. **page 75**

[*from page 44*]

YOUR ANSWER: Log 4 = .602.

You have the correct answer.

It turns out that the log of 2 isn't exactly .301, nor is the log of 5 exactly .699. In fact, seldom can the log of an integer such as 2 or 5 be completely written down, for most logs are unending decimals. For instance the log of 2 starts out:

$$\log 2 = 0.30103010\ldots$$

and keeps on going.

This isn't so good. We've been trying to simplify matters, not complicate them. Besides, how can you find a mark on a scale corresponding to such an endless number? 0.3 isn't hard to find. 0.35 simply requires that the interval between 0.3 and 0.4 be divided in two, but 0.301030 . . . ! Clearly there must be a happy medium. Let's be content with three figures: log 2 = 0.301.

Here is the table of the integers, or whole numbers, from 1 to 10, with their logs computed to three decimal places.

log 1 = 0.000	log 6 = 0.778
log 2 = 0.301	log 7 = 0.845
log 3 = 0.477	log 8 = 0.903
log 4 = 0.602	log 9 = 0.954
log 5 = 0.699	log 10 = 1.000

What integer corresponds to the logarithm indicated below?

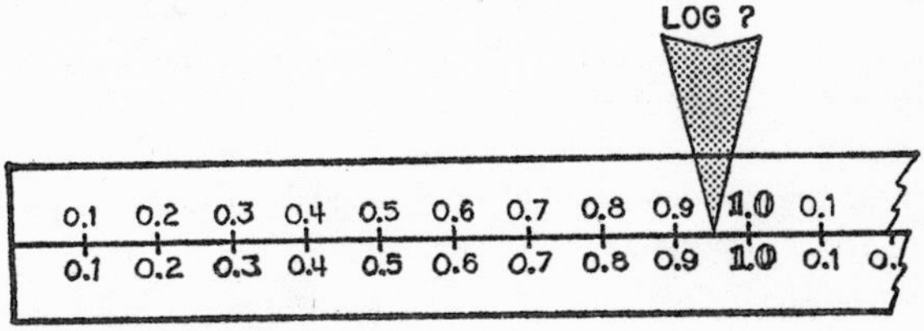

8. **page 41**

9. **page 47**

I don't understand. **page 51**

[*from page 69*]

YOUR ANSWER: The numbers on a slide rule are spaced according to the values of their logarithms, and we can arrive at a product by adding logarithms.

Very good. That is the theory of the slide rule in a nutshell. Let's summarize the important points before going on.

1. Any quantity can be represented by a distance on a scale; two quantities can be added graphically by means of two scales.
2. The common logarithm of a number is the power to which the base 10 must be raised to obtain that number.
3. Numbers can be multiplied by adding their logarithms: the logarithm of the product is the sum of the logarithms of the factors.
4. The slide rule multiplies by graphically adding logarithms. However, the logarithms themselves are not shown. Instead, the numbers corresponding to the logarithms are placed on the scales. Thus, when you add the distance representing one number to the distance representing another on the slide rule, the result is the *product* of the numbers.

Simple, isn't it?

How would division be handled with logs? (Remember that in division, the *dividend* is the number to be divided, the *divisor* is the number that does the dividing, and the *quotient* is the answer.)

The log of the quotient should be added to the log of the divisor to find the log of the dividend. **page 64**

The log of the divisor should be subtracted from the log of the dividend to find the log of the quotient. **page 68**

The log of the dividend should be divided by the log of the divisor to find the quotient. **page 81**

[*from page 67*]

YOUR ANSWER: $\dfrac{1.45 \times 4.90}{2.00} = 3.352.$

No. If you weren't guessing, you slipped up on your readings. On your slide rule follow the procedure below:

To multiply 1.45 by 4.90, set the left index of the C scale over the 1.45 of the D scale. Then slide the hairline indicator over until the hairline is over 4.9 (or 4.90) on the C scale:

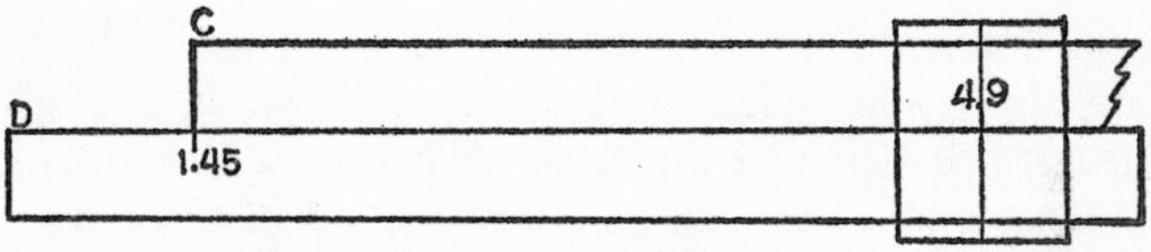

Next, to divide the product of 1.45 and 4.90 by 2.00, shift 2 (or 2.00) on the C scale under the hairline:

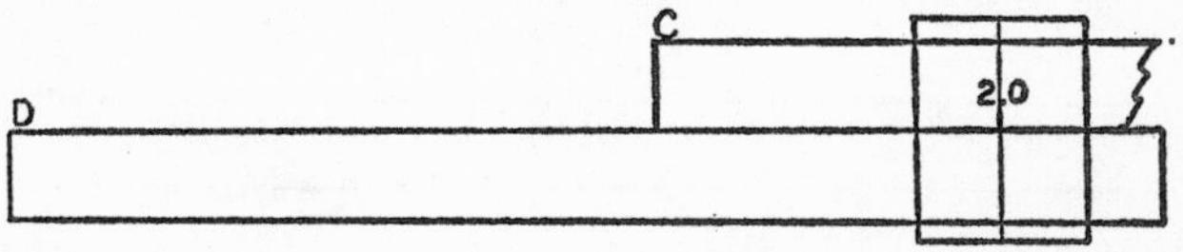

The answer appears on the D scale at the index of the C scale. When you have it, return to page 67 to make the correct selection.

[*from page 68*]

YOUR ANSWER: The indicated number is 2.73.

Let's look at the scale again:

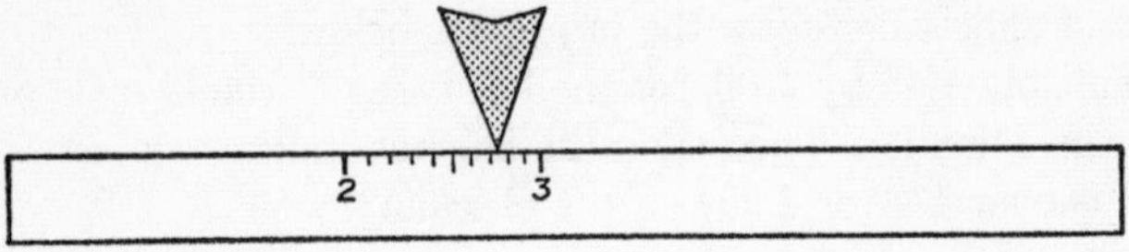

It is clear that the point of the arrow lies between 2.70 and 2.80 —this we can say for sure. And we can feel safe in saying that it lies slightly to the left of 2.75, in the vicinity of 2.73 and 2.74. But that's about as far as we can go. The scale does not have enough markings to let us make a more accurate statement

Similarly, this setting can be taken as 3.66, 3.67, or 3.68:

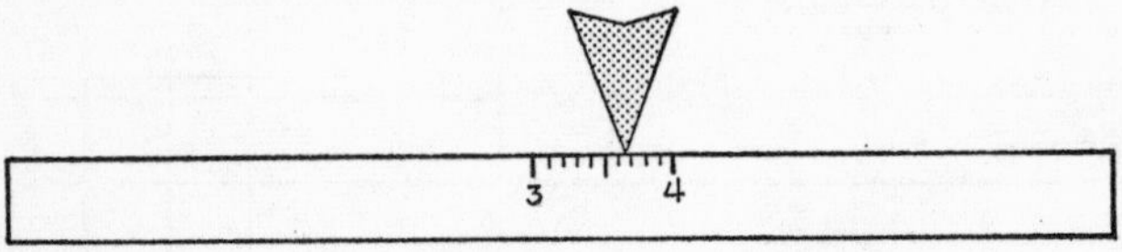

And this could be anything from 5.74 to 5.76:

Without marks indicating still smaller intervals, we can't be more definite than this.

Return to page 68 and answer the question correctly.

[*from page 98*]

YOUR ANSWER: $\frac{3}{2.7} = \frac{4.05}{4.5}$ is a correct proportion.

Is it? Let's check.

If you divide out both fractions to three figures you will see that:

$$\frac{3}{2.7} = 1.11 \quad \text{while} \quad \frac{4.05}{4.5} = 0.900.$$

Clearly, then,

$$\frac{3}{2.7} \neq \frac{4.05}{4.5}$$

To find out what's really happening, look at the setting again:

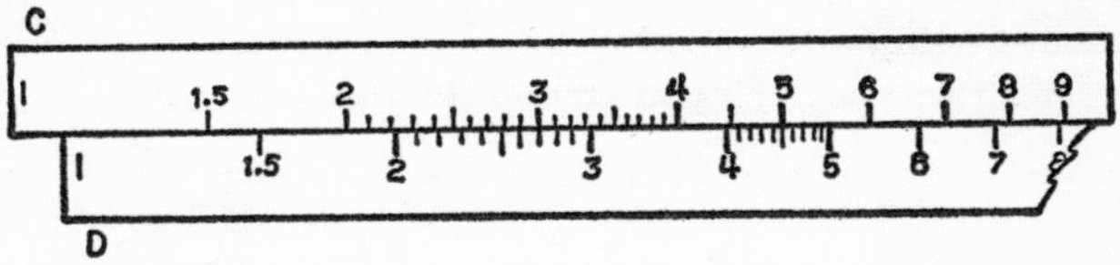

According to this setting,

$$\frac{3}{2.7} = 1.11 \quad \text{and also} \quad \frac{4.5}{4.05} = 1.11.$$

In each case, the number on the C scale is the numerator and the number on the D scale is the denominator.

Therefore, the correct proportion is

$$\frac{3}{2.7} = \frac{4.5}{4.05}.$$

Study this until you're sure you understand why your answer was wrong. Then return to page 98 and select the correct one.

[*from page 60*]

YOUR ANSWER: In division, the log of the quotient should be added to the log of the divisor to find the log of the dividend.

It is true that when you add the log of the quotient to the log of the divisor, you get the log of the dividend as an answer. Or, to put it in non-logarithmic form, when you multiply the quotient by the divisor, your answer is the dividend.

For example, since $12 \div 3 = 4$, it's also true that $3 \times 4 = 12$. Therefore $\log 4 + \log 3 = \log 12$. Or as the answer you chose said, the log of the quotient plus the log of the divisor is equal to the log of the dividend.

But how do you start out with the quotient? In a division problem the quotient will be your answer. You can't start with the answer. You have merely chosen a way in which the accuracy of the original division can be checked.

Please return to page 60 and choose the right answer.

YOUR ANSWER: When we increase 2 units by 3 units we see that $2 + 3 = 5$.

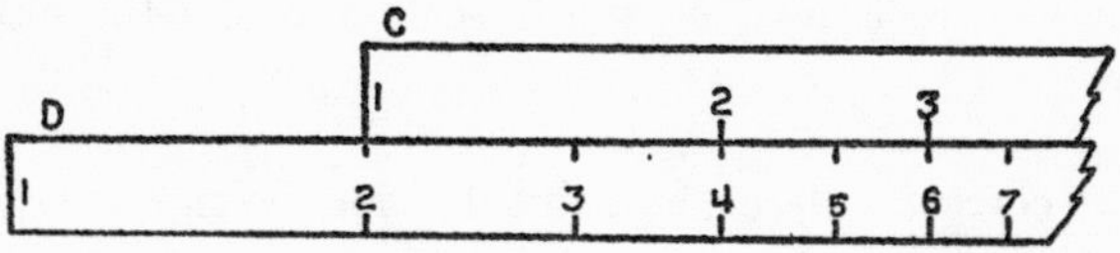

We do not. We put the figure 1 of the top scale (the C scale) opposite the figure 2 of the bottom scale (the D scale). Then, we find the figure 3 on the C scale and notice that it is exactly above the figure 6 on the D scale. While it is true that $3 + 2 = 5$, this clearly doesn't prove it. What it does prove is that the sum of the logarithms of 3 and 2 is equal to the logarithm of 6.

We are adding logarithms, which means we are multiplying their numerical equivalents (remember that the log of $A \times B = \log A + \log B$). However, instead of putting the logarithms on the scales, we have, over the last few pages, substituted the numbers themselves for their logarithms. That is the whole trick of the slide rule. It is not necessary to look up in a table the logarithms of the numbers we want to multiply, then add the logarithms, and finally try to discover the number for which the logarithmic product is the equivalent. Since the numbers have been logarithmically spaced, all those intervening steps are avoided, and we can perform multiplication by adding, and division by subtracting.

So, when 2 units are increased by 3 units on our logarithmic scale, the result is the product of 2 and 3, not their sum.

Here is another example:

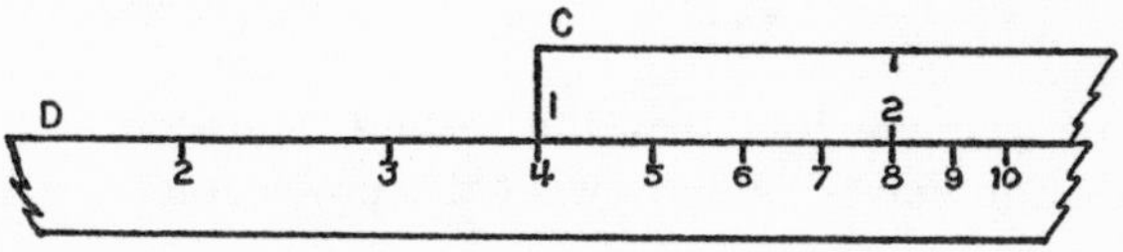

4 units are increased by 2 units. We see that the figure 2 on the top scale falls opposite the 8 on the lower scale. Once again, the result is not the sum but the product of 4 and 2.

Now if you feel you have the right idea, return to page 56 and select the correct answer.

[*from page 86*]

YOUR ANSWER: When the divisor, 3, is set under the hairline on the D scale, and the dividend, 6, is set under the hairline on the C scale, the answer is read on the C scale opposite the index of the D scale.

You are correct. Here's how this division looks:

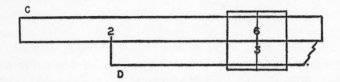

You are reducing the value of the log on the C scale by the value of the log on the D scale; what's left over on the C scale is your answer.

Just for practice, perform the same simple divisions you did on the last page by this method, with the divisor on the D scale and the dividend on the C scale.

$$\frac{3}{2} = ? \qquad \frac{6}{3} = ? \qquad \frac{8}{5} = ? \qquad \frac{2}{5} = ? \qquad \frac{3}{6} = ?$$

Now look at this setting:

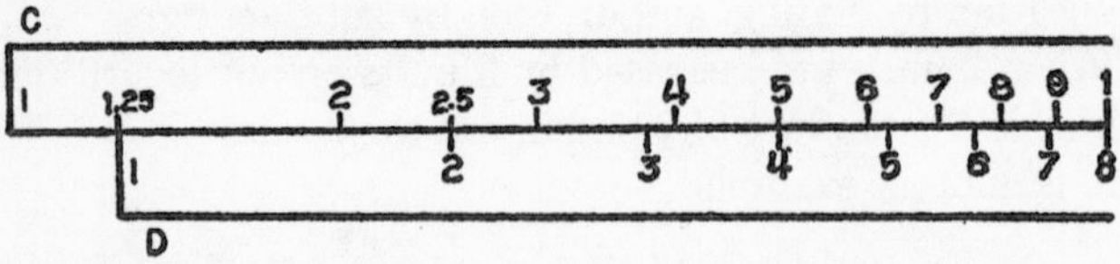

Suppose you are told that the setting represents a problem in division. Can you tell exactly what this problem is?

This setting represents 5 ÷ 4. **page 72**

This setting represents 2.5 ÷ 2. **page 77**

This setting represents both 5 ÷ 4 and 2.5 ÷ 2. **page 92**

This setting represents many divisions. **page 97**

[*from page 88*]

YOUR ANSWER: 1.5 × 3.6 × 1.2 = 6.48.

Fine. Here's the way it goes:

First, find 1.5 on the D scale and align the left index (beginning) of the C scale with it. Next, slide the indicator along until the hairline is at 3.6 on the C scale:

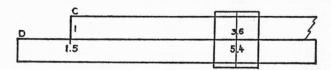

It isn't necessary to read 5.4 on the D scale. Leave the hairline indicator at this point and move the sliding scale to the right until the 1 on the C scale is under the hairline. Once this is done, simply slide the hairline indicator to the right, stopping at 1.2 on the C scale. The answer, 6.48, appears on the D scale.

To divide, of course, we just reverse the order in which we perform these operations. Thus, instead of adding logarithms, we subtract the logarithm of the divisor from the logarithm of the dividend. For instance, let's now divide 6.48 by 3:

1. Slide the hairline indicator to 6.48 on the D scale.
2. Slide 3 on the C scale under the hairline.
3. Read the answer, 2.16, on the D scale at the index of the C scale.

Now try this one:

$$\frac{1.45 \times 4.90}{2.00} = ?$$

3.352 **page 61**

3.552 **page 70**

3.55 **page 86**

[*from page 60*]

YOUR ANSWER: In division, the log of the divisor should be subtracted from the log of the dividend to find the log of the quotient.

Exactly. Division and multiplication are inverse operations, just as addition and subtraction are inverse operations. Since we multiply by adding logs, we can divide by subtracting them.

Here is how we might divide 6 by 2 with a slide rule:

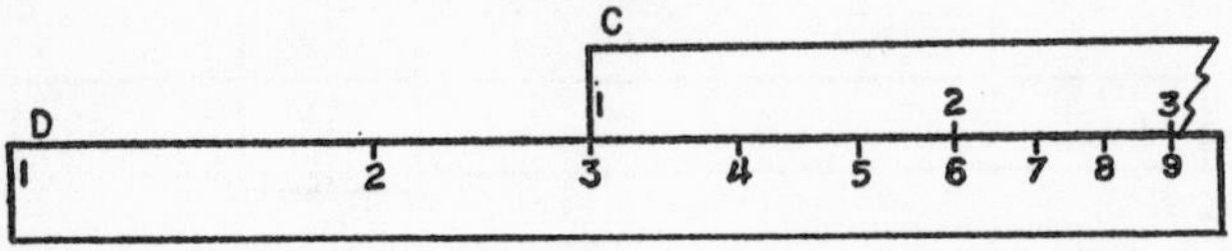

The log of 6 on the lower scale is decreased by the log of 2 on the upper scale. The quotient, 3, is read on the lower scale.

Of course the question of finding a quotient such as $\frac{5.6}{3.2}$ is still with us. That is, we need to be able to read between the integers.

It would be impossible to make marks for every number between 1 and 2, or between 3 and 4, but on all slide rules these spaces are marked off in tenths in a manner similar to the way integers (whole numbers) were, i.e., logarithmically spaced. These marks may be called secondary divisions and are shown in the figure below.

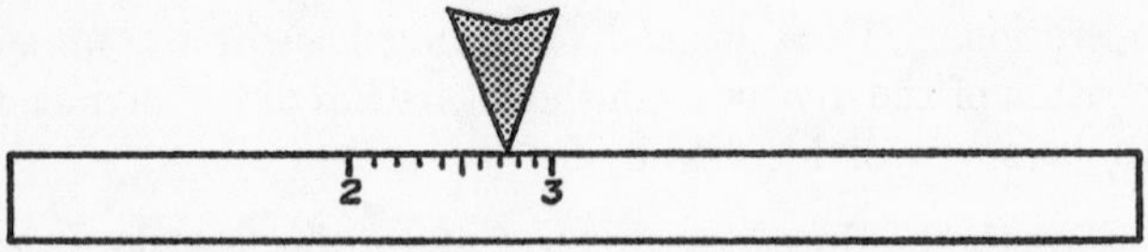

Now we need to be sure that you can read our completed scales. In the figure above, where is the arrow pointing?

2.73. **page 62**

2.74. **page 76**

It might be either one. **page 88**

YOUR ANSWER: When we increase 2 units by 3 units with the C and D scales, we see that $2 \times 3 = 6$.

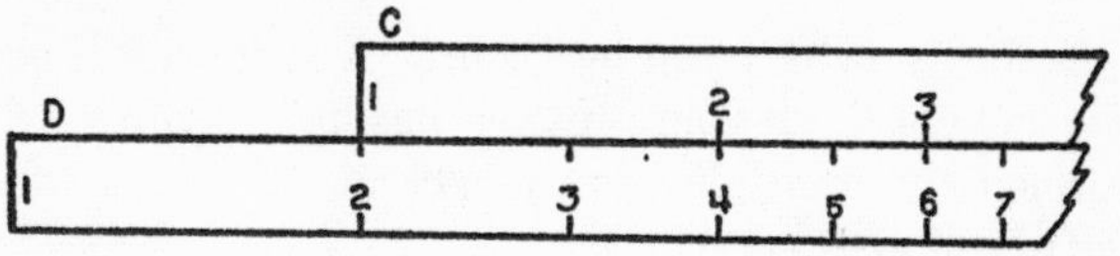

Exactly. Because $\log (A \times B) = \log A + \log B$, we can multiply 2 by 3 simply by adding the logarithm of 3 to the logarithm of 2. On the slide rule, then, we add the distance corresponding to the logarithm of 3 to the distance corresponding to the logarithm of 2. However, instead of marking the values of the logarithms on the scales, we have, over the last few pages, substituted the numbers themselves for their logarithms.

And that is the basic principle of the slide rule. Since the numbers have been logarithmically spaced, we can perform multiplication by adding distances and division by subtracting them.

Here is the setting for the calculation $2 \times 4 = 8$:

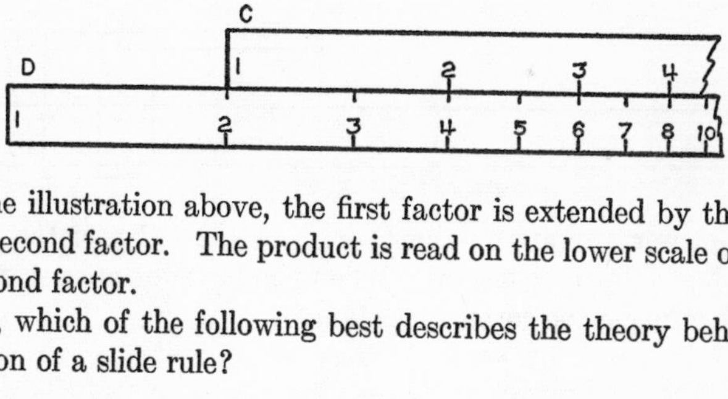

In the illustration above, the first factor is extended by the value of the second factor. The product is read on the lower scale opposite the second factor.

Now, which of the following best describes the theory behind the operation of a slide rule?

We can multiply by adding on a slide rule because any multiplication is a form of addition; 3×4 can be written as $4 + 4 + 4$. **page 57**

The numbers on a slide rule are spaced according to their logarithms, and we can arrive at a product by adding logarithms. **page 60**

The slide rule operates by multiplying the logarithms of numbers instead of multiplying the numbers themselves. **page 73**

[*from page 67*]

YOUR ANSWER: $\dfrac{1.45 \times 4.90}{2.00} = 3.552.$

Well, yes, but how did you get here? A slide rule is accurate to only three figures, and your answer has four figures. Evidently you performed the multiplication longhand, or used a table of logarithms. Or you guessed.

Let's start over.

To multiply 1.45 by 4.90, set the left index of the C scale over the 1.45 of the D scale. Then slide the hairline indicator until the hairline is over 4.9 (or 4.90) on the C scale:

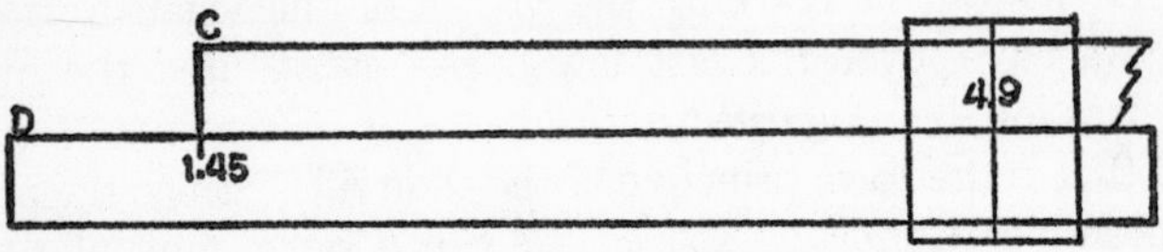

Next, to divide the product of 1.45 and 4.90 by 2.00, shift 2 (or 2.00) on the C scale under the hairline:

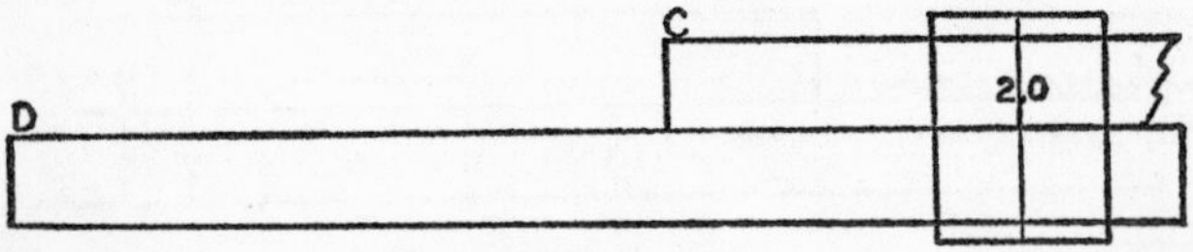

The answer appears on the D scale at the index of the C scale. And it has only three figures. When you have the answer, return to page 67 to make the correct selection.

YOUR ANSWER: 1.5 × 3.6 × 1.2 = 4.50

It looks as if you multiplied 1.5 by 3.6, and then *divided* by 1.2; you should have *multiplied*. Here's the way it goes, step by step:

First, slide the left index of the C scale over the 1.5 of the D scale:

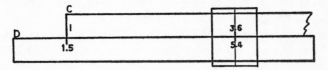

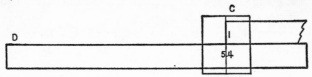

Then slide the indicator until the hairline is at 3.6 on the C scale:

(At this point, if it were necessary, the product of 1.5 and 3.6 could be read from the D scale, directly beneath the hairline. However, since we still have another factor, we just leave the indicator at this point and go on with the problem.)

The next step is to slide the C scale to the right until the left index of the C scale is under the hairline. (Don't move the hairline indicator!)

Finally, slide the indicator to 1.2 on the C scale:

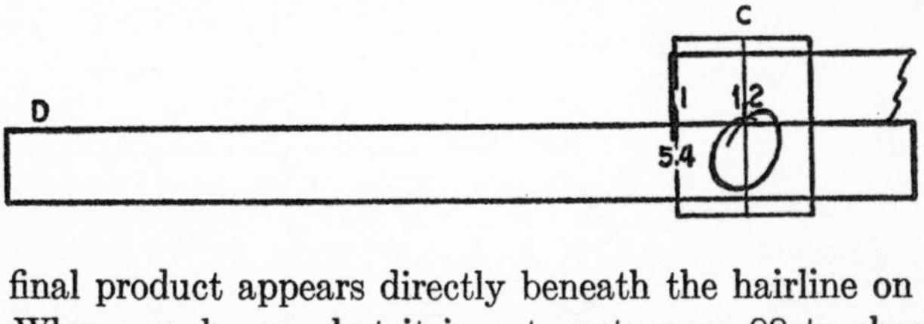

The final product appears directly beneath the hairline on the D scale. When you know what it is, return to page 88 to choose the right answer.

[*from page 66*]

YOUR ANSWER: Yes, we can tell exactly what problem the setting represents: 5 ÷ 4.

Well, let's check. Here's the setting again:

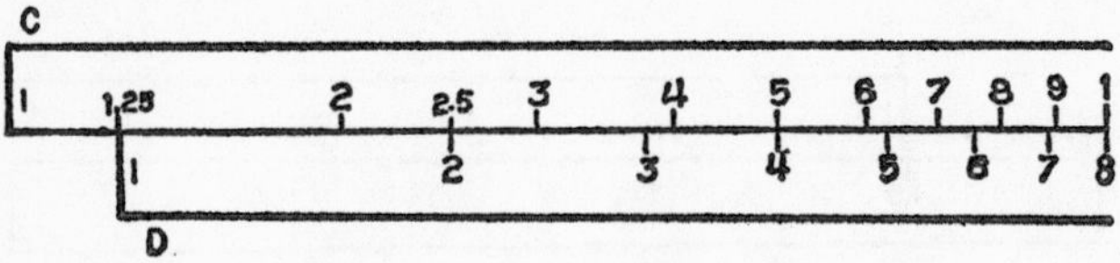

It certainly can be considered a representation of 5 ÷ 4, since 5 on the C scale is directly over 4 on the D scale. The answer, 1.25, is then on the C scale at the end of the D scale.

But how about 2.5 ÷ 2? Since 2.5 on the C scale is in line with 2 on the D scale, the setting also represents the division 2.5 ÷ 2. The answer is again 1.25.

Looking at it another way, we find that this setting can also represent the divisions 4 ÷ 5 and 2 ÷ 2.5. In each of these cases, the answer is 0.8, and it appears on the D scale at the right index of the C scale.

In fact, if we consider each of the numbers on the C scale as being divided by the number directly below it on the D scale, we see that the setting represents all possible divisions for which the answer is 1.25. And going from the D scale to the C scale, the setting represents all the divisions for which the answer is 0.8.

When you're clear on this point, return to page 66 to select the correct answer.

YOUR ANSWER: The slide rule operates by multiplying the logarithms of numbers instead of multiplying the numbers themselves.

Really? You'd better consider what would happen if you multiplied logarithms.

$$1{,}000 \times 1{,}000 = 1{,}000{,}000$$

The logarithm of 1,000 is 3, because $10^3 = 1{,}000$.

If we multiplied logarithms, our product would be $10^{3\times3}$, or 10^9. But $10^9 \neq 1{,}000{,}000$. It equals 1,000,000,000, a difference sufficient to cause some concern, to say the least.

We multiply two numbers by adding their logarithms. Thus $1{,}000 \times 1{,}000 = 10^{3+3}$ or 10^6.

The slide rule works because the units on the scales are spaced according to the value of their logarithms. All the scale does is add the logs.

If this isn't clear, you'd better return to page 40 to get this whole business of logs straightened out.

If you're satisfied that you understand this, you may return to page 69 and pick the correct answer.

[*from page 88*]

YOUR ANSWER: $1.5 \times 3.6 \times 1.2 = 4.13$.

No, and this answer looks like a guess. Here's the way it goes, step by step:

First, slide the left index of the C scale over the 1.5 of the D scale.

Then slide the indicator over until the hairline is at 3.6 on the C scale:

(At this point, if it were necessary, the product of 1.5 and 3.6 could be read from the D scale, directly beneath the hairline. However, since we still have another factor, we just leave the indicator at this point and go on with the problem.)

The next step is to slide the C scale to the right until the 1 of the C scale is under the hairline:

Finally, slide the indicator to 1.2 on the C scale:

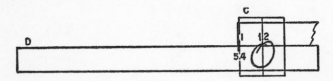

The final product appears directly beneath the hairline on the D scale. When you know what it is, return to page 88 and select the right answer.

[*from page 58*]

YOUR ANSWER: I don't know what whole number is 0.903 of the distance between 0 and 10.

Well, let's go over it carefully.

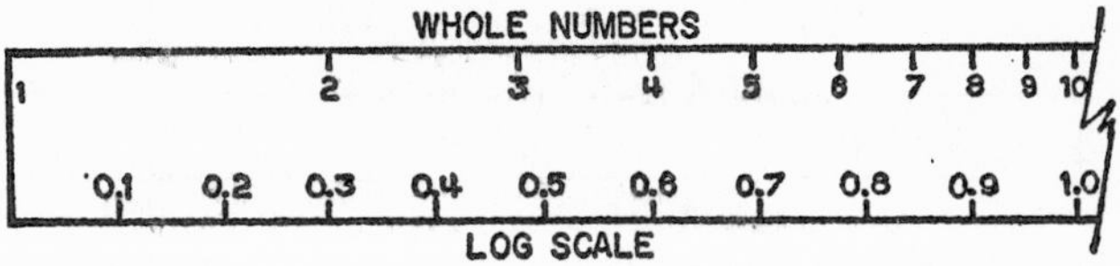

The whole numbers are the figures on the top of the scale above. They are spaced unevenly, as you see.

Beneath them are the evenly-spaced logarithms. The logarithm 0.5 is just half the way up the scale; 0.25 falls one-quarter of the way between 0 and 1, and so on.

The whole numbers are unevenly spaced because each one is placed directly over its own logarithm. Thus 2 is placed above 0.301; 7 is placed above 0.845.

Since the logarithms are evenly spaced, it is correct to say that the number 2 is placed 0.301 of the distance between 0 and 10; and 7 is placed 0.845 of the distance between 0 and 10.

Now, what whole number is placed 0.903 of the distance between 0 and 10? Obviously this is the whole number that has a logarithm of 0.903.

With this information, you should be able to return to page 58 and select the right answer.

[*from page 68*]

YOUR ANSWER: The indicated number is 2.74.

Let's look at the scale again:

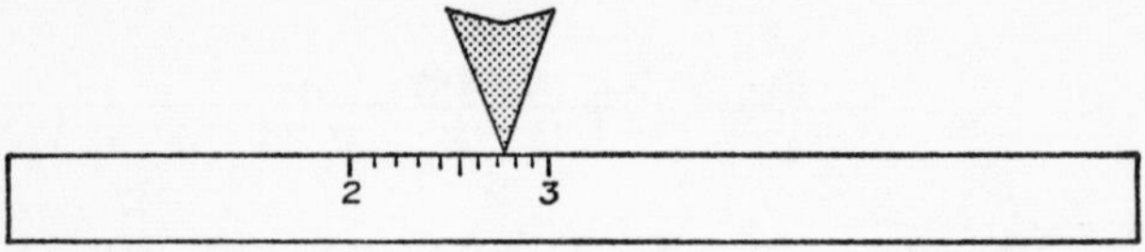

It is clear that the point of the arrow lies between 2.70 and 2.80—this we can say for sure. And we can feel safe in saying that it lies slightly to the left of 2.75, in the vicinity of 2.73 and 2.74. But that's about as far as we can go. The scale does not have enough markings to let us make a more accurate statement.

Similarly, this setting can be taken as 3.66, 3.67, or 3.68.

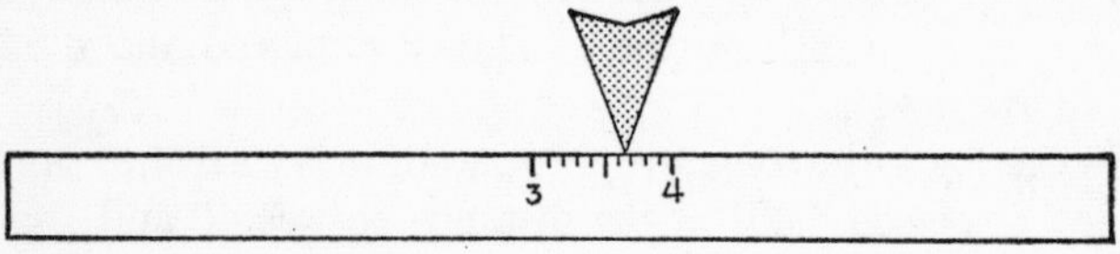

And this could be anything from 5.74 to 5.76:

Without marks indicating still smaller intervals, we can't come to any more concrete conclusion.

Return to page 68 and answer the question correctly.

[*from page 66*]

YOUR ANSWER: Yes, we can tell exactly what problem the setting represents: 2.5 ÷ 2.

Well, let's check. Here's the setting again:

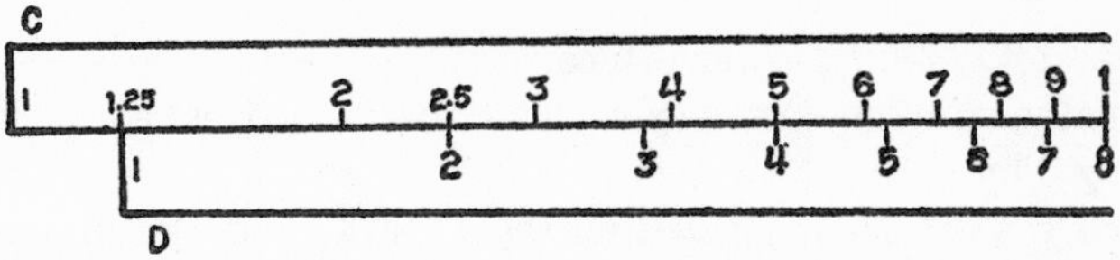

It certainly can be considered a representation of 2.5 ÷ 2, since 2.5 on the C scale is directly over 2 on the D scale. The answer, 1.25, is then on the C scale at the end of the D scale.

But how about 5 ÷ 4? Since 5 on the C scale is in line with 4 on the D scale, the setting also represents the division 5 ÷ 4. The answer is again 1.25.

Looking at it another way, we find that this setting can also represent the divisions 4 ÷ 5 and 2 ÷ 2.5. In each of these cases, the answer is 0.8, and it appears on the D scale at the right index of the C scale.

In fact, if we consider each of the numbers on the C scale as being divided by the number directly below it on the D scale, we see that the setting represents all possible divisions for which the answer is 1.25. And going from the D scale to the C scale, the setting represents all the divisions for which the answer is 0.8.

When you're clear on this point, return to page 66 to select the correct answer.

[*from page 86*]

YOUR ANSWER: When the divisor 3 is set under the hairline on the D scale, and the dividend 6 is set under the hairline on the C scale, the answer is read on the D scale opposite the index of the C scale.

And, if you worked this out, you presumably arrived at the conclusion that $\frac{6}{3} = 5$.

It doesn't. Your answer is incorrect.

Actually, the operation you have performed is equivalent to dividing 3 by 6, and your answer is 0.5.

When the divisor is located on the D scale, and the dividend on the C scale, the quotient will be found on the C scale, too. This is because you are reducing the value of the log on the C scale by the value of the log on the D scale; what's left over on the C scale is your answer.

Now please return to page 86 and select the right answer.

YOUR ANSWER: This group contains an error:

$$415 = 4.15 \times 10^2$$

$$135{,}000{,}000 = 1.35 \times 10^8$$

No, both of these numbers are factored correctly. Let's check them and see. Remember, multiplying by a positive power of ten is equivalent to moving the decimal point toward the right the number of places indicated by the power. To multiply 4.15 by 10^2, we move the decimal point of 4.15 two places to the right:

$$4.15.$$

So the first problem is all right:

$$415 = 4.15 \times 10^2$$

To multiply 1.35 by 10^8, we move the decimal point of 1.35 eight places to the right:

$$1.35000000.$$

So the second problem is also correct:

$$135{,}000{,}000 = 1.35 \times 10^8$$

Return to page 102 and try again.

[*from page 93*]

YOUR ANSWER: $0.0000162 = 1.62 \times 10^{-4}$.

No.
$10^{-4} = \frac{1}{10^4} = \frac{1}{10{,}000}$, so

$$1.62 \times 10^{-4} = 1.62 \times \frac{1}{10{,}000}$$
$$= 0.000162$$

But 0.000162 has only three zeros between the decimal point and the 1. The number we're working with, 0.0000162, has four.

Let's retrace our steps a bit. We've seen that

$$1.62 \times 10^{-1} = 1.62 \times \frac{1}{10^1} = 1.62 \times \frac{1}{10} = 0.162,$$

$$1.62 \times 10^{-2} = 1.62 \times \frac{1}{10^2} = 1.62 \times \frac{1}{100} = 0.0162, \quad \text{and}$$

$$1.62 \times 10^{-3} = 1.62 \times \frac{1}{10^3} = 1.62 \times \frac{1}{1{,}000} = 0.00162$$

You should now be able to see the pattern: When writing a decimal fraction in scientific notation, the power of 10 that's needed is negative, and is always one more than the number of zeros between the decimal point and the first significant digit of the number.

In the number 0.0000162, the first significant figure is 1, of course. And since there are four zeros between the decimal point and the 1, we know immediately that

$$1.62 \times 10^{-5} = 0.0000162$$

Check this out for yourself. Then return to page 93 to choose the right answer.

[*from page 60*]

YOUR ANSWER: In division, the log of the dividend should be divided by the log of the divisor to find the quotient.

No. Absolutely not.

First of all, when working with logarithms, you add to multiply and subtract to divide.

Second, when working with logs, your answer is also a logarithm. Even if your operation were correct, what you'd be getting would have to be the log of the quotient—not the quotient itself. Of course, the slide rule allows you to translate this log directly to the corresponding number.

Please return to page 60 and select the right answer.

[*from page 102*]

YOUR ANSWER: One of these numbers is factored incorrectly:

$$12 = 1.2 \times 10^2$$

$$957{,}346 = 9.57346 \times 10^5$$

Yes; the first is wrong.

$$12 = 1.2 \times 10^1, \quad \text{not } 10^2$$

Factoring a number so that it can be written as the product of some number between 1 and 10 multiplied by a power of 10 is called writing the number in *scientific notation*. With this notation it is possible to do many very involved calculations quickly and easily.

For example, consider the problem

$$\frac{285 \times 3{,}569 \times 92}{9{,}472} = ?$$

We begin by writing in scientific notation each of the numbers involved:

$$\frac{2.85 \times 10^2 \times 3.57 \times 10^3 \times 9.2 \times 10^1}{9.47 \times 10^3}$$

(3.569×10^3 has been rounded off to 3.57×10^3, and 9.472 has been rounded off to 9.47×10^3, because ordinarily the slide rule can't be read accurately to more than three significant figures.)

Next, we make a rough estimate of the final answer, by combining the powers of 10, rounding off each of the other factors to the nearest integer, and performing the indicated multiplication and division. Since 2.85 is almost 3, 3.57 is closer to 4 than to 3, 9.2 is just over 9, and 9.47 is closer to 9 than to 10, we get

$$\frac{3 \times 10^2 \times 4 \times 10^3 \times 9 \times 10^1}{9 \times 10^3} = \frac{3 \times 4 \times \cancel{9} \times 10^6}{\cancel{9} \times 10^3} = 12 \times 10^3,$$

or 1.2×10^4. So the complete answer should be somewhere near 1.2×10^4.

Complete the problem on your slide rule, and select the correct answer below:

9.89×10^3. **page 89**

9.89×10^4. **page 91**

1.012×10^4. **page 96**

YOUR ANSWER: $0.0000162 = 1.62 \times 10^{-5}$.

That's correct.
We've seen that

$$0.162 = 1.62 \times 10^{-1}$$

$$0.0162 = 1.62 \times 10^{-2}$$

$$0.00162 = 1.62 \times 10^{-3}$$

and so on. The pattern is now clear: When we're writing a decimal fraction in scientific notation, the power of 10 we want is negative, and is always one more than the number of zeros between the decimal point and the first significant digit of the number.

$$1.62 \times 10^{-5} = 1.62 \times \frac{1}{10^5}$$

$$= 1.62 \times \frac{1}{100{,}000}$$

$$= 0.0000162$$

In the number 0.0000162, there are four zeros between the decimal point and the first significant figure. So we know immediately that

$$0.0000162 = 1.62 \times 10^{-5}$$

Accordingly, our original problem, $0.0000162 \times 13{,}600$, becomes

$$1.62 \times 10^{-5} \times 1.36 \times 10^{4} = ?$$

Which of the answers below is correct?

2.20×10^{-1}. **page 94**

2.20×10^{9}. **page 101**

[*from page 98*]

YOUR ANSWER: $\frac{3}{2.7} = \frac{4.5}{4.05}$ is a correct proportion.

It certainly is. Here's the setting again:

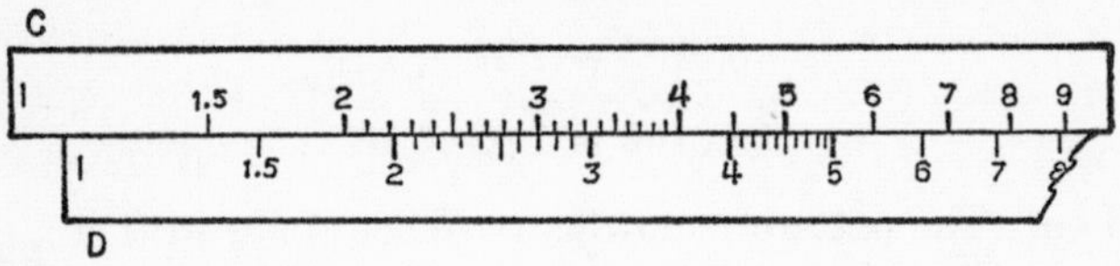

According to this setting,

$$\frac{3}{2.7} = 1.11, \quad \text{and} \quad \frac{4.5}{4.05} = 1.11 \quad \text{also; so} \quad \frac{3}{2.7} = \frac{4.5}{4.05} \quad \left(\text{not } \frac{4.05}{4.5}\right)$$

Enough of that for now.

At first glance, the next problem we're going to consider seems too simple to bother with. How do we multiply 3 by 5 on the slide rule? Let's try the same procedure we've used before:

1. Set the left index of the C scale at 3 on the D scale.
2. Now slide the hairline indicator to 5 on the C scale and read the answer on the D scale.

But wait a minute! If you've been trying this on your rule, you know that at this point the 5 of the C scale is overhanging the lower scale entirely. We need another approach.

Try the procedures below. Which gives the correct answer?

Set 5 on the C scale in line with the right index of the D scale. Slide the hairline indicator to 3 on the C scale and read the answer on the D scale in line with the hairline. **page 87**

Set the right index of the C scale at 3 on the D scale. Slide the hairline indicator to the left, stopping at 5 on the C scale. Read the answer on the D scale in line with the hairline. **page 102**

Neither of these methods works. **page 107**

[*from page 89*]

YOUR ANSWER: $\log (10^3 \div 10^6) = 3$.

Wait a minute! Evidently you've confused the dividend (the number to be divided) with the divisor.

Let's start over.

$10^3 \div 10^6$ means *10^3 divided by 10^6*; 10^3 is the dividend and 10^6 is the divisor. In division, the logarithm of the answer (quotient) is equal to the logarithm of the dividend minus the logarithm of the divisor:

$$\log (A \div B) = \log A - \log B$$

Therefore, in this case,

$$\log (10^3 \div 10^6) = \log 10^3 - \log 10^6$$

Since $\log 10^3 = 3$ and $\log 10^6 = 6$, we see that

$$\log (10^3 \div 10^6) = 3 - 6$$

And $3 - 6$ is -3, of course, not $+3$.

Study this explanation until you're sure you won't make the same mistake again.

Return to page 89 to select the correct answer.

[*from page 67*]

YOUR ANSWER: $\dfrac{1.45 \times 4.90}{2.00} = 3.55.$

Right. It goes like this:

1. Set the left index of the C scale over 1.45 on the D scale.
2. Slide the hairline indicator over 4.90 on the C scale.
3. Shift 2.00 on the C scale under the hairline.
4. Read 3.55 on the D scale at the end of the C scale.

Working the problem on the slide rule like this, we get an answer with only three figures. If we did it in longhand we would get the answer 3.552. But in the vicinity of 3 on the C and D scales we can read only three figures accurately. More about this later.

Follow through each of the following simple divisions on the slide rule, sliding the hairline indicator to the dividend on the D scale, sliding the divisor on the C scale under the hairline, and reading your answer on the D scale at one end of the C scale.

$$\frac{3}{2} = ? \qquad \frac{6}{3} = ? \qquad \frac{8}{5} = ? \qquad \frac{2}{5} = ? \qquad \frac{3}{6} = ?$$

The above instructions show just one way to divide with the C and D scales on the slide rule. You'll remember that when you learned to subtract with two rulers, it didn't make any difference whether you shortened the number of units shown on the bottom scale by the number of units on the top scale or vice versa. Both of these illustrations show methods of subtracting 4 from 6.

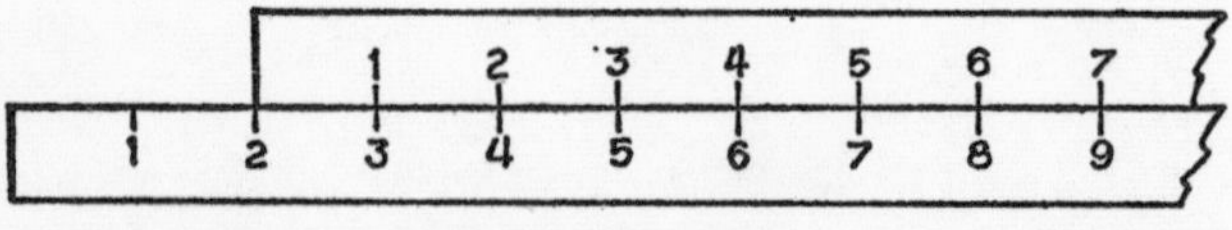

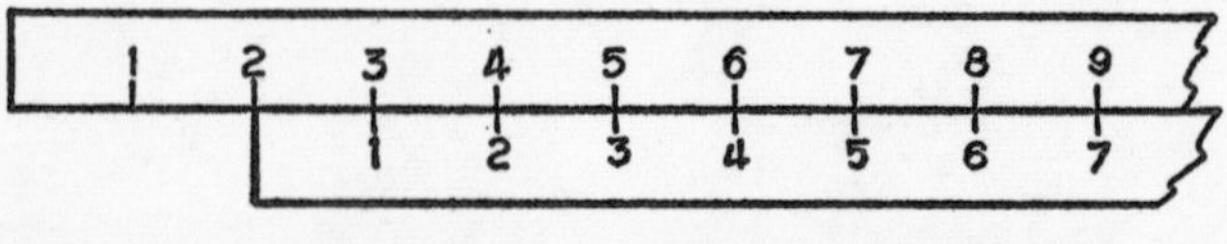

The slide rule is equally impartial. Let's divide 6 by 3 by setting (3) on the D scale under the hairline. Then set (6) on the C scale under the hairline. On what scale do you read your answer?

On the C scale, opposite the index of the D scale. **page 66**

On the D scale, opposite the index of the C scale. **page 78**

[*from page 84*]

YOUR ANSWER: This procedure gives the correct answer to the problem 3 × 5: Set 5 on the C scale at the right index of the D scale. Slide the hairline indicator to 3 on the C scale and read the answer on the D scale in line with the hairline.

No. This procedure is complete nonsense. Here's the way it would look:

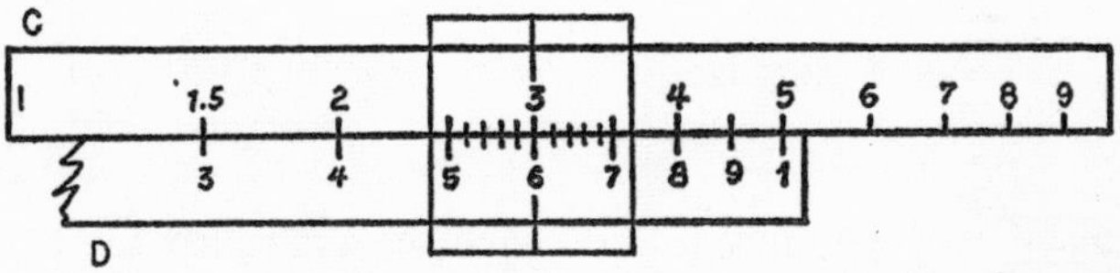

The answer that results is 6. And obviously 3 × 5 is 15, not 6.

But let's look at the other procedure given:

Set the right index of the C scale at 3 on the D scale. Slide the hairline indicator to the left, stopping at 5 on the C scale. Read the answer on the D scale in line with the hairline.

Here's the setting that results:

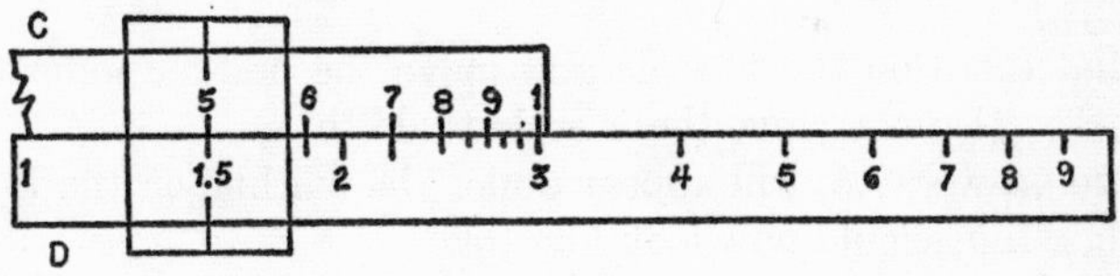

We find that the reading under the hairline on the D scale is 1.5, and 1.5 × 10 = 15, the answer we need. (The 10 came from a "rough estimate" of the answer. You will soon learn to make such estimates for more difficult problems.)

Return to page 84 to select the right answer.

[*from page 68*]

YOUR ANSWER: It might be either one.

Yes, it's rather vague. More marks would be needed.

Notice that there is more room between marks at the beginning of the scale than at the end. It seems only reasonable, then, to mark as many additional values in this area as can be clearly represented. This done, the C and D scales look like this on a five-inch rule:

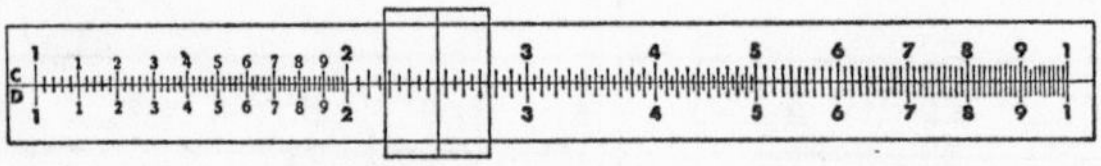

The mark corresponding to 1 on each scale is called the left *index* of that scale. The mark corresponding to 10 is the right index. The vertical hairline indicator is provided to make it easier to read the scales and to line up one number with another.

Let's do a simple computation with our scales. How about 2.5 × 3? Follow along on your own rule.

1. Find 2.5 on the D scale and set the left index (the mark under 1) of the C scale directly above the 2.5. (Slide the C scale to the right to do this.)

2. Find the 3 on the C scale and move the hairline indicator on this mark. (Do not move the C scale to do this!)

3. The answer, 7.5, will appear under the hairline on the D scale. Your slide rule should now look like this.

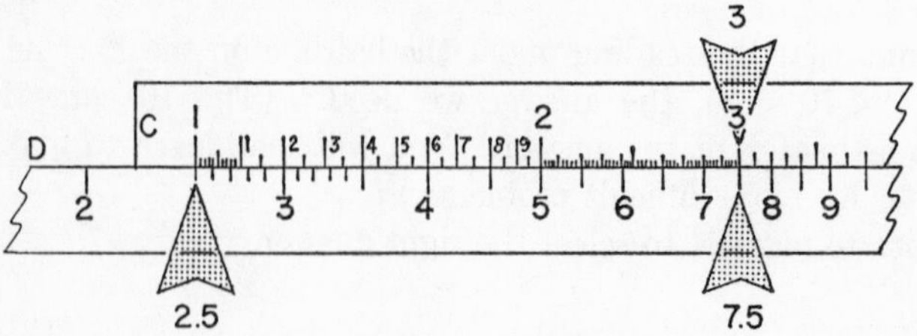

Let's take the big step! Using your slide rule, find the answer to

$$1.5 \times 3.6 \times 1.2 = ?$$

1.5 × 3.6 × 1.2 = 6.48. **page 67** 1.5 × 3.6 × 1.2 = 4.13. **page 74**

1.5 × 3.6 × 1.2 = 4.50. **page 71**

[*from page 82*]

YOUR ANSWER: 9.89×10^3.

Very good. You probably had to make a couple of tries before finding which end of the rule to start with, but having a rough estimate should have helped some.

Now consider the multiplication

$$0.0000162 \times 13{,}600 = ?$$

It's no trick to write 13,600 in scientific notation: 13,600 is the same as 1.36×10^4. But what about 0.0000162? (Remember, in scientific notation, a number is factored into two parts: a number between 1 and 10, and a power of 10. The product of these two parts, of course, is the number.)

Rather than memorize a rule for writing decimal fractions in scientific notation, let's figure it out. We know that the power of 10 we need can't be greater than 1, because

$$10^1 = 10,\ 10^2 = 100,\ 10^3 = 1{,}000, \quad \text{and so on.}$$

Clearly, multiplying 1.62 by any positive power of 10 will increase the size of the number. Since the decimal fraction 0.0000162 is smaller than 1.62, we need to multiply by some power of 10 that will decrease the size of the number.

With what we've learned about multiplying and dividing numbers by adding and subtracting their logarithms, we can find the power of 10 we need.

For instance, what is the logarithm of the answer to the problem

$$10^3 \div 10^6 = ?$$

3. **page 85**

-3. **page 93**

$\frac{1}{1{,}000}$. **page 95**

0.001. **page 99**

[*from page 93*]

YOUR ANSWER: $0.0000162 = 1.62 \times 10^{-6}$.

No.

$$10^{-6} = \frac{1}{10^6} = \frac{1}{1{,}000{,}000}, \text{ so}$$

$$1.62 \times 10^{-6} = 1.62 \times \frac{1}{1{,}000{,}000}$$
$$= 0.00000162$$

But 0.00000162 has five zeros between the decimal point and the 1. The number we're working with, 0.0000162, has only four. Let's retrace our steps a bit. We've seen that

$$1.62 \times 10^{-1} = 1.62 \times \frac{1}{10^1} = 1.62 \times \frac{1}{10} = 0.162,$$

$$1.62 \times 10^{-2} = 1.62 \times \frac{1}{10^2} = 1.62 \times \frac{1}{100} = 0.0162, \quad \text{and}$$

$$1.62 \times 10^{-3} = 1.62 \times \frac{1}{10^3} = 1.62 \times \frac{1}{1{,}000} = 0.00162$$

You should now be able to see the pattern: When writing a decimal fraction in scientific notation, the power of 10 that's needed is negative, and is always one more than the number of zeros between the decimal point and the first significant digit of the number.

In the number 0.0000162, the first significant figure is 1, of course. And since there are four zeros between the decimal point and the 1, we know immediately that

$$1.62 \times 10^{-5} = 0.0000162$$

Check this out for yourself. Then return to page 93 to choose the right answer.

[*from page 82*]

YOUR ANSWER: $\dfrac{2.85 \times 10^2 \times 3.57 \times 10^3 \times 9.2 \times 10^1}{9.47 \times 10^3} = 9.89 \times 10^4.$

No! Wrong exponent.
Let's go back to our approximation.

$$\frac{3 \times 10^2 \times 4 \times 10^3 \times 9 \times 10^1}{9 \times 10^3} = \frac{3 \times 4 \times \not{9} \times 10^6}{\not{9} \times 10^3}$$
$$= 12 \times 10^3$$
$$= 1.2 \times 10^4$$

"Well," you say, "9.89×10^4 is certainly in the vicinity of 1.2×10^4."

Look again. The difference between the two numbers is considerable. Here's why:

$$9.89 \times 10^4 = 98{,}900, \quad \text{but}$$
$$1.2 \times 10^4 = 12{,}000$$

Obviously, there's a sizable difference between 98,900 and 12,000—86,900, or 8.69×10^4, to use scientific notation.

Now, how about the difference between $9.89 \times \underline{10^3}$ and 1.2×10^4? Well, at first glance, there seems to be a great difference. But when we analyze the two numbers, we see that

$$9.89 \times 10^3 = 9{,}890, \quad \text{and}$$
$$1.2 \times 10^4 = 12{,}000$$

Considering the fact that we rounded off to one figure in making our estimate, this is pretty close.

Now return to page 82 and select the correct answer.

[*from page 66*]

YOUR ANSWER: The setting represents both 5 ÷ 4 and 2.5 ÷ 2.

You're on the right track, but you need to go a little further. Look at the setting again:

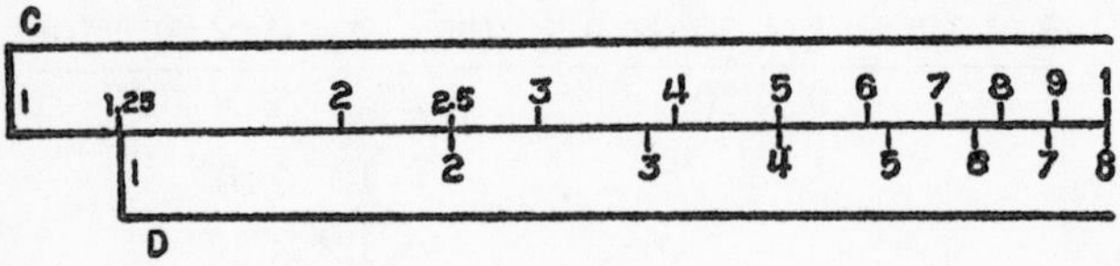

It's true that this setting represents both 5 ÷ 4 and 2.5 ÷ 2. The answer to each of the problems is 1.25, on the C scale in line with the left index of the D scale.

But isn't it also true that this same setting can be considered a representation of 4 ÷ 5 and 2 ÷ 2.5? Of course, but in this case the answer is 0.8, and it appears on the D scale at the right index of the C scale.

In fact, if we consider each of the numbers on the C scale as being divided by the number directly below it on the D scale, we see that the given setting represents all possible divisions for which the answer is 1.25. And going from the D scale to the C scale, it represents all the divisions for which the answer is 0.8.

When you're clear on this point, return to page 66 to select the right answer.

[*from page 89*]

YOUR ANSWER: The logarithm of $10^3 \div 10^6$ is -3.

Right. Very good.

When we are dividing one number by another, the logarithm of the answer is equal to the logarithm of the dividend minus the logarithm of the divisor. Therefore,

$$\log (10^3 \div 10^6) = 3 - 6 = -3$$

This, of course, means that $10^3 \div 10^6 = 10^{-3}$.

Now, what is the significance of the negative exponent? Let's do the problem another way and see.

We know that $10^3 = 1{,}000$ and $10^6 = 1{,}000{,}000$, so

$$10^3 \div 10^6 = \frac{1{,}\not{0}\not{0}\not{0}}{1{,}000{,}\not{0}\not{0}\not{0}} = \frac{1}{1{,}000} = \frac{1}{10^3}$$

Finally, since $10^3 \div 10^6 = 10^{-3}$ and also $\frac{1}{10^3}$, we conclude that $10^{-3} = \frac{1}{10^3}$.

Similarly, we can show that $10^{-1} = \frac{1}{10^1}$, $10^{-2} = \frac{1}{10^2}$, and $10^{-4} = \frac{1}{10^4}$, and so on.

At this point, we're in a position to find the power of 10 we need to write 0.0000162 in scientific notation.

$$1.62 \times 10^{-1} = 1.62 \times \frac{1}{10^1} = 1.62 \times \frac{1}{10} = 0.162$$

$$1.62 \times 10^{-2} = 1.62 \times \frac{1}{10^2} = 1.62 \times \frac{1}{100} = 0.0162$$

$$1.62 \times 10^{-3} = 1.62 \times \frac{1}{10^3} = 1.62 \times \frac{1}{1{,}000} = 0.00162$$

Which of the three expressions below is correct?

$0.0000162 = 1.62 \times 10^{-4}$. **page 80**

$0.0000162 = 1.62 \times 10^{-5}$. **page 83**

$0.0000162 = 1.62 \times 10^{-6}$. **page 90**

[*from page 83*]

YOUR ANSWER: $1.62 \times 10^{-5} \times 1.36 \times 10^{4} = 2.20 \times 10^{-1}$.

Good. You recognized that $10^{-5} \times 10^{4} = 10^{-1}$.

Let's sum up the main points on scientific notation:

In scientific notation, a number is factored into a number between 1 and 10 and a whole-number power of 10:

1. If the original number is between 1 and 10, it is already in scientific notation, since the required power of 10 is 10^0, which equals 1.
2. If the original number is between 10 and 100, the power of 10 will be 10^1, or just 10. Don't overlook the exponent of 10^1 in making estimates.
3. If the original number is more than 100, the exponent of the power of 10 will be 2 or more.
4. If the original number is less than 1, the exponent of the power of 10 will be negative.

Every number can be written in scientific notation.

When attacking a problem involving multiplication or division, or both, first write each of the numbers involved in scientific notation:

$$\frac{0.0000842 \times 6{,}396 \times 1{,}846{,}000}{6{,}530 \times 0.779} = \frac{8.42 \times 10^{-5} \times 6.396 \times 10^{3} \times 1.846 \times 10^{6}}{6.53 \times 10^{3} \times 7.79 \times 10^{-1}} = \frac{8.42 \times 6.396 \times 1.846}{6.53 \times 7.79} \times 10^{2}$$

Then make an approximation (replacing the number in the last expression above with the nearest integers),

$$\frac{8 \times 6 \times 2}{7 \times 8} \times 10^{2} = 1.7 \times 10^{2}$$

Use your slide rule to find the complete answer. (Hint: first divide 8.42 by 6.53, then multiply by 6.396, then divide by 7.79, and finally multiply by 1.846.)

The answer is

1.95×10^{2}. **page 103** 1.98×10^{2}. **page 109**

1.21×10^{2}. **page 105**

[*from page 89*]

YOUR ANSWER: $\log (10^3 \div 10^6)$ is $\dfrac{1}{1{,}000}$.

Well, it's true that $10^3 \div 10^6 = \dfrac{1}{1{,}000}$, but that isn't what you were asked. You were asked for the *logarithm* of the answer, not the answer itself.

Let's start over.

In division, the logarithm of the answer is equal to the logarithm of the dividend minus the logarithm of the divisor:

$$\log (A \div B) = \log A - \log B$$

Since $10^3 \div 10^6$ means *10^3 divided by 10^6*, 10^3 is the dividend and 10^6 is the divisor. Hence,

$$\log (10^3 \div 10^6) = \log 10^3 - \log 10^6$$

The log of 10^3 is just 3, and that of 10^6 is simply 6, so we see that

$$\log (10^3 \div 10^6) = 3 - 6$$

Now return to page 89 and select the correct answer.

[*from page 82*]

YOUR ANSWER: $\dfrac{2.85 \times 10^2 \times 3.57 \times 10^3 \times 9.2 \times 10^1}{9.47 \times 10^3} = 1.012 \times 10^4.$

No. Evidently you are confused about which end of the scale you should be reading. And unfortunately, comparison of your answer with the approximate answer we calculated wouldn't have shown up the error. The approximate figure, 1.2×10^4, and your answer, 1.012×10^4, are fairly close.

$$1.2 \times 10^4 = 12{,}000$$

$$1.012 \times 10^4 = 10{,}120$$

See whether you can discover where you went wrong as we go through the solution step by step:

First, multiply 2.85 by 3.57: Place the *right-hand* index of the C scale over 2.85 on the D scale. Then move the hairline indicator to 3.57 on the C scale.

Next, multiply by 9.2: Align the *left-hand* index of the C scale with the hairline. Then move the hairline to 9.2 on the C scale.

Finally, divide by 9.47: Align 9.47 on the C scale with the hairline.

The answer will be on the D scale, directly beneath the *right-hand* index of the C scale.

Now return to page 82 and select the right answer.

[*from page 66*]

YOUR ANSWER: No, we can't tell exactly what division is indicated; the setting represents many divisions.

You are right.

Here's the setting again, with just a few of the many possible divisions emphasized:

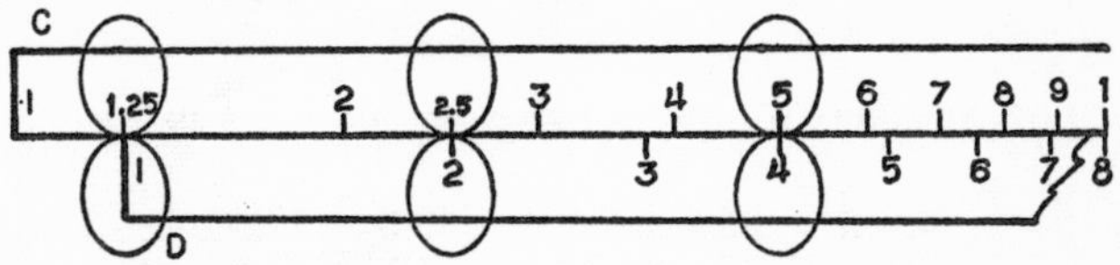

Clearly, this setting can be used to divide 2 on the D scale by 2.5 on the C scale; or 4 on the D scale by 5 on the C scale; and so on. For these problems, the answer 0.8 appears on the D scale at the right index of the C scale.

Furthermore, the same setting can be used to divide 2.5 on the C scale by 2 on the D scale; or 5 on the C scale by 4 on the D scale; and so on. For each of these problems, the answer is 1.25, and it appears on the C scale at the left index of the D scale.

These ideas shouldn't give you any trouble. Just remember that the answer to any division problem will appear on the same scale as the number being divided.

Now let's take a closer look at two of the divisions shown above. Since $\frac{5}{4} = 1.25$ and $\frac{2.5}{2} = 1.25$ also, we see that $\frac{5}{4} = \frac{2.5}{2}$.

An expression of this form, where one fraction is said to be equal in value to another, is called a *proportion*.

Please go on to page 98.

[*from page 97*]

These expressions are all proportions:

$$\frac{15}{25} = \frac{3}{5} \qquad \frac{1.7}{3.4} = \frac{1}{2} \qquad \frac{19}{2} = \frac{57}{6}.$$

In fact, the expressions

$$\frac{5}{4} = 1.25 \qquad \text{and} \qquad \frac{2.5}{2} = 1.25.$$

can also be considered proportions, since we could just as well have written

$$\frac{5}{4} = \frac{1.25}{1} \qquad \text{and} \qquad \frac{2.5}{2} = \frac{1.25}{1}.$$

Proportions are especially useful for converting a quantity given in one kind of unit to its equivalent in another kind of unit. One simple setting of the rule, and we can convert any number of dollars to an equivalent number of francs. Another setting, and we can convert kilometers to miles. We'll become quite familiar with this sort of operation a little later on.

Look at the setting below:

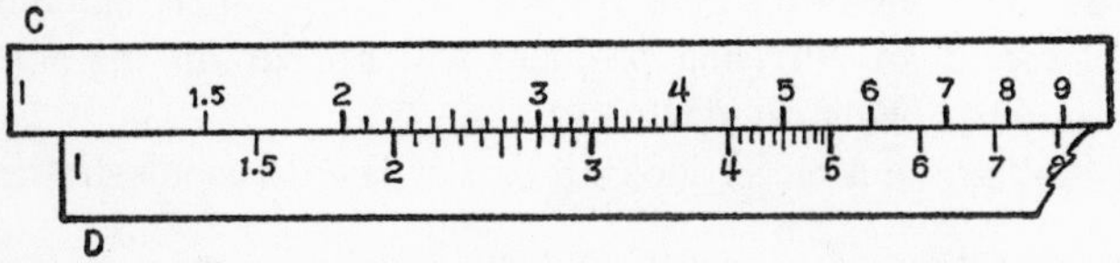

According to this setting, which of these proportions is correct?

$\frac{3}{2.7} = \frac{4.05}{4.5}$. **page 63**

$\frac{3}{2.7} = \frac{4.5}{4.05}$. **page 84**

[*from page 89*]

YOUR ANSWER: $\log (10^3 \div 10^6) = 0.001$.

Well, it's true that $10^3 \div 10^6 = 0.001$, but that isn't what you were asked. You were asked to find the *logarithm* of the answer, not the answer itself.

Let's start over.

In division, the logarithm of the answer is equal to the logarithm of the dividend (the number to be divided) minus the logarithm of the divisor:

$$\log (A \div B) = \log A - \log B$$

Since $10^3 \div 10^6$ means *10^3 divided by 10^6*, 10^3 is the dividend and 10^6 is the divisor. Hence,

$$\log (10^3 \div 10^6) = \log 10^3 - \log 10^6$$

The log of 10^3 is just 3, and that of 10^6 is simply 6, so we see that

$$\log (10^3 \div 10^6) = 3 - 6$$

Complete the subtraction and then return to page 89 to select the correct answer.

[*from page 103*]

YOUR ANSWER: The first pair of problems contains an error.

No, it doesn't. Look at the problems again:

The first one is $\dfrac{6.28 \times 0.00102 \times 946}{0.000184} = 3.29 \times 10^4$.

The left side of this expression simplifies to $\dfrac{6.28 \times 1.02 \times 9.46}{1.84} \times 10^3$.

If we make a rough approximation by using the integers nearest to the actual numbers of the problem, we see that $\dfrac{6 \times 1 \times 9}{2} \times 10^3 = 27 \times 10^3$, or 2.7×10^4. For the whole solution,

1. Multiply 6.28 by 1.02: set the left-hand index of the C scale over 6.28 on the D scale, and move the indicator to 1.02 on the C scale.
2. Divide by 1.84: move the C scale until its 1.84 is under the hairline. Then move the hairline to the left index of the C scale.
3. Multiply by 9.46: slide the right-hand index of the C scale under the hairline. Then move the hairline to 9.46 on the C scale.
4. Read the answer, 3.29, beneath the hairline on the D scale.

The second problem is similar:

$$\frac{8.305 \times 0.046 \times 1{,}350{,}000}{11} \text{ simplifies to } \frac{8.305 \times 4.6 \times 1.35}{1.1} \times 10^3.$$

The answer should be roughly 40×10^3, or 4.0×10^4. The actual solution is found in much the same way as that of the first problem: Multiply 8.305 (you'll have to use 8.31) by 4.6, divide by 1.1, and multiply by 1.35. You should find that the answer is 4.68×10^4.

When you've seen for yourself that these answers are correct, return to page 103 for another try.

[*from page 83*]

YOUR ANSWER: $1.62 \times 10^{-5} \times 1.36 \times 10^{4} = 2.20 \times 10^{9}$.

No, the exponent's wrong. Since you seem to be a little hazy on this score, let's review. First, we have seen that we *add* exponents to multiply powers of 10:

$$\begin{array}{ccccc} \text{this} & + & \text{this} & = & \text{this} \\ \downarrow & & \downarrow & & \downarrow \\ 10^2 & \times & 10^4 & = & 10^6 \end{array} \quad \text{because} \quad \begin{aligned} 10^2 \times 10^4 &= 100 \times 10{,}000 \\ &= 1{,}000{,}000 \\ &= 10^6 \end{aligned}$$

We also learned that 10^{-1} means $\frac{1}{10}$, or 0.1; 10^{-2} means $\frac{1}{100}$, or 0.01; 10^{-3} means $\frac{1}{1{,}000}$, or 0.001, and so on.

Now, then, we have two possible ways to deal with the powers of 10 in the given problem. We can add exponents:

$$1.62 \times 10^{-5} \times 1.36 \times 10^{4} = 1.62 \times 1.36 \times 10^{-1}$$

Or we can use the fact that $10^{-5} = \frac{1}{100{,}000}$ to write

$$\begin{aligned} 1.62 \times 10^{-5} \times 1.36 \times 10^{4} &= 1.62 \times 1.36 \times \frac{1}{10\cancel{0},\cancel{0}\cancel{0}\cancel{0}} \times 1\cancel{0},\cancel{0}\cancel{0}\cancel{0} \\ &= 1.62 \times 1.36 \times \frac{1}{10} \\ &= 1.62 \times 1.36 \times 10^{-1} \end{aligned}$$

Either way, our final answer is

$$2.20 \times 10^{-1}, \quad \textit{not} \quad 2.20 \times 10^{9}$$

Study this carefully. Then return to page 83 to select the correct answer.

[*from page 84*]

YOUR ANSWER: To multiply 3 × 5, set the right end of the C scale at 3 on the D scale, slide the hairline to 5 on the C scale, and read the answer on the D scale under the hairline.

Right. We then read 1.5 on the D scale. And 1.5 × 10 = 15, the correct answer.

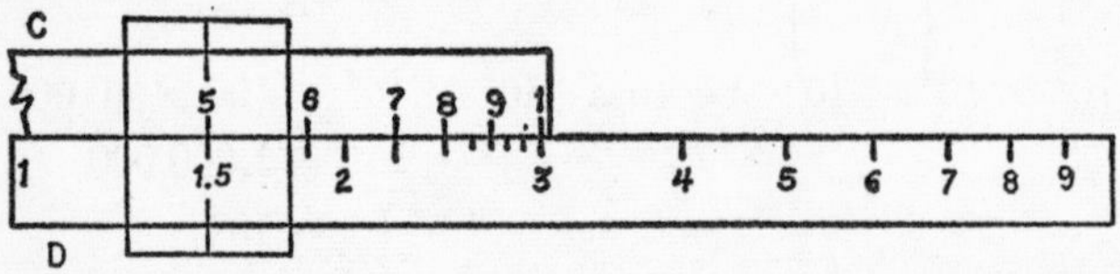

It looks as though we are multiplying by subtracting one logarithm from another. That is just what we are doing, but we'll postpone a detailed explanation until later. For now, just accept the fact that you can begin a multiplication by placing *either* index of the C scale over the first factor on the D scale. If the answer falls beyond the end of the D scale, simply start over, using the other C-scale index to locate the first factor.

Of course 3 × 5 is not 1.5, but 15. We can't rely on the slide rule to place the decimal point, for the numbers on the C and D scales could just as well represent 100 to 1,000 as 1 to 10. So the normal procedure is to read only the sequence of numbers from the slide rule and place the decimal by making a very rough estimate of what the answer should be.

The key to making a rough estimate is factoring for powers of 10. As a start in this direction, select the group that contains an error in factoring:

$415 = 4.15 \times 10^2.$
$135{,}000{,}000 = 1.35 \times 10^8.$ **page 79**

$12 = 1.2 \times 10^2.$
$957{,}346 = 9.57346 \times 10^5.$ **page 82**

$2{,}000 = 2 \times 10^3.$
$614{,}000 = 6.14 \times 10^5.$ **page 110**

[*from page 94*]

YOUR ANSWER: $\dfrac{0.0000842 \times 6{,}396 \times 1{,}846{,}000}{6{,}530 \times 0.779} = 1.95 \times 10^2.$

Good. You were given a hint; here's the complete solution:

1. Set the hairline indicator over 8.42 on the D scale.
2. Shift 6.53 on the C scale under the hairline.
3. Slide the hairline indicator left to 6.40 on the C scale.
4. Slide 7.79 on the C scale under the hairline.
5. Slide the hairline indicator to the left to 1.846 on the C scale.
6. Read the answer, 1.95, on the D scale under the hairline.

The approximate solution was 2.25×10^2, so the complete answer is 1.95×10^2.

In general, the number of shifts of sliding scale and hairline indicator should be kept at a minimum. Every time you have to make a reading, the likelihood of error increases.

Here are three pairs of problems. Which pair contains an incorrect solution?

$$\frac{6.28 \times 0.00102 \times 946}{0.000184} = 3.29 \times 10^4$$

$$\frac{8.305 \times 0.046 \times 1{,}350{,}000}{11} = 4.68 \times 10^4$$

page 100

$$\frac{1}{17{,}300{,}000} \times \frac{1}{493} = 1.17 \times 10^{-10}$$

$$\frac{69.41 \times 0.5 \times 380 \times 16}{35 \times 1{,}683 \times 0.524 \times 666} = 1.03 \times 10^{-2}$$

page 111

$$\frac{1{,}570{,}000 \times 0.00000165}{6{,}380 \times 14 \times 7{,}800 \times 1} = 3.72 \times 10^{-9}$$

$$\frac{0.00135 \times 1.005 \times 0.174}{0.00000627} = 3.79 \times 10^1$$

page 113

[*from page 113*]

YOUR ANSWER: 70 miles per hour.

No. Here's the problem again: You have driven 326 kilometers in $7\frac{1}{2}$ hours. Using the distance formula (distance = rate of speed $\times$ time) and the fact that 1 kilometer = 0.621 miles, find your average rate in miles per hour.

In decimal form, $7\frac{1}{2}$ hours is expressed as 7.5 hours. Then, according to the distance formula, 326 kilometers = $r \times 7.5$ hours (where r is the rate, of course). From this we see that

$$r = \frac{326 \text{ kilometers}}{7.5 \text{ hours}}$$

This expression will give us the rate in terms of kilometers per hour. We need to find the rate in terms of miles per hour.

Since 1 kilometer = 0.621 miles, then

$$326 \text{ kilometers} = 326 \times 0.621 \text{ miles}$$

and our rate is given by

$$r = \frac{326 \times 0.621 \text{ miles}}{7.5 \text{ hours}}$$

This gives us the answer in miles per hour.

On the slide rule:

1. Slide the hairline indicator to 3.26 on the D scale.
2. Shift 7.5 on the C scale under the hairline.
3. Slide the hairline indicator to 6.21 on the C scale.
4. Read the answer under the hairline on the D scale.

Thus

$$\frac{326 \times 0.621}{7.5} = \frac{3.26 \times 10^2 \times 6.21 \times 10^{-1}}{7.5} = \frac{3.26 \times 6.21}{7.5} \times 10^1.$$

The answer will be roughly $\frac{3 \times 6}{8} \times 10^1$, or 25 miles per hour.

When you have the answer, return to page 113 to make the correct choice.

[*from page 94*]

YOUR ANSWER: 1.21×10^2.

No. It looks as if you multiplied by 6.53 instead of dividing. Here's the problem again:

$$\frac{0.0000842 \times 6.396 \times 1{,}846{,}000}{6{,}530 \times 0.779}$$

This simplifies to

$$\frac{8.42 \times 6.396 \times 1.846}{6.53 \times 7.79} \times 10^2$$

Now, if we try to do all the multiplications in the numerator before performing any division, we must make many moves with the sliding scale and the indicator. Each move increases the possibility of error. So you were given a hint about how to do the problem. Following this suggestion, the procedure would be:

1. Divide 8.42 by 6.53: set the indicator hairline over 8.42 on the D scale, and slide the C scale to the right until 6.53 is under the hairline.
2. Multiply by 6.396: slide the hairline left to 6.40 (you can't read 4 figures here) on the C scale.
3. Divide by 7.79: slide the C scale until 7.79 is under the hairline.
4. Multiply by 1.846: slide the indicator to the left, stopping when 1.846 of the C scale is under the hairline.
5. Read the final answer under the hairline on the D scale.

If you follow this procedure carefully, you should have no trouble arriving at the right answer. Return to page 94 for another try.

[*from page 113*]

YOUR ANSWER: 54 miles per hour.

No. And this looks like a guess. Here's the problem again: You have driven 326 kilometers in $7\frac{1}{2}$ hours. Using the distance formula (distance = rate of speed × time) and the fact that 1 kilometer = 0.621 miles, find your average rate in miles per hour.

In decimal form, $7\frac{1}{2}$ hours is expressed as 7.5 hours. Then, according to the distance formula, 326 kilometers = $r \times 7.5$ hours (where r is the rate, of course). From this we see that

$$r = \frac{326 \text{ kilometers}}{7.5 \text{ hours}}$$

This expression will give us the rate in terms of kilometers per hour. We need to find the rate in terms of miles per hour.

Since 1 kilometer = 0.621 miles, then

$$326 \text{ kilometers} = 326 \times 0.621 \text{ miles}$$

and our rate is given by

$$r = \frac{326 \times 0.621 \text{ miles}}{7.5 \text{ hours}}$$

This gives us the answer in miles per hour.

On the slide rule:

1. Slide the hairline indicator to 3.26 on the D scale.
2. Shift 7.5 on the C scale under the hairline.
3. Slide the hairline indicator to 6.21 on the C scale.
4. Read the answer under the hairline on the D scale.

Thus

$$\frac{326 \times 0.621}{7.5} = \frac{3.26 \times 10^2 \times 6.21 \times 10^{-1}}{7.5} = \frac{3.26 \times 6.21}{7.5} \times 10^1.$$

The answer will be roughly $\frac{3 \times 6}{8} \times 10^1$, or 25 miles per hour.

When you have the answer, return to page 113 to make the correct choice.

YOUR ANSWER: Neither of the given methods works.

But one of them does. Let's try them both.

Here's the first method: Set 5 on the C scale in line with the right index of the D scale. Slide the hairline indicator to 3 on the C scale and read the answer on the D scale in line with the hairline.

And here's the setting that would result:

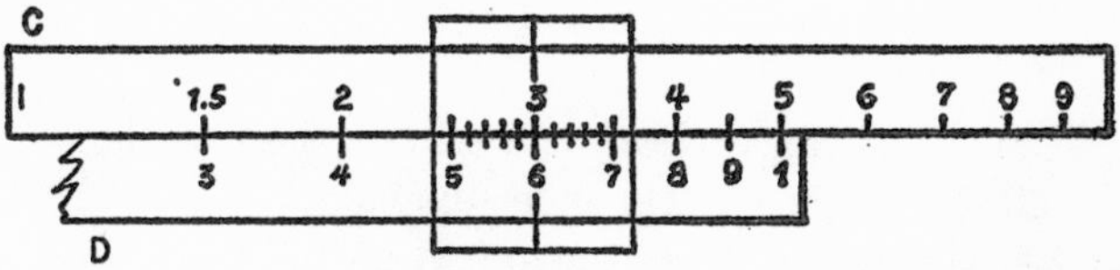

The number under the hairline is 6. And obviously 3 × 5 = 15, not 6.

So the first method is no good.

Here is the second procedure: Set the right index of the C scale at 3 on the D scale. Slide the hairline indicator to the left, stopping at 5 on the C scale. Read the answer on the D scale in line with the hairline.

Here's the setting that is the result of this procedure:

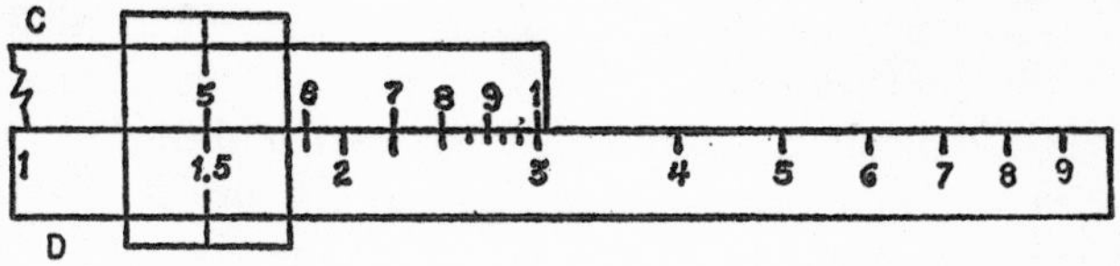

The number under the hairline is 1.5. And 1.5 × 10 = 15, the answer we want. (You will soon learn why we have to supply the 10 to get the final answer.)

Return to page 84 and select the right answer.

[*from page 113*]

YOUR ANSWER: 27 miles per hour.

Very good. Distance = rate of speed × time, so rate = $\frac{\text{distance}}{\text{time}}$. In the given problem, $r = \frac{326 \text{ kilometers}}{7.5 \text{ hours}}$ (r, of course, stands for rate). To convert the answer we get to miles per hour, we simply multiply by $\frac{0.621 \text{ miles}}{1 \text{ kilometer}}$.

On the slide rule:

1. Slide the hairline indicator to 3.26 on the D scale.
2. Shift 7.5 on the C scale under the hairline.
3. Slide the hairline indicator to 6.21 on the C scale.
4. Read the answer, 2.7, under the hairline on the D scale.

Since you should have seen by estimating that r is roughly 2.5×10^1, or 25 miles per hour, you know that the final answer is 27 miles per hour.

But how dependable is this answer? The usual automobile mileage gauge is accurate to within about 10%. So the actual distance covered could be as much as 359 kilometers (326 kilometers + 10% of 326 kilometers) or as little as 293 kilometers (326 kilometers − 10% of 326 kilometers). So all we can really say from the given measurements is that the average rate was somewhere between 25 and 30 miles per hour. The three-figure accuracy of the slide rule is ample for many such problems.

As was said before, all units obey the rules of addition, subtraction, multiplication, and division. In figuring the problem above, we divided miles by hours to get the number of miles per hour.

Here are two problems involving units which occur often in physics. Which one is incorrect? (*Dyne-cm.* means *dyne* × *cm.*)

$$\frac{6.28 \text{ lb.} \times \frac{32 \text{ ft.}}{\text{sec.}^2}}{60 \text{ lb.}} = \frac{3.35 \text{ ft.}}{\text{sec.}^2}.$$ **page 112**

$$\frac{725 \text{ gm.} \times 3.87 \times \frac{10^6 \text{ dyne-cm.}}{\text{gm.}} \times 373}{\frac{1{,}013{,}000 \text{ dyne}}{\text{cm.}^2}} = 1.04 \times 10^6 \text{ cm.}^2$$ **page 114**

[*from page 94*]

YOUR ANSWER: $\dfrac{0.0000842 \times 6{,}396 \times 1{,}846{,}000}{6{,}530 \times 0.779} = 1.98 \times 10^2.$

No. The problem simplifies to

$$\frac{8.42 \times 6.396 \times 1.846}{6.53 \times 7.79} \times 10^2$$

You seem to have followed the right procedure, since you arrived at an answer that is reasonably close to correct. But in case you didn't, let's go over it again:

1. Divide 8.42 by 6.53.
2. Multiply by 6.396.
3. Divide by 7.79.
4. Multiply by 1.846.

Your mistake may have been in reading your final answer wrong or rounding off 1.846 before locating it on your slide rule. If you read the answer wrong, all we can say is, *be more careful, and practice taking readings.*

But rounding off 1.846 is something else again. Between the 6 and 7 on the C and D scales, we cannot read more than three figures. This is a consequence of the nature of the slide rule—the distance between the logarithm of 6 and that of 7 is relatively small. Therefore, when we multiply by 6.396, we have to round it off to 6.4 in order to locate it on the scale. However, the distance between 1 and 2 on these scales is large enough to be marked in very small quantities. So we can read all four figures of the number 1.846.

Return to page 94 for another try.

[*from page 102*]

YOUR ANSWER: This group contains an error:

$$2{,}000 = 2 \times 10^3$$

$$614{,}000 = 6.14 \times 10^5$$

Sorry—both of these problems are correct. Let's check them and see. Remember, multiplying by a positive power of ten is just a matter of moving the decimal point toward the right the number of places indicated by the power of ten.

To multiply 2 by 10^3, we move the decimal point of 2 three places to the right:

$$2.\underset{\frown}{000}.$$

So it is true that

$$2{,}000 = 2 \times 10^3$$

To multiply 6.14 by 10^5 we move the decimal point of 6.14 five places to the right:

$$6.\underset{\frown}{14000}.$$

So this problem is all right:

$$614{,}000 = 6.14 \times 10^5$$

Return to page 102 and try again.

YOUR ANSWER: The second series of problems contains an error.

No, it doesn't. Here's the way they go:

The first problem is $\frac{1}{17,300,000} \times \frac{1}{493} = 1.17 \times 10^{-10}$.

This may have seemed confusing, but don't let it throw you—it can be done just like the others. The left side of the equation can be simplified:

$$\frac{1}{17,300,000} \times \frac{1}{493} = \frac{1}{1.73 \times 4.93 \times 10^{9}} = \frac{1}{1.73 \times 4.93} \times 10^{-9}$$

Substituting 2 for 1.73 and 5 for 4.93, we find that our answer should be roughly 0.1×10^{-9}, or 1.0×10^{-10}. To find the complete solution

1. Divide 1 by 1.73: set 1.73 on the C scale over 1 on the D scale. Then move the indicator hairline to the right-hand index on the C scale.
2. Divide by 4.93: slide 4.93 on the C scale under the hairline.

The answer, 117, will appear under the left-hand index of the C scale, on the D scale.

The second problem is

$$\frac{69.41 \times 0.5 \times 380 \times 16}{35 \times 1,683 \times 0.524 \times 666} = 1.03 \times 10^{-2}$$

Approximate the answer first—it should be roughly 1.0×10^{-2}. In finding the actual solution to this problem, it is easiest to alternate multiplication and division operations: Divide 6.94 by 3.5, then multiply by 5.0, then divide by 1.683, then multiply by 3.8, then divide by 5.24, then multiply by 1.6, then divide by 6.66. (These numbers are in their simplified form, of course.) The main trick to all this is to remember where you are. If you get lost, just start over.

When you've seen for yourself that these answers are correct, return to page 103 for another try.

[*from page 108*]

YOUR ANSWER: $\dfrac{6.28 \text{ lb.} \times \dfrac{32 \text{ ft.}}{\text{sec.}^2}}{60 \text{ lb.}} = \dfrac{3.35 \text{ ft.}}{\text{sec.}^2}$.

No, this problem is all right. Remember, all units obey all the rules of multiplication and division. So we can write

$$\frac{6.28 \text{ lb.} \times \dfrac{32 \text{ ft.}}{\text{sec.}^2}}{60 \text{ lb.}} = \frac{6.28 \text{ lb.}}{60 \text{ lb.}} \times \frac{\dfrac{32 \text{ ft.}}{\text{sec.}^2}}{1}$$

But $\dfrac{6.28 \text{ lb.}}{60 \text{ lb.}} = \dfrac{6.28}{60}$, because we can cancel the pound unit that appears in both the numerator and the denominator. So

$$\frac{6.28 \text{ lb.}}{60 \text{ lb.}} \times \frac{\dfrac{32 \text{ ft.}}{\text{sec.}^2}}{1} = \frac{6.28}{60} \times \frac{\dfrac{32 \text{ ft.}}{\text{sec.}^2}}{1}$$

As you can easily check on your slide rule, $\dfrac{6.28}{60} = 0.1046$, so

$$\frac{6.28}{60} \times \frac{32 \text{ ft.}}{\text{sec.}^2} = 0.1046 \times \frac{32 \text{ ft.}}{\text{sec.}^2}$$

$$= 3.35 \text{ ft/sec}^2$$

This problem is all right—the units are right and so are the numbers.

Return to page 108 and study it carefully. This business of units can cause you plenty of trouble unless you get it down pat, once and for all. When you feel that you know what you are doing, choose the right answer.

YOUR ANSWER: One of these is wrong:

$$\frac{1{,}570{,}000 \times 0.00000165}{6{,}380 \times 14 \times 7{,}800 \times 1} = 3.72 \times 10^{-9}.$$

$$\frac{0.00135 \times 1.005 \times 0.174}{0.00000627} = 3.79 \times 10^{1}.$$

You are correct. It may have taken you quite a while to find this error, for it is a relatively small one; the second answer should be 3.77×10^1.

The incorrect answer given results from rounding 1.005 to 1.01. It's all right to round off a number such as 9.005 to 9.01, because the markings on the right-hand part of the scales are too close together to let you read more than three figures accurately; but the distance between 1 and 2 on the C and D scales is enough to allow all four significant figures of the number 1.005 to be read.

Before we go any further in our discussion of the slide rule, let's discuss the problem of units. A *unit* is simply any standard of measurement. For example, the second is a unit of time. So is the hour. Similarly, the foot is a unit of distance, as is the meter. All of these examples are familiar to you.

There are many units besides the ones we've mentioned. Since you are likely to encounter problems with units at one time or another, you need to learn how to manipulate them.

Basically, it's very simple: any unit can be treated as an algebraic quantity. That is, units can be added, subtracted, multiplied, and divided as if they were algebraic symbols. For instance, 2 ft. $\times$ 2 ft. = 4 ft.^{2} or 4 square feet. In an expression such as $\frac{miles}{hour}$, the bar means *per*. $\frac{3 \text{ miles}}{\text{hour}}$ = 3 miles per hour.

Here is a fairly commonplace problem:

You've been driving a small foreign car along winding mountain roads. Actual driving time is $7\frac{1}{2}$ hours, and you have covered 326 kilometers. Using the distance formula (distance = rate of speed $\times$ time), and the fact that 1 kilometer = 0.621 miles, calculate your average rate in miles per hour.

70 miles per hour. **page 104**

27 miles per hour. **page 108**

54 miles per hour. **page 106**

[*from page 108*]

YOUR ANSWER: This problem has an error:

$$\frac{725 \text{ gm.} \times 3.87 \times \dfrac{10^6 \text{ dyne-cm.}}{\text{gm.}} \times 373}{\dfrac{1{,}013{,}000 \text{ dyne}}{\text{cm.}^2}} = 1.04 \times 10^6 \text{ cm.}^2$$

Yes, it has.

The answer is numerically correct, but the units were not correctly manipulated. Let's consider the units alone, apart from their numbers. Then the problem is as follows:

$$\frac{\text{gm.} \times \dfrac{\text{dyne-cm.}}{\text{gm.}}}{\dfrac{\text{dyne}}{\text{cm.}^2}} = ?$$

The grams (gm.) in the numerator cancel one another out, and the remainder is:

$$\frac{\text{dyne-cm.}}{\dfrac{\text{dyne}}{\text{cm.}^2}} = ?$$

(That's a hyphen in dyne-cm., not a minus sign. *Dyne-cm.* means *dyne* $\times$ *cm.*)

To divide by a fraction, we invert the divisor and multiply:

$$\frac{\text{dyne-cm.}}{\dfrac{\text{dyne}}{\text{cm.}^2}} = \text{dyne-cm.} \times \frac{\text{cm.}^2}{\text{dyne}}$$

The dynes cancel, leaving cm. $\times$ cm.^{2}, or cm.^{3}, as the unit for the answer.

Thus, the answer should have been 1.04×10^6 cm.^{3} (cubic centimeters).

In this chapter, you have really come to grips with the slide rule, and have progressed to a point where you can handle most problems in multiplication and division. In the succeeding lessons, you will be given a chance to sharpen your new-found skill, and acquire others that will enable you to solve even thornier problems.

CHAPTER 3

The A, B, and K Scales

Many of the practical problems faced by the engineer, the architect, and the scientist or technician involve factors that must be squared or cubed. It may be necessary to find the surface area of a square wall, the volume of a cube, or the reduction of an electrical or magnetic force over distance. Most slide rules have two scales, called the A and K scales, that are of special help in solving such problems.

Let us take a specific problem and solve it first with ordinary arithmetic and then with the C and D scales. Then we will take up the new scales.

Assume that it is necessary to determine the weight of a concrete block that is to be used in the construction of a building. The block is a cube 2.1 feet on a side. You know that the concrete that you will be using weighs 131 pounds per cubic foot. The volume (v) of the block is the cube of the length of one side:

$$\begin{aligned} v &= 2.1 \text{ ft.} \times 2.1 \text{ ft.} \times 2.1 \text{ ft.} = 2.1^3 \text{ ft.}^3 \\ &= 9.26 \text{ cubic feet} \end{aligned}$$

The weight of the block is found by multiplying the weight of the concrete per cubic foot by the total number of cubic feet in a block:

$$\frac{131 \text{ lb.}}{\underset{1}{1\,\cancel{\text{cubic ft.}}}} \times 9.26\,\overset{1}{\cancel{\text{cubic ft.}}} = (131 \times 9.26) \text{ lb.} = 1{,}212 \text{ lb.}$$

Considering that there is some likelihood of error in measurement, a good answer from a slide rule would be approximately 1,210 pounds.

Solving the same problem with the C and D scales, we would find the volume by adding log 2.1 + log 2.1 + log 2.1. From this we can conclude:

The log of the cube of a number is three times the log of the number.
page 119

The log of the cube of a number is the cube of the log of the number.
page 121

[*from page 126*]

YOUR ANSWER: The full length of the D scale represents the number 20 on the A scale.

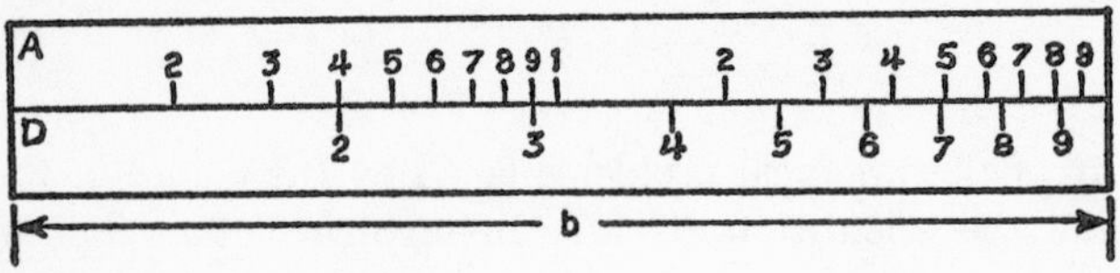

Your answer is incorrect.

Each number on the A scale is the square of the number opposite it on the D scale:

4 on A is opposite 2 on D $\quad 4 = 2^2$

9 on A is opposite 3 on D $\quad 9 = 3^2$

49 on A is opposite 7 on D $\quad 49 = 7^2$

and so on.

In terms of logarithms, we can look at it this way: The length of the left half of the A scale can represent the logarithm of 10. The length of the right half is the same, so that the whole scale represents log 10 + log 10. By now you should recall that the sum of the logarithms of two numbers is the logarithm of the product of the numbers:

$$\log A + \log B = \log (A \times B)$$

In this case,

$$\log 10 + \log 10 = \log (10 \times 10) = \log 100$$

Therefore, the full length of the A scale represents 100, not 20. And the 100 at the right index of the A scale is directly opposite 10 on the D scale, as it should be, since $100 = 10^2$.

The left half of the A scale is read from 1 to 10; the right half is read from 10 to 100.

Now return to page 126 and select the correct answer.

[*from page 130*]

YOUR ANSWER: $(x \times y)^2 = x^2 + y^2$.

Well, let's see. To test that conclusion, let $x = 3$ and $y = 4$.

If	$(x \times y)^2 = x^2 + y^2$
then	$(3 \times 4)^2 = 3^2 + 4^2$
and	$12^2 = 9 + 16$
But obviously	$144 \neq 25$

Your answer can't be right. 144 does not equal 25.
Better return to page 130 and select the correct answer.

[*from page 123*]

YOUR ANSWER: To square 130,000, I would first factor this number into 1.3×10^5.

Very good. Having correctly factored the number into the product of a number between 1 and 10 and a power of 10, all that remains is to square both factors and multiply them.

$$\begin{aligned} 130{,}000^2 &= 1.3^2 \times (10^5)^2 \\ &= 1.69 \times 10^{10} \end{aligned}$$

Suppose we wanted to square 0.013. The same procedure will work.

$$0.013^2 = 1.3^2 \times (10^{-3})^2 = 1.69 \times 10^{-6}$$

There's no problem with negative exponents. Just remember that the product of a positive and a negative number is negative. Multiplying two numbers of the same sign, whether positive or negative, gives a positive result.

Now you try one. Using your slide rule, find the square of 568.

323,000. **page 124**

238,000. **page 128**

2,380. **page 132**

[*from page 115*]

YOUR ANSWER: The log of the cube of a number is three times the log of the number.

Correct. Cubing a number by slide rule consists of adding the same distance three times. Doubling the distance gives us the square of a number. Mathematically, we express these as:

$$\log N^3 = 3 \times \log N$$

$$\log N^2 = 2 \times \log N$$

Or, generally, $$\log N^n = n \times \log N$$

This can be demonstrated readily by squaring the number 10^3. According to our formula,

$$\log N^2 = 2 \times \log N$$

If N is 10^3, $\log N = 3$, so that

$$2 \times \log N = 2 \times 3 = 6$$

It follows that

$$\log N^2 = 6$$

And this checks, because

$$(10^3)^2 = (10 \times 10 \times 10) \times (10 \times 10 \times 10) = 10^6$$

Now, let's look at the A scale which is on the body of the rule, right above the slide on most slide rules. If you move the hairline to the figure 9 near the center of the A scale, you will notice that the same distance from the left index corresponds to 3 on the D scale.

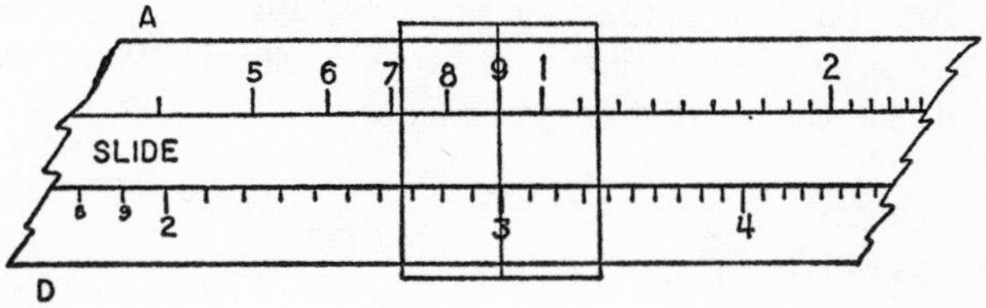

The conclusion is that when these scales are compared:

Any number on the A scale will be three times the number opposite it on the D scale. **page 122**

The distance from the index to a number on the A scale will be half the distance from the index to the same number on the D scale. **page 126**

[*from page 124*]

YOUR ANSWER: $360^{\frac{1}{2}} = 19$.

You are correct, within reasonable limits of accuracy. Actually, $19^2 = 361$, which is close enough for many practical purposes.

In extracting square roots the need to keep track of the power of 10 is not simply a question of keeping the decimal point in the right place. Failure can lead to the quandary of trying to decide whether 6 or 60 is the square root of 360. The key is proper factoring.

When squaring a number, we factored the number to be squared into the product of a number between 1 and 10 and a power of 10. Then the square of the first factor fell between 1 and 100 on the A scale. The square of the second factor, the power of 10, was found by doubling the exponent.

When extracting the square root of a number, we factor the number into the product of a number between 1 and 100, and an *even* power of 10. Then we can read the square root of the first factor off the D scale, and we can find the square root of the even power of 10 by dividing the exponent by 2.

If we wanted to find the square root of 528,000, for instance, we would factor it into 52.8×10^4. Since 52.8 is more than 10, it will be located on the right half of the A scale. With the indicator over 52.8 on the A scale, we read 7.26 on the D scale. Since the square root of 10^4 is 10^2, our answer will be 7.26×10^2, or 726.

It would be possible to factor to 5.28×10^5, which would give us a reading of 2.30 on the D scale to be multiplied by the square root of 10^5. Though it can be done, it is not as easy as finding the square root of 10^4. So stick to the even powers of 10.

One of the problems below is incorrectly solved. Work the problems and pick the set that contains an error.

$(0.00863)^2 = (0.0000745)$
$(0.000000763)^{\frac{1}{2}} = (0.000873)$ } **page 125**

$(0.702)^2 = (0.493)$
$(1{,}326{,}000{,}000)^{\frac{1}{2}} = (36{,}500)$ } **page 131**

$(4{,}925)^{\frac{1}{2}} = (22.2)$
$(0.9)^{\frac{1}{2}} = (0.949)$ } **page 135**

[*from page 115*]

YOUR ANSWER: The log of the cube of a number is the cube of the log of the number.

No, you haven't quite got the idea. Follow this closely.

It is true that we cube a number by using it as a factor three times, for example, 2.1 × 2.1 × 2.1 = 9.26. But, with logs, we multiply by adding. So the log of 9.26, for example, is log 2.1 + log 2.1 + log 2.1, or just three times the log of 2.1. What you said is log 9.26 = log 2.1 × log 2.1 × log 2.1. That is simply not true.

If we set the index of the C scale on 2.10 of the D scale, and then move the indicator hairline to 2.10 of the C scale, we have, in essence, added the log of 2.10 to the log of 2.10:

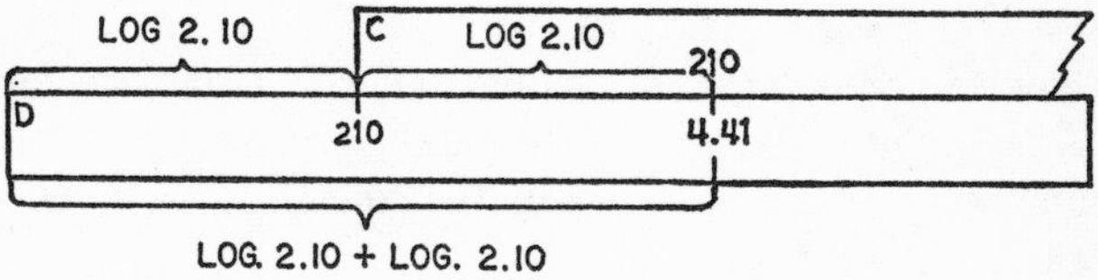

Sliding the index of the C scale to the hairline and then moving the hairline to 2.10 on the C scale is equivalent to adding another log 2.10:

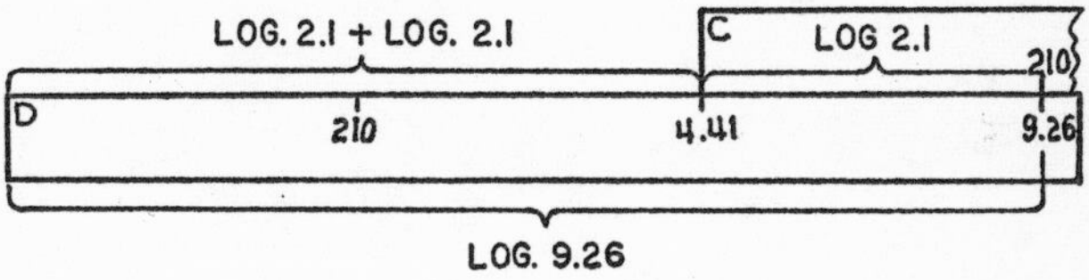

Thus we have multiplied 2.1 × 2.1 × 2.1 by adding logs. The resulting distance from the index of the D scale to 9.26 on that scale represents the log of 9.26. So it is true that log 9.26 = log 2.1 + log 2.1 + log 2.1, or 3 × log 2.1.

Now return to page 115 and select the other answer.

[*from page 119*]

YOUR ANSWER: Any number on Scale A will be three times the number opposite it on Scale D.

Really? Look at Scale A and Scale D next to each other.

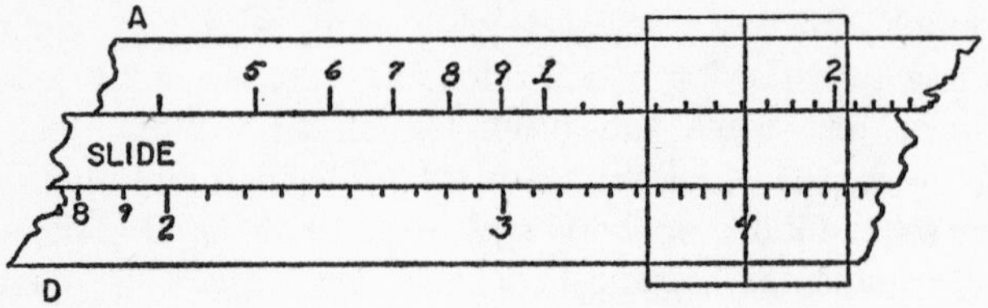

True, the number 3 on Scale D is opposite 9 on Scale A. But 2 is opposite 4, and 4 is opposite 16.

In fact, either observation should tell you that the numbers on Scale A represent the squares of the numbers on Scale D. Conversely, the numbers on Scale D represent the square roots of the numbers on Scale A.

Please return to page 119 and select the correct answer.

YOUR ANSWER: $(x \times y)^2 = x^2 \times y^2$.

Right. If we let $x = 3$ and $y = 4$, then

$$(3 \times 4)^2 = 3^2 \times 4^2$$
$$(12)^2 = 9 \times 16$$
$$144 = 144$$

The formula above is useful in finding the square of a number that doesn't fall between 1 and 10, the range of the D scale. As you know from Chapter 2, any number can be written in scientific notation: the number is written as a product of two factors, one a number between 1 and 10, and the other a power of 10. Using scientific notation and the relationship shown above, it is simple to keep track of the decimal point when squaring numbers of any size with the slide rule.

Let us suppose that we want to find the square of 400, using the slide rule. First, we need to factor 400 into a number between 1 and 10 and a power of 10: $400 = 4.0 \times 10^2$. Then, since $(x \times y)^2 = x^2 \times y^2$,

$$400^2 = 4.0^2 \times (10^2)^2$$

All we need to do now is locate 4.0 on the D scale and read its square on the A scale. (In this case you really don't need the slide rule, since you know by inspection that $4.0^2 = 16$.) Then we need to find $(10^2)^2$. Remembering that

$$(a^n)^m = a^{n \times m} \quad (\textit{not } a^{n+m})$$

we see that $$(10^2)^2 = 10^{2 \times 2} = 10^4$$

So $$400^2 = 16 \times 10^4 = 160{,}000$$

Suppose you wanted to square 130,000 with the slide rule. How would you factor it?

1.3×10^5. **page 118**

13×10^4. **page 129**

[*from page 118*]

YOUR ANSWER: The square of 568 is 323,000.

Yes. In the example, 568 was factored into 5.68×10^2. Setting the hairline at 5.68 on the D scale, we read 32.2 on the right-hand half of the A scale. The square of 10^2 is 10^4, so the entire answer is 32.3×10^4, or 323,000.

The steps in squaring any number (N) other than those between 1 and 10 are:

1. Write the number (N) as a product of two factors (X and Y), one a number between 1 and 10 (X), and the other a power of 10 (Y).
2. Set the indicator hairline at X on the D scale.
3. Obtain the square of X on the A scale.
4. Square Y, the power of 10, by doubling its exponent.
5. The square of N will be the product of the squares of X and Y. That is, since $N = X \times Y$, $N^2 = X^2 \times Y^2$.

The A and D scales can also be used for the extraction of square roots. For purposes of analysis, let us assume that N is the unknown square root of another number, M. Therefore, $M = N^2$, or $\sqrt{M} = N$ (the latter equation is read, *the square root of M equals N*). But we've seen before that: $2 \log N = \log N^2$, so $2 \log N = \log M$.

That being the case,

$$\log N = \frac{\log M}{2}$$

Since we said that N is the square root of M (that is, $N = \sqrt{M}$), we conclude that the log of the square root of M equals $\frac{1}{2} \log M$. The usual notation for the log of the square root of M is $\log M^{\frac{1}{2}}$.

A small complication arises in extracting square roots. The fact that $N = M^{\frac{1}{2}}$ or $\sqrt{M}$ does not mean that $10 \times N$ is the square root of $10 \times M$. For example, 2 is the square root of 4, but 2×10 is not the square root of 4×10. However, 2×10 *is* the square root of 4×10^2.

In extracting square roots, as in all other slide rule operations, you must keep your powers of 10 straight. Try your hand at this: $36^{\frac{1}{2}} = 6$, but what is $360^{\frac{1}{2}}$?

19. **page 120**		60. **page 133**

[*from page 120*]

YOUR ANSWER: The first pair contains an error.

Sorry—both of the problems in the first group are correct.

The first problem was $(0.00863)^2$. To find the square of a number, begin by writing the number as a product of two factors, one a number between 1 and 10, and the other a power of 10:

$$0.00863 = 8.63 \times 10^{-3}$$

Next, set the indicator hairline at the given number (8.63) on the D scale, and read its square on the right-hand A scale: $8.63^2 = 74.5$. (We can determine the placement of the decimal point with no difficulty, even if we forget that the right-hand A scale is read from 10 to 100, because we know that the square of 8.63 must lie between 64 and 81, the squares of 8 and 9.) Next, square the power of 10: $10^{-3} \times 10^{-3} = 10^{-6}$.

Since the square of 0.00863 will be the product of the squares of its factors,

$$(0.00863)^2 = 74.5 \times 10^{-6} = 0.0000745$$

The second problem was to find the square root of 0.000000763. First, we reduce the number to two factors, one a number between 1 and 100 and the other an even power of 10:

$$0.000000763 = 76.3 \times 10^{-8}$$

Then set the indicator at 76.3 on the A scale (that's between 10 and 100, remember). Read the square root of 76.3 from the D scale as 8.73. The square root of 10^{-8} is 10^{-4} (since $10^{-4} \times 10^{-4} = 10^{-8}$), so

$$(0.000000763)^{\frac{1}{2}} = 8.73 \times 10^{-4} = 0.000873$$

Return to page 120 and try again.

[*from page 119*]

YOUR ANSWER: The distance from the index to a number on Scale A will be half the distance from the index to the same number on Scale D.

Very good. It was clear from the illustration that the numbers appearing on the A scale are the squares of the corresponding numbers on the D scale. Now, if we make one entire scale from 1 to 10 that is just half as long as another corresponding scale, a distance on the shorter scale will represent the square of the number represented by the same distance on the longer scale ("*a*" on the diagram).

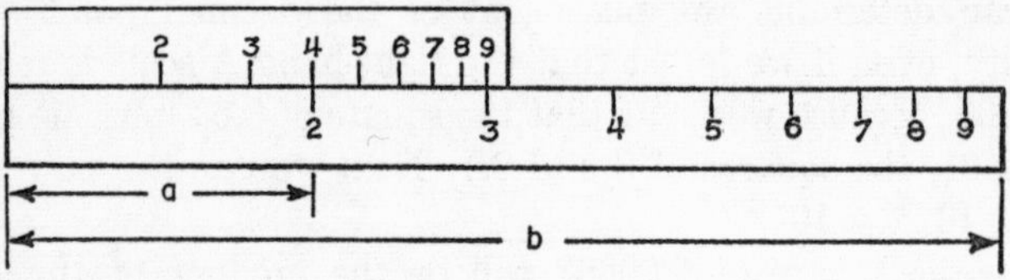

This is a consequence of the fact that

$$\log N^2 = 2 \times \log N$$

We can divide both sides by 2 to get

$$\frac{\log N^2}{2} = \log N$$

So when we transfer readings from a scale of one size to another half the size, we find the square of the number setting of the longer scale. Reading from the shorter to the longer scale, we obtain square roots.

Of course, the A scale is not physically half as long as the D scale. Rather, it consists of two shorter scales, end to end.

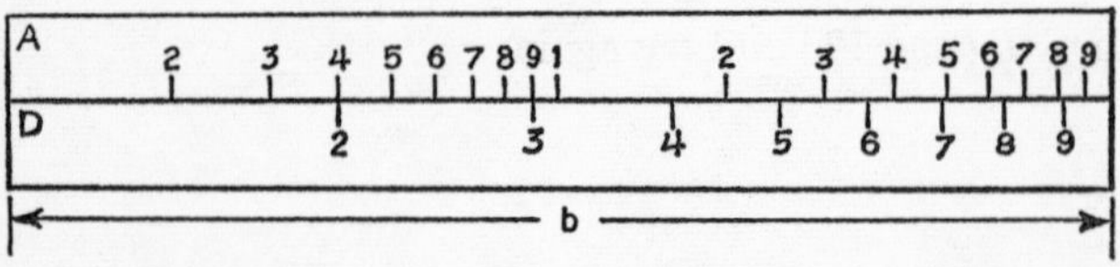

Here are the complete A and D scales next to each other. Now what number on the A scale is represented by distance *b*, the full length of the D scale?

20. **page 116**   100. **page 130**

[*from page 135*]

YOUR ANSWER: On the left side of the B scale.

It's there, all right. But it appears twice.

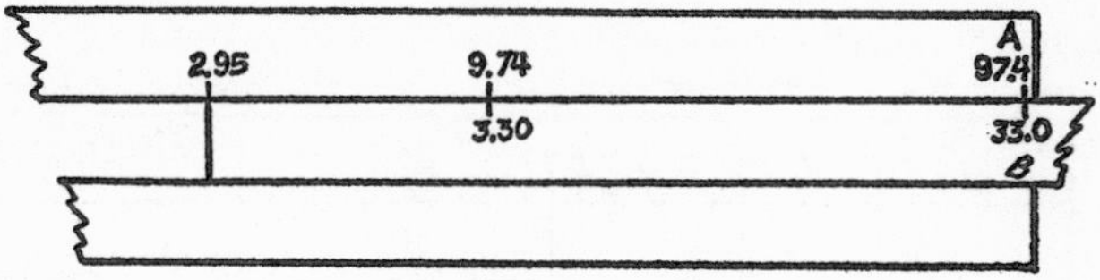

Some time ago—and it probably seems like a very long time indeed—you found that multiplying 3 × 5 with the C and D scales wasn't as easy as it seemed. Adding the distances corresponding to log 3 and log 5, you ended up off the scale.

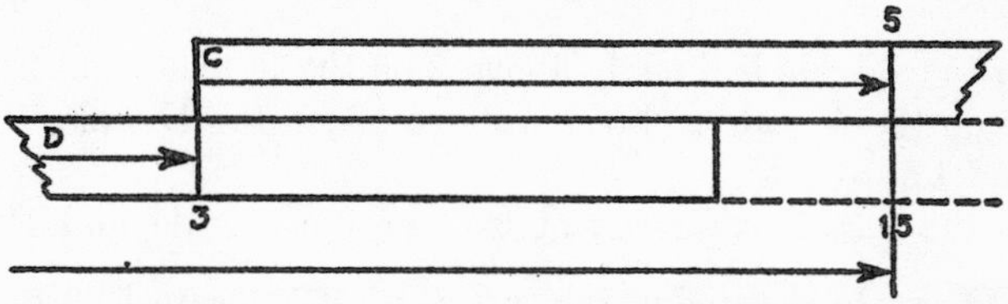

This didn't mean that the method was wrong, for if the scale hadn't stopped at 10 it would have worked. The A and B scales don't stop at 10; they both go to 100. With the hairline at 3.3 on the left-hand B scale, the problem is properly 2.95 × 3.30 = 9.74. At 33 on the right-hand B scale, the problem can be seen as 2.95 × 33.0 = 97.4. However, you've learned to place the decimal correctly, so this shouldn't cause any trouble.

Return to page 135 and choose a better answer.

[*from page 118*]

YOUR ANSWER: $568^2 = 238{,}000$.

Well, you've got the right power of 10, but you're confused about which scale does what. Let's look at a portion of the A and D scales again:

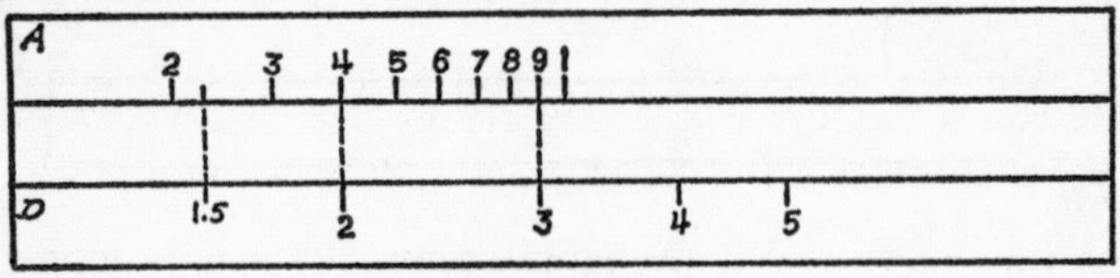

As you can see, a number appearing on the D scale has its square directly over it on the A scale. Here are some examples to check for yourself:

4 on the A scale is directly above 2 on the D scale, and $2^2 = 4$.
2.25 on the A scale is directly above 1.5 on the D scale, and $1.5^2 = 2.25$.
9 on the A scale is directly above 3 on the D scale, and $3^2 = 9$.

Therefore, to determine the square of 568, locate 5.68 on the D scale with the hairline. Then the square of 5.68 will appear on the A scale in line with the hairline. (To get the answer you chose, you must have done the reverse. You located 5.68 on the A scale and read 2.38 from the D scale.)

Rework the problem, and return to page 118 to choose the correct answer.

[*from page 123*]

YOUR ANSWER: To square 130,000, I would first factor this number into 13×10^4.

You could do it that way, but not for easiest operation of a slide rule. Remember, we think of the number on the D scale as being between 1 and 10, in order to keep track of the decimal point as easily as possible.

To square a number larger than 10 or less than 1, we first must write the number as a product of two factors, one a number between 1 and 10, and the other a power of 10.

But 13 is not between 1 and 10. Return to page 123 and select the better answer.

[*from page 126*]

YOUR ANSWER: 100.

Right. In the illustration below, showing a complete A scale, we can consider the numbers on the left half as 1 through 10, while the right half of the scale takes us through 100. This should be clear if we consider our general formula once more. We will let N stand for 10.

$$2 \log N = \log N^2$$

$$2 \log 10 = \log 10^2$$

$$N^2 = 10^2 = 100$$

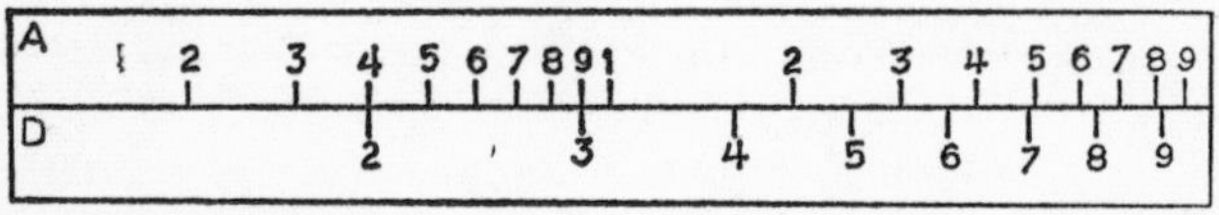

For reasons that will become apparent later, the scale is not marked as from 1 through 100, but as 1 through 10 twice. That means that care must be taken to avoid losing the decimal point. In simple calculations, there is no problem. Thus, we know that the number on the A scale above the 6 on the D scale will be read as 36 rather than 3.6.

Since the D scale is read from 1 to 10, numbers outside that range must be factored before their squares can be found on the A scale.

Before we get into the details of this factoring process, think about the following question for a moment. Which of these equations is correct?

$(x \times y)^2 = x^2 + y^2$. **page 117**

$(x \times y)^2 = x^2 \times y^2$. **page 123**

[*from page 120*]

YOUR ANSWER: The second pair contains an error.

No, it doesn't. Follow the explanations below and see whether you can find where you went wrong.

The first problem in this group was to find the square of 0.702. We start by writing the number as a product of two factors, one a power of 10, and the other a number between 1 and 10:

$$0.702 = 7.02 \times 10^{-1}$$

Then we set the indicator hairline at 7.02 on the D scale, and read its square, 49.3, from the right-hand A scale. (It has to be 49.3, rather than, say, 4.93, because, as you should know immediately, $7^2 = 49$. And also, of course, the right-hand A scale is read from 10 to 100.) Next, we square the power of 10: $10^{-1} \times 10^{-1} = 10^{-2}$. The square of a product is equal to the product of the squares of its factors, so:

$$(0.702)^2 = (7.02)^2 \times (10^{-1})^2 = 49.3 \times 10^{-2} = 0.493$$

The other problem was to find the square root of 1,326,000,000. First, factor the number as a product of two factors, one a number between 1 and 100, and the other an *even* power of 10:

$$1{,}326{,}000{,}000 = 13.26 \times 10^8$$

Then we locate 13.26 on the A scale (between 10 and 100, remember), and with the hairline indicator read its square root on the D scale as 3.65. The square root of 10^8 is 10^4 (since $10^4 \times 10^4 = 10^8$), so:

$$(1{,}326{,}000{,}000)^{\frac{1}{2}} = 3.65 \times 10^4 = 36{,}500$$

Return to page 120 for another try.

[*from page 118*]

YOUR ANSWER: $568^2 = 2{,}380$.

No, you've got a couple of errors here. Let's reduce the problem to scientific notation:

$$568^2 = (5.68 \times 10^2)^2$$

5.68 is reasonably close to 6, so we can use 6 in place of 5.68 to arrive at an approximation of the answer:

$$(6 \times 10^2)^2 = 6^2 \times (10^2)^2 = 36 \times 10^4$$

So our answer should be in the neighborhood of 36×10^4, or 360,000. And 2,380 obviously isn't.

Now, let's look at a portion of the A and D scales:

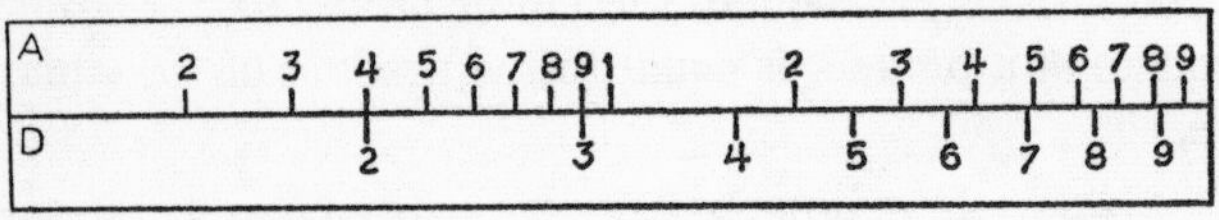

As you can see, a number appearing on the D scale has its square directly above it on the A scale. Therefore, to determine the square of any number, locate the number on the D scale with the hairline. Then its square will appear on the A scale in line with the hairline. Apparently you reversed this procedure, locating 5.68 on the A scale and reading its "square" from the D scale. To make sure you have it straight, we'll say it once more:

> To determine the square of any number, locate the number on the *D scale* with the hairline. Then its square will appear on the *A scale* in line with the hairline.

Now, return to page 118 and rework the problem. Keep in mind the approximation we calculated.

[*from page 124*]

YOUR ANSWER: $360^{\frac{1}{2}} = 60$.

No. You're looking for the square root of 360. But 360 doesn't appear directly on the A scale, which runs from 1 to 100 and no higher.

Working it out in your head, you can see that:

$$6 \times 6 = 36 \qquad 60 \times 60 = 3{,}600$$

So your answer won't even begin with a 6. You do know that the square root of 400 is 20, so the square root of 360 must be just a little less.

How do you use the slide rule to find the square root of 360? The key is to break 360 into two factors, each of whose square roots you can find easily. The square root of 360 will be the product of the square roots of the two factors. Factoring,

$$360 = 3.6 \times 10^2$$

The square root of 3.6 is found on the slide rule by setting the hairline at 3.6 on the left side of the A scale and reading the square root, 1.9, on the D scale under the hairline. The square root of 10^2 is simply 10. Therefore, the square root of 360 is 1.9×10, or 19.

Written in mathematical terms:

$$\begin{aligned} 360 &= 3.6 \times 10^2 \\ \sqrt{360} &= \sqrt{3.6} \times \sqrt{10^2} \\ &= 1.9 \times 10 \\ &= 19 \quad \text{to two-figure accuracy.} \end{aligned}$$

You must keep track of the power of 10 to avoid serious errors in taking square roots on the slide rule.

Please return to page 124 and pick the correct answer.

[*from page 141*]

YOUR ANSWER: 1.

No, more than one shift is necessary. This couldn't help but be a guess. A little help in solving the problem would probably be in order. Turn to page 150 where aid is available.

YOUR ANSWER: The third pair contains an error.

Yes. Let's see which of the two was wrong.

For the first problem, $(4{,}925)^{\frac{1}{2}} = (22.2)$, we reduce 4,925 to two factors:

A number between 1 and 100 $\longrightarrow 49.25 \times 10^2 \longleftarrow$ An even power of 10

The first factor, 49.25, is greater than 10, so it's on the right half of the A scale. The reading on the D scale is 7.03. The square root of 10^2 is 10^1, so:

$$(4{,}925)^{\frac{1}{2}} = 7.03 \times 10^1 = 70.3$$

The answer is not 22.2.

The second problem, $(0.9)^{\frac{1}{2}} = (0.949)$, becomes 90×10^{-2} in factored form. Reading from A to D, we find that the square root of 90 is 9.49. The square root of 10^{-2} is 10^{-1}, of course. So:

$$(0.9)^{\frac{1}{2}} = 9.49 \times 10^{-1} = 0.949$$

Now, let's review the steps in finding a square root:

1. Write the number as the product of two factors, one a number between 1 and 100, the other an even power of 10.
2. Find the square root of the first factor by locating the number on the A scale, and, with the aid of the hairline, reading the result directly below on the D scale.
3. Find the root of the power of 10 by dividing its exponent by 2.
4. Obtain the final result by multiplying the two square roots just obtained.

Now let's look at the B scale, which is an exact counterpart of the A scale located on the slide. The A and B scales can be used as a pair in exactly the same manner as the C and D scales.

If we want to multiply 2.95×3.30, we would simply move the left index of the B scale in line with 2.95 on the A scale. The product of this multiplication is found on the A scale in line with 3.30 on:

The left side of the B scale. **page 127**

The right side of the B scale. **page 137**

Either side of the B scale. **page 141**

[*from page 144*]

YOUR ANSWER: The first group of problems contains an error.

No, both of these problems are correct. Here are the shortest ways to do them:

$$\sqrt{8.47} \times 37.6^2 = \sqrt{8.47} \times 3.76^2 \times 10^2,$$

so the correct answer is approximately $3 \times 16 \times 10^2$, or 4.8×10^3. To find the whole answer:

1. Locate 8.47 on the A scale with the hairline indicator. Then $\sqrt{8.47}$ is under the hairline on the D scale.
2. Multiply $\sqrt{8.47}$ by 3.76 by sliding the right index of the C scale under the hairline and moving the hairline to 3.76 on the C scale. (You may have to turn your slide rule over to do this, depending on what type you have.)
3. Multiply by 3.76 again by again sliding the left index of the C scale under the hairline and again moving the hairline to 3.76 on the C scale. The answer, 4.12, will be on the D scale under the hairline.

Then, from our estimate, the complete answer is 4.12×10^3, or 4,120.

$\left(\frac{2.39^2}{2.04}\right)^{\frac{1}{2}}$ is approximately equal to $\left(\frac{4}{2}\right)^{\frac{1}{2}} = \sqrt{2}$. To find the actual answer:

1. Locate 2.39 on the D scale with the hairline indicator. Then 2.39^2 is on the A scale underneath the hairline.
2. Divide 2.39^2 by 2.04 by sliding 2.04 on the B scale under the hairline. Then move the hairline to the index of the B scale. Read 1.675 on the D scale underneath the hairline.

Then the full answer is 1.675.

Study these problems until you're sure you understand how to do them. Then return to page 144 for another try.

[*from page 135*]

YOUR ANSWER: On the right side of the B scale.

Some time ago—and it probably seems like a very long time indeed—you found that multiplying 3 × 5 with the C and D scales wasn't as easy as it seemed to be. Adding the distances corresponding to log 3 and log 5, you ended up off the scale.

This didn't mean that the method was wrong, for if the scale hadn't stopped at 10 it would have worked. The A and B scales don't stop at 10; they go to 100. With the hairline at 33 on the right-hand B scale, the problem is properly read as 2.95 × 33.0 = 97.4. Since you know how to place decimal points, this shouldn't cause any trouble. You know from the factors that the product must be around 9 or 10.

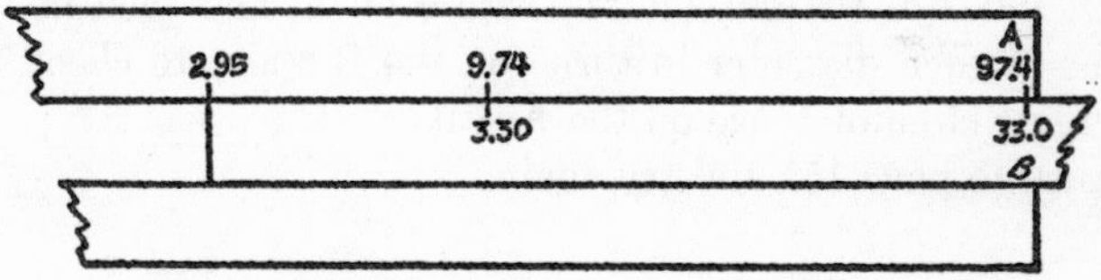

If 33 on the right-hand B scale stands for 33.0, 33 on the left-hand B scale stands for 3.3. Note that 974 appears on the A scale under the hairline here also, and is read directly as 9.74 rather than 97.4.

Now, return to page 135 and select a better answer.

[*from page 151*]

YOUR ANSWER: This pair of values is incorrect: $c = 722$, $d = 230$.

No, these values are all right. And there are two ways you could have checked for yourself.

First, since the formula for the circumference of a circle is $c = \pi d$, you could have used the given diameter, 230, to calculate c:

$$\begin{aligned} c &= \pi \times 230 \\ &= 3.1416 \times 230 \\ &= 722 \end{aligned}$$

Or you could have solved the equation $c = \pi d$ for d, getting $d = \frac{c}{\pi}$. Then, plugging in 722 for c,

$$\begin{aligned} d &= \frac{722}{\pi} \\ &= 230 \end{aligned}$$

Either way, then, it is clear that if $d = 230$, $c = 722$. This should tell you how to check the other two pairs of values: The simplest method is to use $c = \pi d$. All three pairs can be checked by setting the left index of the B scale opposite π on A, and then moving the hairline to each diameter in turn (on the B scale) to check the corresponding circumference on the A scale.

Return to page 151 and try again.

[*from page 144*]

YOUR ANSWER: The second group of problems contains an error.

No, both of the problems in this group are correct.

$$\frac{0.00363 \times 9{,}550 \times (1.33)^2}{1.863} \text{ or approximately } \frac{4 \times 10 \times 2}{2}$$

which is roughly 40.0, or 4.0×10^1. For the complete answer:

1. Locate 1.33 on the D scale with the hairline indicator. Then 1.33^2 will appear on the A scale under the hairline.
2. Multiply 1.33^2 by 3.63 by sliding the index of the B scale under the hairline and moving the hairline to 3.63 on the B scale.
3. Divide by 1.863 by sliding 1.863 on the B scale under the hairline.
4. Multiply by 9.55 by sliding the hairline over 9.55 on the B scale. The result, 3.29, will be under the line on the A scale.

And this is the answer given.

$$\sqrt{\frac{7{,}921 \times 0.031 \times 43}{29{,}642 \times 361}} \text{ or approximately}$$

$$\sqrt{\frac{8 \times \cancel{3} \times \cancel{4} \times 10^2}{\cancel{3} \times \cancel{4} \times 106}} = 3 \times 10^{-2}$$

1. Set the hairline at 7.92 on the A scale. Divide by 2.96 by sliding 2.96 on the B scale under the hairline.
2. Multiply by 3.1 by moving the hairline to 3.1 on the B scale.
3. Divide by 3.61 by moving the B scale so that 3.61 is under the hairline.
4. Multiply by 4.3 by moving the hairline to 4.3 on the B scale.

The answer, 3.14, will be on the D scale (because we want the square root of the whole thing) underneath the hairline. So the complete answer is 3.14×10^{-2}, or 0.0314, as was stated.

Notice the alternation of multiplication and division used to simplify the problem.

Now return to page 144 and try to find the error.

[*from page 159*]

YOUR ANSWER: About 11 gallons of paint would be required to paint the tank.

Excellent. The top is a circle with a diameter of 58 feet. To find the area, use

$$a = \frac{\pi}{4} d^2$$

$$a_{\text{top}} = \frac{\pi}{4} \times (58)^2 = 2{,}640 \text{ square feet}$$

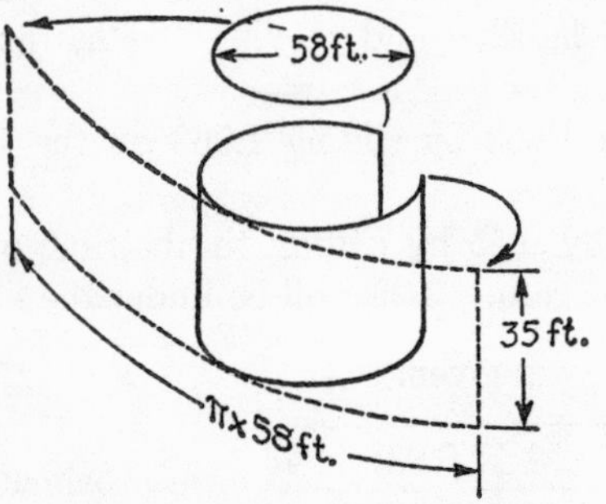

The circumference is $c = \pi \times d = \pi \times 58$ ft.
Therefore, the area of the side is:

$$a_{\text{side}} = 35 \times \pi \times 58 \text{ ft.} = 6{,}370 \text{ square feet}$$

This makes the total area to be covered 2,640 plus 6,370, or 9,010, square feet. The total amount of paint is 9,010 square feet divided by 850 square feet per gallon or 10.6 gallons.

$$\frac{9{,}010 \text{ ft.}^2}{850 \text{ ft.}^2/\text{gal.}} = 10.6 \text{ gal., or about 11 gal.}$$

Here are three problems and solutions. Which one is incorrect?

1. A wheel with a radius of 8.55 inches will roll 53.7 inches per revolution. **page 145**

2. The label of a can has an area of 43.7 sq. in. If it completely covers the side of a can 3.13 in. across, the can must be 4.45 sq. in. tall. **page 149**

3. The weight of iron for manhole covers is 36.9 lb/ft.² The weight of a cover one yard across will be 261 lb. **page 158**

[*from page 135*]

YOUR ANSWER: On either side of the B scale.

Good. Ignoring the decimal point, the answer, 974, will be under the hairline in either position.

Here are the possible settings:

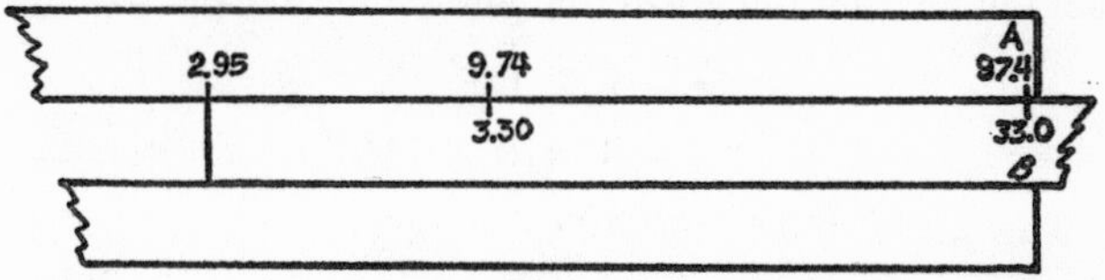

The reason we can do this is that both the A and B scales are doubled, and there are two settings for every one on the C-D combination. Of course, one of these scales can be considered as representing 1 through 10, the other as representing 10 through 100. But as long as we know from the factors where the decimal point will go, it doesn't make any difference in this problem which setting is read.

The problem could have been done in at least two ways on the A and B scales.

To find the answer to 2.95×3.30, ignore the decimal point and shift the left- or right-hand B scale index under 295 on the left- or right-hand A scale, and slide the hairline to 330 on the left- or right-hand B scale. The answer will be found under the hairline.

There is a very real advantage to using the A and B scales for combined operations because of the greater range of the scales. However, it is obviously more difficult to read the shorter scale accurately because the numbers are closer together. So the greater range is obtained at a price. But where accuracy is not critical, you can use the A and B scales.

The principal advantage of these scales, though, is for combined operations in conjunction with the C and D scales. Here's an example of such a problem:

$$\left(\frac{3{,}760 \times 241^2}{1.68}\right)^2 = 1.69 \times 10^{16}$$

How many shifts of the moving scales are necessary to solve it?

1. **page 134** 3. **page 147**

2. **page 144** I don't know how to begin. **page 150**

[*from page 151*]

YOUR ANSWER: This pair of values is incorrect: $d = 145$, $c = 456$.

No, these values are all right. And there are two ways you could have checked for yourself.

First, since the formula for the circumference of a circle is $c = \pi d$, you could have used the given diameter, 145, to calculate c:

$$\begin{aligned} c &= \pi \times 145 \\ &= 3.1416 \times 145 \\ &= 456 \end{aligned}$$

Or you could have solved the equation $c = \pi d$ for d, getting $d = \frac{c}{\pi}$. Then, plugging in 456 for c,

$$\begin{aligned} d &= \frac{456}{\pi} \\ &= 145 \end{aligned}$$

Either way, then, it is clear that if $d = 145$, $c = 456$. This should tell you how to check the other two pairs of values: The simplest method is to use $c = \pi d$, for then all three pairs can be checked by setting the left index of the B scale opposite π on A, and then moving the hairline to each diameter in turn (on the B scale) to check the corresponding circumference on the A scale.

Return to page 151 and try again.

[*from page 159*]

YOUR ANSWER: $5\frac{1}{2}$ gallons would be enough to paint the tank.

No, $5\frac{1}{2}$ gallons won't do the trick.

We want to paint the top and side of a circular tank 35 feet high and 58 feet in diameter. The total area to be covered is the area of the top plus the area of the side: $a_{\text{total}} = a_{\text{top}} + a_{\text{side}}$.

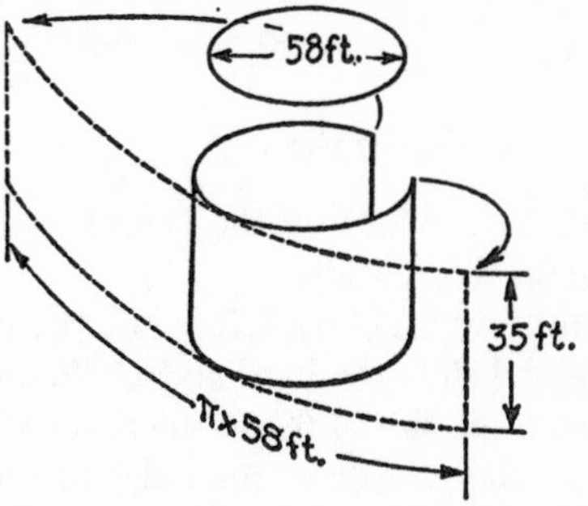

The area of the top is given by the formula for the area of a circle:

$$a_{\text{top}} = \frac{\pi}{4} \times d^2 = \frac{\pi}{4} \times 58^2$$

which is roughly 3,000 square feet. The area of the side can be considered a rectangle whose width is the height of the tank and whose length is the circumference of the circle:

$$\text{width} = 35 \text{ feet} \qquad \text{length} = c = \pi \times d = \pi \times 58$$

Since the area of a rectangle is the product of its length times its width,

$$a_{\text{side}} = 35 \times \pi \times 58$$

So the area of the side will be about 6,000 square feet.

Now, the number of gallons necessary to paint the tank is found by dividing the total number of square feet of area by the number of square feet that can be covered by one gallon of paint:

$$\text{number of gallons necessary} = \frac{a_{\text{total}}}{850}$$

Complete the problem, using the actual figures (not the approximations), and then return to page 159 to select the correct answer.

[*from page 141*]

YOUR ANSWER: 2.

Right. The problem can be performed with two shifts of the slide. Here is the solution, step by step. Check it against your own work.

$$\left(\frac{3{,}760 \times 241^2}{1.68}\right)^2 = \left(\frac{3.76 \times 2.41^2}{1.68}\right)^2 \times 10^{14}$$

or approximately, $\left(\frac{4 \times 2.5^2}{2}\right)^2 \times 10^{14} = 1.25^2 \times 10^{16} = 1.56 \times 10^{16}$

Now for the manipulation of the rule:

1. Slide the hairline to 2.41 on the D scale. Then 2.41^2 is under the hairline on the A scale.
2. Then, to multiply 2.41^2 by 3.76, shift the left B index under the hairline and slide the hairline to 3.76 on the B scale.
3. To divide by 1.68, shift 1.68 on the B scale under the hairline.
4. Read 13.0 on the A scale at the index of the B scale. This is the value of everything within the parentheses.
5. Slide the hairline indicator to 130 on the B scale (ignore the decimal point) to square the value of everything within the parentheses.
6. Read 169 on the A scale under the hairline. The complete answer is 1.69×10^{16}.

Here are three pairs of problems. One of the six problems is incorrectly solved. Select the pair that includes an error.

$$\sqrt{8.47} \times 37.6^2 = 4{,}120$$

$$\left(\frac{2.39^2}{2.04}\right)^{\frac{1}{2}} = 1.675$$

page 136

$$\frac{0.00363 \times 9{,}550 \times 1.33^2}{1.863} = 32.9$$

$$\frac{\sqrt{7{,}921 \times 0.031 \times 43}}{29{,}642 \times 361} = 3.14 \times 10^{-2}$$

page 139

$$\frac{0.00631 \times 3{,}682^2 \times 1.002}{43.4^2} = 21.9$$

$$\frac{81.6 \times 32{,}400 \times \sqrt{160}}{\sqrt{802}} = 1.18 \times 10^7$$

page 151

[*from page 140*]

YOUR ANSWER: This problem was incorrectly solved: A wheel with a radius of 8.55 inches will roll 53.7 inches per revolution.

No, the problem was solved correctly. Here's why:

When a wheel has rolled through one complete revolution, it has rolled the length of its circumference:

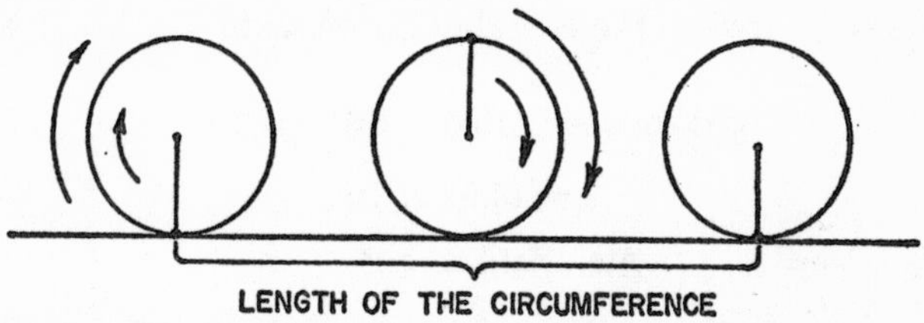

The diameter of a circle is twice its radius, so a wheel with a radius of 8.55 inches has a diameter of 2×8.55 inches.

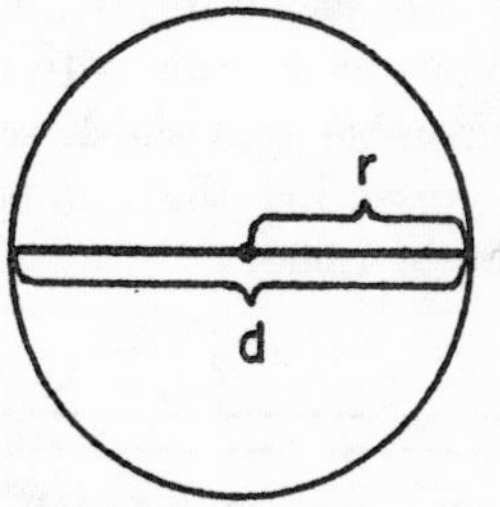

The circumference of this wheel, which is also the distance it will roll in one revolution, is calculated from the circumference formula, $c = \pi d$.

$$\begin{aligned} c &= \pi \times 2 \times 8.55 \\ &= \pi \times 17.1 \\ &= 53.7 \text{ inches} \end{aligned}$$

Now return to page 140 for another try.

[*from page 152*]

YOUR ANSWER: $\sqrt[3]{15{,}600{,}000} = 116.$

It looks as if you read the K scale in the wrong place. Let's start from the beginning.

First, we factor 15,600,000 into two factors, one of which must be a power of 10 in which the exponent is a multiple of 3. The other number must be between 1 and 1,000; that is, it must be a number that can be located on the K scale. So we write

$$15{,}600{,}000^{\frac{1}{3}} = (15.6 \times 10^6)^{\frac{1}{3}}$$
$$= 15.6^{\frac{1}{3}} \times 10^2$$

because $(10^6)^{\frac{1}{3}} = 10^{\frac{6}{3}} = 10^2$

to check: $(10^2)^3 = 10^2 \times 10^2 \times 10^2 = 10^6$

Since $2^3 = 8$, and $3^3 = 27$, the cube root of 15.6 must be between 2 and 3. This gives us a fairly good approximation of our answer.

The next step—and this seems to be where you made your mistake—is to locate 15.6 on the K scale with the hairline. To do this correctly, you must remember that the K scale is divided into three identical segments, representing the numbers from 1 to 10, from 10 to 100, and from 100 to 1,000:

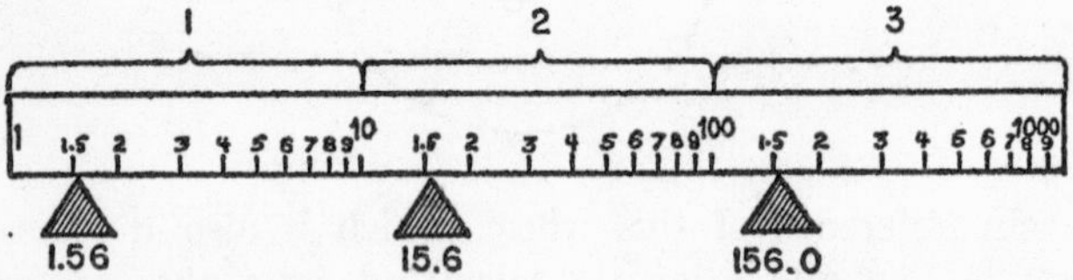

Since 15.6 is between 10 and 100, we must locate it on the *second* segment. Then we can read its cube root from the D scale. Evidently you aligned the hairline with 1.56 in the first segment, giving you the cube root of 1.56 rather than that of 15.6.

Return to page 152 and select the correct answer.

YOUR ANSWER: 3.

Actually, 2 shifts of the slide are enough, if you use the shortest, most efficient procedure. Until you become more familiar with the slide rule, however, you will probably have to work most problems several times before you find the shortest method.

The given problem reduces to $\left(\frac{3.76 \times 2.41^2}{1.68}\right)^2 \times 10^{14}$. Substituting 4 for 3.76, 2.5 for 2.41, and 2 for 1.68, we find that the correct answer is roughly 1.56×10^{16}.

Since we have an estimate of the answer, we can disregard the decimal point during the slide rule operations and read only the sequence of numbers for each setting.

It seems most practical to perform the operations within the parentheses first and then square the answer we get, rather than square everything first. Therefore:

1. Locate 241 on the D scale with the hairline indicator. This automatically locates 2.41^2 on the A scale.
2. Next, to multiply 2.41^2 by 3.76, shift the index of the B scale under the hairline, and slide the hairline to 3.76 on the B scale.
3. To divide by 1.68, shift 1.68 under the hairline.

Now—and this is a timesaving trick—take a reading from the A scale at the index of the B scale. It should be 130, which is the value of $\frac{3.76 \times 2.41^2}{1.68}$ (without the decimal). Therefore, to get our final answer, we just square 130 by moving the hairline indicator to 130 on the B scale and reading from the A scale. Last of all, we place the decimal according to the estimate.

Perform the operations for yourself. You should be able to get the correct answer, 1.69×10^{16}. When you feel that you understand why this procedure works and why it's the shortest method, return to page 141 and choose the correct answer.

[*from page 157*]

YOUR ANSWER: One of these is incorrect:

$$(699)^{\frac{1}{3}} = 8.87 \qquad (42.1)^{\frac{1}{3}} = 3.48$$

No, they're both right. Let's run through the procedure again:

1. Factor the number as a product of two factors. One must be a power of 10 whose exponent is a multiple of 3. The other factor may be any number between 1 and 1,000, but it is chosen to satisfy the need for a power of 10 divisible by 3.
2. Extract the cube root of the power of 10 by dividing its exponent by 3.
3. Locate the second factor on the proper part of the K scale. Remember that the left-hand section runs from 1 to 10, the center section runs from 10 to 100, and the right-hand section runs from 100 to 1,000.
4. Read the root of the second factor directly on the D scale. It will be a number between 1 and 10.
5. Multiply the cube root of the first factor (the power of 10) by that of the second factor to obtain the complete cube root.

With this procedure in mind, look at the two problems again. Both 699 and 42.1 are between 1 and 1,000, so they do not need to be factored. If you like, you can look at them this way:

$$699 = 699 \times 10^0 \quad \text{and} \quad 42.1 = 42.1 \times 10^0,$$

and 0 can be considered a multiple of any number. So just locate 699 on the last section of the K scale and read its cube root directly on the D scale. Similarly, locate 42.1 on the center section of the K scale and read its cube root on the D scale. That's all there is to it.

Now return to page 157 and try to find the error.

[*from page 140*]

YOUR ANSWER: The second problem is incorrect.

Of course. Although the numerical calculation is correct, the height of the can would not be expressed in square inches. Linear measure is not made in squared units.

Sometimes it is necessary to operate with the cube of a number, or to extract a cube root. A scale to operate with cubes is developed in the same manner as the A and B scales for squares and square roots. That is, just as the A scale was made of two half-size C scales because the log of $N^2 = 2 \log N$, the cube scale consists of three such scales of one-third size because the log of $N^3 = 3 \log N$. Thus, the scale is in three sections, 1 to 10, 10 to 100, and 100 to 1,000.

On many slide rules, the K scale is on the body of the rule, above the A scale. Although a Mannheim standard rule doesn't have a K scale, users of that rule should read along anyway. You can work the problems with the scales you have.

To cube any number, first factor it into the product of a number between 1 and 10 and a power of 10. Then locate the first factor on the D scale and read its cube on the K scale. The cube of the number is the cube of the first factor times the cube of the power of 10. For example, $4{,}720^3 = (4.72 \times 10^3)^3 = 4.72^3 \times 10^9$. This will be roughly equivalent to $5^3 \times 10^9 = 125 \times 10^9$, or 1.25×10^{11}. Sliding the hairline indicator to 4.72 on the D scale, we read 105 on the center K scale. So $4{,}720^3 = 1.05 \times 10^{11}$.

Here is another "one-wrong" series:

1. $(9.29)^3 = 802$
   $(0.000464)^3 = 0.000000000999$ } **page 152**

2. $(14.1)^3 = 2{,}800$
   $(0.267)^3 = 0.019$ } **page 155**

3. $(792)^3 = 4.97 \times 10^8$
   $(40.4)^3 = 65{,}900$ } **page 161**

[*from page 141*]

YOUR ANSWER: I don't know how to begin.

The problem may look confusing for a moment, but it is not really as difficult as it may seem.

$$\left(\frac{3{,}760 \times 241^2}{1.68}\right)^2 = \left(\frac{3.76 \times 10^3 \times (2.41 \times 10^2)^2}{1.68}\right)^2$$

$$= \left(\frac{3.76 \times 2.41^2}{1.68}\right)^2 \times 10^{14}$$

In approximation form,

$$\left(\frac{4 \times 2.5^2}{2}\right)^2 \times 10^{14} = \left(\frac{4 \times 6.25}{2}\right)^2 \times 10^{14} = 12.5^2 \times 10^{14}$$

$$= 1.25^2 \times 10^{16} = 1.56 \times 10^{16}$$

The estimate will tell us where the decimal point belongs in the final answer, so we need not worry about keeping track of the decimal during the slide rule operations.

It seems most practical to perform the operations within the parentheses first and then square the answer we get, rather than square everything first. Therefore:

1. Locate 2.41 on the D scale with the hairline indicator. This automatically locates 2.41^2 on the A scale.
2. Next, to multiply 2.41^2 by 3.76, shift the index of the B scale under the hairline, and slide the hairline to 3.76 on the B scale.
3. To divide by 1.68, shift 1.68 on the B scale under the hairline.

Now—and this is a timesaving trick—take a reading from the A scale at the index of the B scale. It should be 130, representing the value of $\frac{3.76 \times 2.41^2}{1.68}$ (without the decimal, of course). Therefore, to get our final answer, we just square 130 by moving the hairline indicator to 130 on the B scale and reading from the A scale under the hairline. Last, we locate the decimal, using the rough estimate.

This is only one of several possible ways of solving this problem. It is one of the simplest. As you read the above, you should have been performing the steps. If you didn't, do so now, and see whether you get the correct answer, which is 1.69×10^{16}. Then return to page 141 to select the correct answer.

[*from page 144*]

YOUR ANSWER: One of these is wrong:

$$\frac{0.00631 \times 3{,}682^2 \times 1.002}{43.4^2} = 21.9$$

$$\frac{81.6 \times 32{,}400 \times \sqrt{160}}{\sqrt{802}} = 1.18 \times 10^7$$

Yes, the first one is incorrect. And it's a little tricky if you have a slide rule on which A, B, C, and D scales are not all on the same side. In this case you will find that you must turn the slide rule over twice. However, you needn't change the settings because they are the same on either side. Now estimate and follow the steps below.

$$\frac{6 \times 10^{-3} \times (4 \times 10^3)^2}{(4 \times 10)^2} = 6 \times 10^1$$

1. Index the B scale at 1.002 on A scale.
2. Slide the hairline indicator to 6.31 on the left-hand B scale.
3. Index the left end of the B scale at the hairline.
4. Slide the hairline to 3.68 on C scale (turn the rule over, if necessary).
5. Shift the sliding scale to the left. Stop when 4.34 on the C scale is under the hairline.
6. Read 4.55 on the A scale (turn over, if necessary). The result is 4.55×10, not 21.9.

Don't be discouraged if you had to work some of these problems several times in several ways. The only way to become proficient with the slide rule is to practice.

It is often necessary to find the circumference of a circle. The usual formula for the circumference of a circle is: $c = \pi d$, where d is the diameter and π (pi) is the symbol for the ratio of circumference to diameter. That ratio is the same for all circles; its value is 3.1416 to five figures. That is, $\pi = 3.1416$.

Using the formula $c = \pi d$, check the three pairs of values below. Turn to the page corresponding to the pair that is incorrect.

$c = 722$, $d = 230$. **page 138**

$d = 145$, $c = 456$. **page 142**

$c = 1{,}940$, $d = 628$. **page 159**

[*from page 149*]

YOUR ANSWER: One of the first pair is incorrect.

Yes; let's see which one. The first was $(9.29)^3 = 802$.
Written in form for estimating: $10^3 = 1{,}000$. On the slide rule:

1. Set 9.29 on the D scale.
2. Read the answer, 802, on the K scale.

The second was $(0.000464)^3$ which was said to equal 0.000000000-999. Estimating, $(5 \times 10^{-4})^3 = 125 \times 10^{-12}$.

On the slide rule, set 4.64 on the D scale. The 99.9 on the K scale is read 99.9×10^{-12}. That means, we move the decimal point 12 places to the left, so

$$(0.000464)^3 = 99.9 \times 10^{-12} = 0.0000000000999$$

Extracting a cube root is a bit more involved. As with the square root, the number whose root is to be found must be factored. For the cube root, the power of ten must have an exponent that is a multiple of 3. The other factor must be between 1 and 1,000.

Consider the cube root of 125,000, which can be written as $(125{,}000)^{\frac{1}{3}}$ or $\sqrt[3]{125{,}000}$:

Factoring 125,000 in the prescribed manner gives 125×10^3.

As with the square root, the cube root is the product of the roots of its factors:

$$\sqrt[3]{125{,}000} = (125)^{\frac{1}{3}} \times (10^3)^{\frac{1}{3}} = \underset{\substack{\uparrow \\ \text{because } 10 \times 10 \times 10 = 10^3}}{\overset{\substack{\text{because } 5 \times 5 \times 5 = 125 \\ \downarrow}}{5 \times 10}} = 50$$

Suppose you try this one:

$$\sqrt[3]{15{,}600{,}000} = ?$$

116. **page 146**

250. **page 157**

I don't know how to start. **page 162**

[*from page 157*]

YOUR ANSWER: One of the second pair is incorrect.

Right. Let's check them. The first is factored this way:

$$(9{,}850)^{\frac{1}{3}} = 9.85^{\frac{1}{3}} \times (10^3)^{\frac{1}{3}} = 9.85^{\frac{1}{3}} \times 10^1$$

Locate 9.85 on the left-hand K scale and read 2.14 on the D scale. The result is 2.14×10^1, or 21.4. So 46.2, the answer given for this problem, was wrong, apparently an error resulting from use of the center K scale.

The second problem, $(78.7 \times 10^{-8})^{\frac{1}{3}}$, can be written as $(787 \times 10^{-9})^{\frac{1}{3}}$, which becomes $787^{\frac{1}{3}} \times 10^{-3}$. Finding 787 on the right-hand K scale we read 9.23 on the D scale. $(78.7 \times 10^{-8})^{\frac{1}{3}}$, then, is 9.23×10^{-3}, as shown.

While roots and powers other than squares and cubes do occur in many problems, there is not a special scale for each power and its corresponding root. However, by combining the scales you have already learned about, it is possible to use a slide rule to find those roots and powers for which the exponents can be broken down into combinations of 2's and 3's.

Some of these are rather obvious. Since $3^2 = 9$, and $9^2 = 81$, $(3^2)^2 = 81$. Going one step further, $3^4 = 81$. So, to find the fourth power of a number, first square it (reading from D to A), then set the hairline at the square on the D scale. The fourth power of the original number is then on the A scale under the hairline. It is possible to extract the fourth root of any number by reversing this procedure.

Is the following true or false?

The fifth and eleventh powers and roots may be found in similar fashion.

True. **page 160**

False. **page 165**

[*from page 159*]

YOUR ANSWER: I don't know where to start.

Well, start by deciding just exactly what areas are to be painted. The top of the tank is a circle, with a diameter of 58 feet. The formula for the area of a circle is

$$a = \frac{\pi}{4} \times d^2,$$

so $$a_{top} = \frac{\pi}{4} \times 58^2, \quad \text{which is about 3,000 square feet.}$$

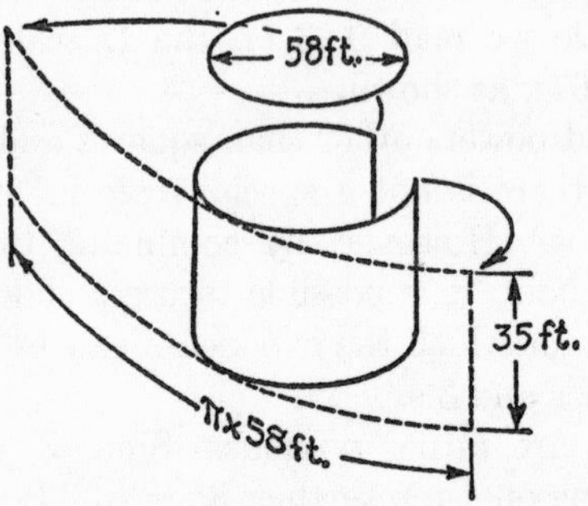

The side of the tank can be thought of as a rolled-up rectangle. The area of a rectangle is the product of its width times its length. In this case, the width is the height of the tank, 35 feet, and the length is the circumference of the tank. Since the circumference is

$$c = \pi \times d = \pi \times 58,$$

the side area of the tank is $a_{side} = 35 \times \pi \times 58$.

The total area to be painted is the side area plus the top area:

$$a_{total} = a_{side} + a_{top}$$

The total area divided by the number of square feet that can be covered by one gallon of paint will give the number of gallons necessary to do the job:

$$\text{Number of gallons needed} = \frac{a_{total}}{850}$$

Complete the problem, and then return to page 159 to select the correct answer.

YOUR ANSWER: One of these is wrong:

$$(14.1)^3 = 2{,}800$$
$$(0.267)^3 = 0.019$$

No, consider them again: $(14.1)^3 = (1.41 \times 10)^3 = 1.41^3 \times 10^3$. In estimating form:

$$1.5^3 \times 10^3 = 3.38 \times 10^3$$

For the complete answer:

1. Slide the hairline to 1.41 on the D scale.
2. Read 2.8 from the left-hand K scale.

The desired cube is 2.8×10^3, or 2,800. So that answer is correct.

$$(0.267)^3 = (2.67 \times 10^{-1})^3 = 2.67^3 \times 10^{-3}$$

In estimating form:

$$3^3 \times 10^{-3} = 27 \times 10^{-3}$$

To find the complete answer:

1. Slide the hairline to 2.67 on the D scale.
2. Read 19.0 on the center K scale.

The cube is 19.0×10^{-3}, or 0.019, as stated.

When you're working with the K scale, remember that it is divided into three identical segments, just as the A and B scales are divided into two identical segments. Thus, on the K scale, the first segment represents the numbers from 1 to 10, the second represents the numbers from 10 to 100, and the third represents the numbers from 100 to 1,000.

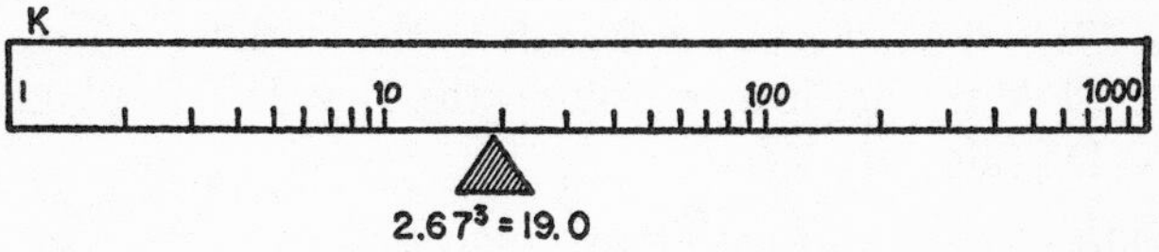

In order that the decimal point may be placed correctly, keep in mind what range you are in. Thus, we read the cube of 2.67 as 19.0, *not* 1.9.

Now return to page 149 and try to find the error.

[*from page 160*]

YOUR ANSWER: One of the problems in the first pair requires more than the listed number of moves.

Well, let's check.

$$\frac{(6.38 \times 10^8 \times 108.5)^2}{36.8 \times 10.9 \times 444} = \frac{(6.38 \times 10^8 \times 1.085 \times 10^2)^2}{3.68 \times 10 \times 1.09 \times 10 \times 4.44 \times 10^2}$$

$$= \frac{(6.38 \times 1.085)^2}{3.68 \times 1.09 \times 4.44} \times 10^{16}$$

In approximation form, $\frac{6^2 \times 1^2}{4 \times 1 \times 4} \times 10^{16} = 2.25 \times 10^{16}$

1. Slide the hairline indicator to 6.38 on the D scale.
2. Shift the slide until 3.68 on the B scale is under the hairline.
3. Slide the hairline indicator to 1.085 on the C scale.
4. Shift the slide until 1.09 on the B scale is under the hairline.
5. Slide the hairline to the left index of the B scale.
6. Shift the slide until 4.44 of the B scale is under the hairline.

The answer 2.69 is at the left index of the B scale on the A scale. The complete answer is 2.69×10^{16}.

The operation requires three shifts and three slides—the listed number of moves.

How about the second?

$$\sqrt[2]{639} \times \sqrt[3]{9{,}640} = (6.39 \times 10^2)^{\frac{1}{2}} \times (9.640 \times 10^3)^{\frac{1}{3}}$$

$$= 6.39^{\frac{1}{2}} \times 9.64^{\frac{1}{3}} \times 10^2$$

which will be about 5.25×10^2. Here are the minimum number of moves:

1. *Slide* the hairline indicator to 9.64 on the K scale.
2. *Shift* the index of the B scale to the hairline.
3. *Slide* the hairline to 6.39 on the B scale. Read 5.38 on the D Scale.

One shift and two slides, so that's right too.

Now return to page 160 and try again.

[*from page 152*]

YOUR ANSWER: $\sqrt[3]{15{,}600{,}000} = 250.$

Yes.

Factoring into the product of a number between 1 and 1,000 and a power of 10 whose exponent is divisible by 3, we get $15{,}600{,}000 = 15.6 \times 10^6$, so $15{,}600{,}000^{\frac{1}{3}} = (15.6)^{\frac{1}{3}} \times (10^6)^{\frac{1}{3}}$.

The cube root of 10^6 is clearly 10^2: $(10^6)^{\frac{1}{3}} = 10^{\frac{6}{3}} = 10^2$. Checking: $(10^2)^3 = 10^2 \times 10^2 \times 10^2 = 10^6$.

To find the cube root of 15.6 you had to decide which section of the K scale you needed:

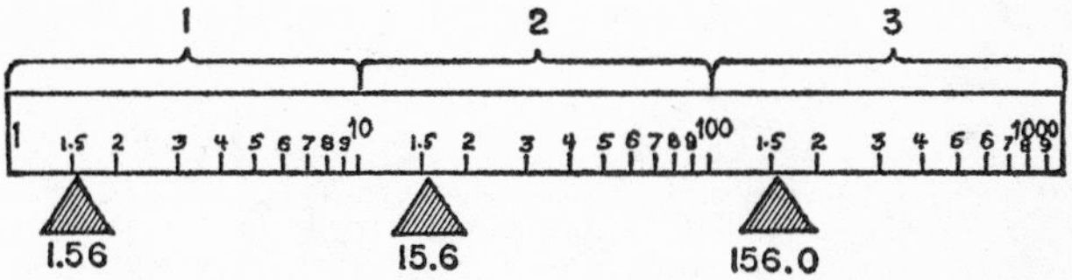

According to the illustration, 15.6 would be found on the center scale. Its cube root, 2.5, is then found on the D scale. The complete cube root of 15,600,000 is 2.5×10^2 or 250.

In review, to find the cube root:

1. Factor the number as a product of two factors, one a power of 10 whose exponent is divisible by 3, the second a number between 1 and 1,000.
2. Extract the cube root of the power of ten by finding $\frac{1}{3}$ of its exponent, that is, by dividing its exponent by 3.
3. Locate the second factor properly on the K scale.
4. Read the root of the second factor directly on the D scale, and finally
5. Multiply the cube roots of the two factors.

In which of the following pairs can you find an error?

$(699)^{\frac{1}{3}} = 8.87$
$(42.1)^{\frac{1}{3}} = 3.48$ } **page 148**

$(9{,}850)^{\frac{1}{3}} = 46.2$
$(78.7 \times 10^{-8})^{\frac{1}{3}} = 9.23 \times 10^{-3}$ } **page 153**

$(0.00239)^{\frac{1}{3}} = 0.134$
$(12{,}812)^{\frac{1}{3}} = 23.4$ } **page 164**

[*from page 140*]

YOUR ANSWER: This problem was incorrectly solved: The weight of iron for manhole covers is 36.9 lb/ft.^{2} The weight of a cover 1 yard across will be 261 lb.

No, the weight of the sewer cover was correctly determined. Here's the way it goes:

Because the weight is given in pounds per sq. ft., we must convert the 1-yard diameter into 3 feet (1 yd. = 3 ft.). Area is calculated by our formula, as follows:

$$a = \frac{\pi}{4} d^2$$

$$= \frac{\pi}{4} 3^2$$

$$= 7.07 \text{ square feet} \quad (\text{or ft.}^2)$$

The whole weight of the cover is determined by this formula: weight (wt.) = area in square feet × pounds per square foot. If each square foot of this cover weighs 36.9 lb., and there are 7.07 square feet,

$$\text{wt.} = 7.07 \text{ ft.}^2 \times 36.9 \frac{\text{lb.}}{\text{ft.}^2}$$

$$= 7.07 \times 36.9 \text{ lb.}$$

$$= 261 \text{ lb.}$$

Now return to page 140 to try again.

[*from page 151*]

YOUR ANSWER: This pair of values is incorrect: $c = 1{,}940$, $d = 628$.

Good. Using the diameter given and $c = \pi d$, you could have calculated the corresponding circumference and compared it with the 1,940. If this were done, the calculated circumference would have come out about 1,970.

Though you could solve for d $\left(d = \dfrac{c}{\pi}\right)$, the method above is easiest, for it allows the checking of all three problems with one movement of the slide. Setting the left index of the B scale opposite π, we move the hairline along B to each of the values of d, finding the corresponding values of c on the A scale.

Another common problem is finding the area of a circle, given only its diameter or radius. The formula for area in terms of the diameter (which is twice the radius) is $a = \dfrac{\pi}{4} d^2$. The factor $\dfrac{\pi}{4}$ is approximately 0.78539. On most rules there is a gauge mark at 785 on the right-hand A scale to make calculations with $\dfrac{\pi}{4}$ faster. It is on the right-hand scale so it will be read as 78.539×10^{-2}, with an even power of 10.

To find the area of a circle with a diameter of 296 inches:

1. Index the right-hand end of the B scale at the $\dfrac{\pi}{4}$ mark.
2. Slide the hairline to 2.96 on the C scale (turn over?).
3. Read 6.88 on the A scale, and place the decimal (6.88×10^5).

By this time you should be beginning to visualize these operations as the addition of distances corresponding to logarithms of the numbers used. If not, try consciously to think in those terms.

Here's a typical problem combining area and circumference:

The top and sides of an oil storage tank, 35 feet high and 58 feet in diameter, are to be painted. The paint covers about 850 square feet per gallon. About how much paint is needed?

11 gallons. **page 140**

$5\frac{1}{2}$ gallons. **page 143**

I don't know where to start. **page 154**

[*from page 153*]

YOUR ANSWER: Yes, the fifth and eleventh powers and roots can be found in much the same fashion as the fourth.

Right. Since $2^5 = 2^2 \times 2^3$, $\log 2^5 = \log 2^2 + \log 2^3$, so we can find 2^5 in the following manner:

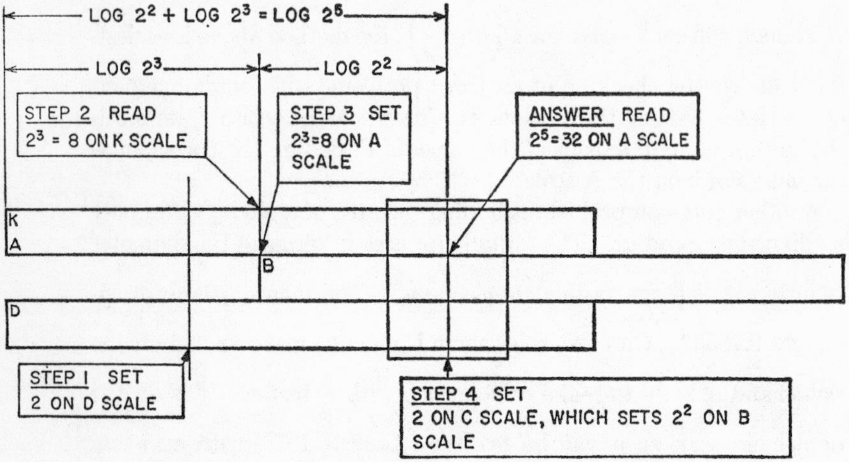

Here is a series of problems, with the answers all correct for a change. Their purpose is to give you practice in working efficiently. Select the group in which the minimum number of *slides* of the hairline and *shifts* of the sliding scale is not given correctly.

	Shifts	*Slides*	
$\dfrac{(6.38 \times 10^8 \times 108.5)^2}{36.8 \times 10.9 \times 444} = 2.69 \times 10^{16}$	3	3	**page 156**
$\sqrt[2]{639} \times \sqrt[3]{9{,}640} = 538$	1	2	
$\sqrt[3]{\dfrac{932 \times 0.00387}{6{,}430 \times 173}} = 0.014{,}8$	2	3	**page 163**
$\sqrt[3]{696} \times \sqrt[3]{0.143} = 4.63$	1	2	
$\dfrac{148 \times (0.096)^2}{3{,}650} = 0.000374$	2	1	**page 166**
$\sqrt[3]{0.000636} = 0.086$	1	1	

[*from page 149*]

YOUR ANSWER: One of these is incorrect:

$$(792)^3 = 4.97 \times 10^8$$

$$(40.4)^3 = 65,900$$

No, both of them are correct. Here's how they would have been been done: $(792)^3 = (7.92 \times 10^2)^3 = 7.92^3 \times 10^6$. To estimate, $8^3 \times 10^6 = 512 \times 10^6$. For the actual answer:

1. Slide the hairline to 7.92 on the D scale.
2. Read 497 on the K scale, recalling that you are in the third range, 100–1,000.

So the cube of 792 is 497×10^6, or 4.97×10^8, the answer stated.

$(40.4)^3 = (4.04 \times 10)^3 = 4.04^3 \times 10^3$. In estimating form, $4^3 \times 10^3 = 64 \times 10^3$. For the complete answer:

1. Slide the hairline to 4.04 on the D scale.
2. Read 6.59 on the K scale.

So the cube of 40.4 is 65.9×10^3, or 65,900, as given.

When you're working with the K scale, remember that it is divided into three identical segments, just as the A and B scales are divided into two identical segments. On the K scale, the first segment represents the numbers from 1 to 10, the second represents the numbers from 10 to 100, and the third represents the numbers from 100 to 1,000:

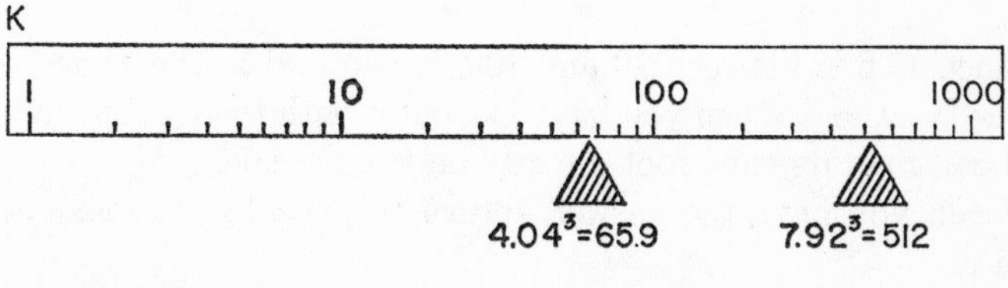

In order that the decimal point may be placed correctly, keep in mind the range you are in. Thus, we read the cube of 7.92 as 512, not 5.12 or 51.2, and we read the cube of 4.04 as 65.9 rather than 6.59.

Now return to page 149 and try to find the error.

[*from page 152*]

YOUR ANSWER: I don't know how to start.

The first thing to do to find a cube root is factor the number as a product of two factors. One of these factors must be a number between 1 and 1,000 (the range of the K scale), and the second must be a power of 10 whose exponent is divisible by 3.

$$(15{,}600{,}000)^{\frac{1}{3}} = (15.6 \times 10^6)^{\frac{1}{3}}$$
$$= 15.6^{\frac{1}{3}} \times 10^2$$

because $$(10^6)^{\frac{1}{3}} = 10^{\frac{6}{3}} = 10^2$$

to check: $$(10^2)^3 = 10^2 \times 10^2 \times 10^2 = 10^6$$

Since 15.6 is between 8, the cube of 2, and 27, the cube of 3, we know that the cube root of 15.6 must be between 2 and 3. So the final answer will be about 2.5×10^2.

The next step is to locate 15.6 on the K scale with the hairline indicator. As you should have noticed, the K scale is divided into three identical segments. The first represents the numbers from 1 to 10, the second those from 10 to 100, and the third those from 100 to 1,000:

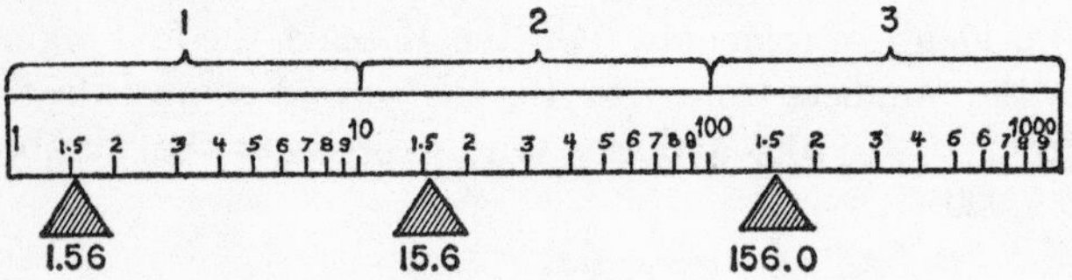

Since 15.6 is between 10 and 100, it is found in the *second* section of the K scale. When you have located it with the hairline indicator, you can read its cube root directly on the D scale.

When you have the answer, return to page 152 to make another choice.

[*from page 160*]

YOUR ANSWER: One of the problems in the second pair requires more than the listed number of moves.

Let's check them.

$$\sqrt[3]{\frac{932 \times 0.00387}{6{,}430 \times 173}} = \sqrt[3]{\frac{9.32 \times 10^2 \times 3.87 \times 10^{-3}}{6.43 \times 10^3 \times 1.73 \times 10^2}}$$

$$= \sqrt[3]{\frac{9.32 \times 3.87}{6.43 \times 1.73}} \times 10^{-2}$$

In estimating form,

$$\sqrt[3]{\frac{9 \times 4}{6 \times 2}} \times 10^{-2} = \sqrt[3]{3} \times 10^{-2}$$

Since $1^3 = 1$ but $2^3 = 8$, the answer will be just a little over 1×10^{-2}.

1. Slide the hairline indicator to 9.32 on the D scale.
2. Shift the sliding scale so that 6.43 on the C scale is under the hairline.
3. Slide the hairline indicator to 3.87 on the C scale.
4. Shift the sliding scale until 1.73 on the C scale is under the hairline. Read 3.24 on the D scale at the index of the C scale.
5. Slide the hairline indicator to 3.24 on the K scale, and read the answer, 1.48, on the D scale.

Two shifts and three slides; this problem is all right.

Now, the second problem:

$$\sqrt[3]{696} \times \sqrt[3]{0.143} = \sqrt[3]{6.96 \times 10^2 \times 14.3 \times 10^{-2}} = \sqrt[3]{6.96 \times 14.3}$$

To estimate,

$$\sqrt[3]{7 \times 14} = \sqrt[3]{98}$$

Since $4^3 = 64$ and $5^3 = 125$, the complete answer will be between 4 and 5.

1. Shift the index of the C scale to 6.96 on the D scale.
2. Slide the indicator to 1.43 on the C scale. Read 9.96 on the D scale.
3. Slide the indicator to 99.6 on the K scale. Read the answer, 4.63, on the D scale.

One shift and two slides was the answer given. Return to page 160.

[*from page 157*]

YOUR ANSWER: One of the third pair is incorrect.

$$(0.00239)^{\frac{1}{3}} = 0.134 \qquad (12{,}812)^{\frac{1}{3}} = 23.4$$

No, they're both right. Follow the explanations below:

Reduce 0.00239 to two factors, one of which is a number between 1 and 1,000 chosen so that the other, a power of 10, will have an exponent divisible by 3.

$$(0.00239)^{\frac{1}{3}} = (2.39 \times 10^{-3})^{\frac{1}{3}} = 2.39^{\frac{1}{3}} \times (10^{-3})^{\frac{1}{3}}$$

The cube root of 10^{-3} is 10^{-1} because $\frac{1}{3}$ of -3 is -1.

This checks: $(10^{-1})^3 = 10^{-1} \times 10^{-1} \times 10^{-1} = 10^{-3}$. So,

$$(0.00239)^{\frac{1}{3}} = 2.39^{\frac{1}{3}} \times 10^{-1}$$

Since 2.39 is between 1 and 10, we locate it on the first section of the K scale and read its cube root directly from the D scale:

$$2.39^{\frac{1}{3}} = 1.34$$

So

$$(0.00239)^{\frac{1}{3}} = 1.34 \times 10^{-1} = 0.134$$

which was the answer given.

In the second problem, we see that

$$(12{,}812)^{\frac{1}{3}} = (12.812 \times 10^3)^{\frac{1}{3}} = 12.812^{\frac{1}{3}} \times (10^3)^{\frac{1}{3}} = 12.812^{\frac{1}{3}} \times 10^1$$

12.812 is between 10 and 100, so we locate it on the center section of the K scale. (Actually, the best we can do is to locate 12.8.) Its cube root, read directly from the D scale, is 2.34. So

$$(12{,}812)^{\frac{1}{3}} = 2.34 \times 10^1 = 23.4$$

just as we said.

Return now to page 157 and try to find the error.

YOUR ANSWER: False.

No, it's true. The fifth and eleventh powers and roots can be found in much the same way as the fourth root.

The fifth power of a number (N) can be thought of as the product of the second and third powers:

For example, $$2^5 = 2^2 \times 2^3$$

Therefore, $$\log 2^5 = \log 2^2 + \log 2^3$$

Accordingly, we can obtain the fifth power of 2 as follows:

1. Slide the hairline indicator to 2 on the D scale.
2. Read 2^3, or 8, on the K scale under the hairline.
3. Index the B scale at 8 on the A scale.
4. Slide the hairline indicator to 2 on the C scale, which puts the hairline at 2^2 on the B scale, thereby adding $\log 2^2$ to $\log 2^3$.
5. Read the answer, 32, on the A scale under the hairline.

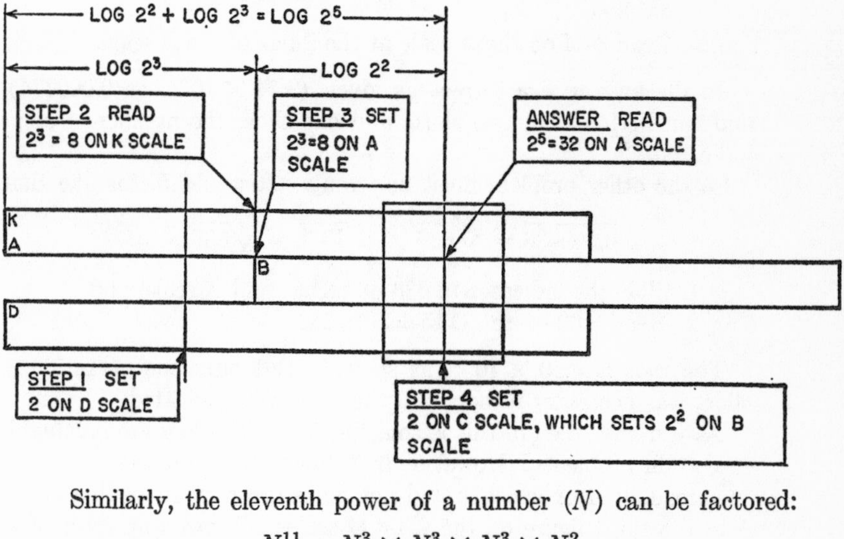

Similarly, the eleventh power of a number (N) can be factored:

$$N^{11} = N^3 \times N^3 \times N^3 \times N^2$$

You shouldn't have any trouble seeing how this can be done on the slide rule.

Return to page 153 to select the correct answer.

[*from page 160*]

YOUR ANSWER: One of the problems in the third pair requires more than the listed number of moves.

Yes. Let's see which one. Here's the first:

$$\frac{148 \times (0.096)^2}{3{,}650} = \frac{1.48 \times 10^2 \times (9.6 \times 10^{-2})^2}{3.65 \times 10^3}$$

$$= \frac{1.48 \times 9.6^2}{3.65} \times 10^{-5}$$

In approximation form,

$$\frac{1.5 \times 10^2}{4} \times 10^{-5} = \frac{1.5}{4} \times 10^{-3} = 0.375 \times 10^{-3} = 3.75 \times 10^{-4}$$

On the slide rule:

1. Shift the right-hand C index to 9.60 on the D scale.
2. Slide the hairline indicator to 1.48 on the B scale.
3. Shift the sliding scale until 3.65 on the B scale is under the hairline.
4. Read 37.4 on the A scale at the index of the B scale.

So the answer was correct as given (3.74×10^{-4}, or 0.000374), and can be found in two shifts and one slide, the number of steps indicated.

So the other problem must be wrong. It would factor like this:

$$\sqrt[3]{0.000636} = \sqrt[3]{636} \times \sqrt[3]{10^{-6}} = \sqrt[3]{636} \times 10^{-2}$$

1. Slide the indicator to 636 on right-hand K scale, and
2. Read 8.60 on the D scale.

The root is 8.60×10^{-2}, as shown. But only one operation, a slide, was necessary rather than the two steps indicated.

As you have seen in this lesson, the A and K scales are invaluable in certain problems. However, they have shortcomings.

A reading error which would not quite throw your reading off by 1 in the third figure on the C or D scales will mean an error of at least 1 on the A scales, and perhaps 2 or more on the K scales. You will have to judge whether speed or accuracy is more important in a given situation.

Now go on to Chapter 4, which begins on page 167.

CHAPTER 4

The CI Scale

The CI scale is located just above the C scale on your rule. This scale increases the speed and accuracy with which you can perform certain kinds of calculations. Before you can understand how it works, however, you need to know something about reciprocals.

The reciprocal of any number is simply 1 divided by that number. For example,

the reciprocal of 5 is $\frac{1}{5}$, or 0.2;

the reciprocal of 40 is $\frac{1}{40}$, or 0.025; and

the reciprocal of $\frac{1}{3}$ is $\frac{1}{\frac{1}{3}}$, or 3 $\left(\text{because } \frac{1}{\frac{1}{3}} = 1 \times \frac{3}{1} = \frac{3}{1} = 3\right)$.

To divide a number by a fraction, we must invert the divisor (in this case, the fraction) and multiply. That is,

$$3 \div \frac{1}{5} = 3 \times \frac{5}{1} = 15$$

But $\frac{5}{1}$ is just 5, so

$$3 \div \frac{1}{5} = 3 \times 5$$

In terms of reciprocals, dividing by a number is equivalent to multiplying by its reciprocal.

$$a \div b = a \times \frac{1}{b}$$

Is it also true that $\frac{a}{c} = a \times \frac{1}{c}$?

Yes. **page 174**

I don't know. **page 179**

No. **page 177**

[*from page 174*]

YOUR ANSWER: The correct pair of reciprocals is 0.316 and 0.316.

No, you read the numbers correctly from the rule, but you have misplaced the decimal point.

We may write 0.316 as 3.16×10^{-1}. Consider the reciprocal of this:

$$\frac{1}{3.16 \times 10^{-1}} = \frac{1}{3.16} \times 10^{1}$$

You can see that the answer is going to be about 0.3×10^{1} or 3.0, so the reciprocal of 0.316 must be 3.16.

Let's review the method of reading reciprocals from the slide rule. As you can see, the C and the CI scales are already lined up, so it's best to read from them. Slide the hairline to a number on the C scale, and you will find the reciprocal of that number directly above it on the CI scale.

The reciprocal of a number, of course, is found by dividing that number into 1. The C and CI scales on the slide rule are set up to do this automatically. The distance from the left-hand index of the CI scale to the number 9 represents the log of the reciprocal of 9, and you may read the actual reciprocal on the C scale below: 0.111. Likewise, the distance from the left-hand index of the CI scale to 8 represents the log of the reciprocal of 8; below on the C scale you read 0.125.

Now return to page 174 and pick out the correct pair of reciprocals.

YOUR ANSWER: The distance from the right end of the C or D scale to 2 on that scale represents the log of the reciprocal of 2.

Yes. Very good. The distance from the left index of the CI scale to 2 on that scale represents the log of the reciprocal of that number. The sum of this distance and the distance from the left index of the D scale to 2 is the entire length of the D scale. In other words, the distance from 2 on the D scale to the right index of that scale represents the log of the reciprocal of 2. (This is also true of the C scale, of course, since the C and D scales are identical.)

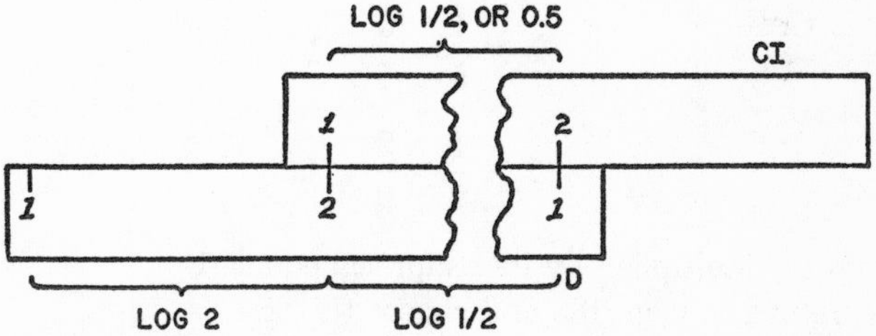

The same relationship holds true for every number on the C and D scales: the distance from the left index of the number represents the log of the number, and the distance from the right index to the number represents the log of the reciprocal of the number.

Now, notice that if we set 2 on the CI scale at the left index of the D scale, the right index of the CI scale is at 2 on the D scale. Clearly, the distance from the right index of the CI scale to 2 on that scale must represent log 2.

Which of the statements below is false?

The distance from the right index to 5 on the CI scale represents the log of $\frac{1}{5}$. **page 172**

The distance from the right index to 7 on the D scale represents the log of 0.143. **page 175**

The CI scale is simply the C scale reversed. **page 182**

[*from page 183*]

YOUR ANSWER: The sum of a number and its reciprocal is equal to 1.

No, this is not true. The reciprocal of a number is found by dividing that number into 1. For instance, the reciprocal of 5 is $\frac{1}{5}$ or 0.2. The sum of these two numbers is 5.2 as you can see. The reciprocal of 2 is $\frac{1}{2}$ or 0.5, and the sum of these two is 2.5. These sums are greater than 1.

On the other hand, look at what happens when you *multiply* the reciprocals together:

$$5 \times \frac{1}{5} = \frac{5}{5} = 1$$

$$2 \times \frac{1}{2} = \frac{2}{2} = 1$$

Any number multiplied by its reciprocal equals 1.

Now return to page 183 and choose the other answer.

[*from page 174*]

YOUR ANSWER: The correct pair of reciprocals is 52.5 and 0.195.

No, this is doubly wrong. First of all, you made a slight mistake in your reading. When you set the hairline on 52.5 of the C scale, you see that it falls just beyond 19 on the CI scale. In fact it is about halfway to the first line. However, since the first line beyond 1.9 represents 1.91, you must read this as 1.905 and not 1.95.

Also, you misplaced your decimal point. By approximation:

$$\frac{1}{50} = \frac{1}{5 \times 10^1} = 0.2 \times 10^{-1}$$

This means that the reciprocal of 50 is approximately 0.02. So the reciprocal of 52.5 is 0.01905.

Let's review the method of reading reciprocals from the slide rule. As you can see, the C and CI scales are already lined up, so it's best to read from them. Slide the hairline to a number on the C scale, and you will find the reciprocal of that number directly above it on the CI scale.

The reciprocal of a number, of course, is found by dividing that number into 1. The C and CI scales on the slide rule are set up to do this automatically. The distance from the left-hand index of the CI scale to the number 9 represents the log of the reciprocal of 9, and you may read the actual reciprocal on the C scale below: 0.111. Likewise, the distance from the left-hand index of the CI scale to 8 represents the log of the reciprocal of 8; below on the C scale you read 0.125.

Now return to page 174 and pick out the correct pair of reciprocals.

[*from page 169*]

YOUR ANSWER: This statement is false: The distance from the right index to 5 on the CI scale represents the log of $\frac{1}{5}$.

You're right; it's wrong. $\frac{1}{5}$ is the reciprocal of 5, and on the CI scale the log of the reciprocal of a number is represented by the distance from the *left* index to the number.

The other two statements are correct. The reciprocal of 7 is $\frac{1}{7}$, or 0.143 to three figures. Since on the D scale the log of the reciprocal of a number is represented by the distance from that number to the right index of the scale, the distance from 7 to the right index does represent the log of 0.143.

It should now be fairly obvious to you that the CI scale is simply the C scale reversed. For any number, the distance from the left index of the C scale to that number corresponds to the distance of that number from the right index of the CI scale, and vice versa. In other words, the CI scale is essentially just a C scale turned around to read from right to left.

Now, remembering that multiplying one number by another is equivalent to dividing one of them by the reciprocal of the other, decide whether the statement below is true or false.

To multiply 2 by 4 with the D and CI scales, set 4 on the CI scale opposite 2 on the D scale and read the answer on the D scale at the index of the CI scale.

True. **page 181**

False. **page 189**

[*from page 180*]

YOUR ANSWER: The distance from the right end of the CI scale to 2 on that scale represents the log of the reciprocal of 2.

No, either you are momentarily confused or else you do not understand how the CI scale is laid out. The CI scale can be used to find reciprocals, but you must know where to look for them.

Take a good look at the CI scale again. Beginning at the index on the right end and reading toward the left, you will see the numbers laid out in a logarithmic scale, with the intervals between the units becoming smaller and smaller until you reach the left index of the CI scale.

As we have explained, the CI scale is laid out like this because its spacing corresponds to the logs of the reciprocals of the numbers when measured from the *left-hand* index. The reciprocal of 2 is 0.5, so the distance from the left-hand index of the CI scale to 2 corresponds to the log of 0.5. You can see this is true, for the number 5 appears on the C scale just below the 2 on the CI scale.

But the distance from the right-hand index to 2 on the CI scale represents the log of 2, just as the distance from the left-hand index to 2 on the C or D scale represents the log of 2. You can set the right-hand index of the CI scale on 2 of the D scale and check this, if you want.

Now return to page 180 and choose the correct answer.

[*from page 167*]

YOUR ANSWER: Yes, it's true that $\frac{a}{c} = a \times \frac{1}{c}$.

Of course. This is true regardless of whether one or both of the numbers happen to be fractions. The reciprocal of $\frac{1}{c}$ is c $\left(\text{because } \frac{1}{\frac{1}{c}} = 1 \times \frac{c}{1} = c\right)$, so multiplying by $\frac{1}{c}$ is equivalent to dividing by c.

Now, let's look at the CI scale. Line it up with the D scale, and slide the hairline indicator to 2 on the D scale. Then 5 appears on the CI scale under the hairline; 0.5 is the reciprocal of 2. Similarly, if you slide the hairline to 25 on the D scale, 4 appears on the CI scale under the hairline; 0.4 is the reciprocal of 2.5.

By now you should be able to see what's happening: the distance from the left index of the CI scale to a number on that scale represents the log of the reciprocal of that number. Therefore, a number on the CI scale is lined up with the number on the C or D scale that is its reciprocal, and vice versa. To find the reciprocal of any number, then, simply slide the hairline to that number on the C scale and read its reciprocal on the CI scale. (Or align the D and CI scales and read from D to CI.) Notice, however, that the numbers on the CI scale get larger as you read from *right to left*. For example, 2.50 on the CI scale is to the *left* of 2.00, between 2.00 and 3.00. Just keep this in mind when you're taking readings: use the ordinary approximation method to place the decimal point correctly, and you'll have no trouble finding reciprocals.

Using the C and CI scales, determine which of the following is a correct pair of reciprocals.

0.316 and 0.316. **page 168**

52.5 and 0.195. **page 171**

3.57 and 0.320. **page 178**

2,578 and 0.000388. **page 183**

[*from page 169*]

YOUR ANSWER: This statement is false: The distance from the right index to 7 on the D scale represents the log of 0.143.

No, this statement is correct.

The distance from the *left* index to 7 on the D scale represents the log of 7, of course, and the distance from the *right* index to 7 on the D scale represents the log of the reciprocal of 7. Set the hairline on 7 on the C scale and you will see from the CI scale that 0.143 is the reciprocal of 7.

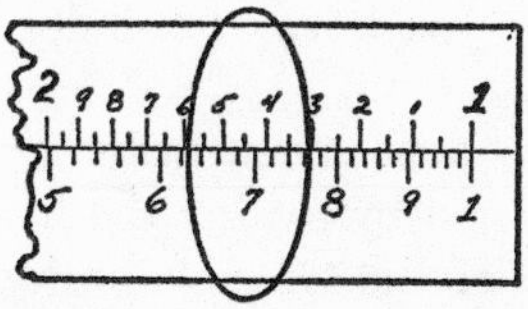

As you can see, the distance representing the log of 7 plus the distance representing the log of the reciprocal of 7 equals the full length of the scale. This is the same thing as saying:

$$7 \times \frac{1}{7} = 1$$

This is true for any number and its reciprocal, of course.

Now return to page 169 and pick out the statement that is false.

[*from page 181*]

YOUR ANSWER: 19.2 × 546 × 861 × 2.33 = 2.32 × 10^7.

No. And this looks like a wild guess on your part. Unless your slide or indicator slipped a great deal, you should not have found anything close to this result.

You could, of course, do the whole problem with the C and D scales. After multiplying 19.2 by 546, you would find the result at approximately 1.05 on the D scale. Then you could set the index of the C scale at that point to multiply by the next number, 861, and so on. But every time you have to re-index you are increasing the chance for error.

The problem can be done much faster and more accurately by using the CI scale. Begin by setting the hairline at 1.92 on the D scale. Now shift 5.46 of the CI scale under the hairline. As you see, you are now *dividing* 1.92 by the reciprocal of 5.46, and this is the same as multiplying by 5.46. The answer is on the D scale at the left index of the C scale, though you don't need to read it yet.

Now proceed to multiply this partial result by 8.61, using the C scale in the normal manner. Just slide the hairline to 8.61 on the C scale. Don't read the answer here, either. Finally, divide by the reciprocal of 2.33. Simply slide 2.33 on the CI scale under the hairline.

You should now find the correct answer on the D scale under the left index of the C (or CI) scale. Return to page 181 and find the corresponding page reference.

[*from page 167*]

YOUR ANSWER: No, it is not true that $\frac{a}{c} = a \times \frac{1}{c}$.

Not so fast! We used this same equation in the first chapter. Let's look at this part of it alone:

$$a \times \frac{1}{c}$$

As you know, in order to multiply a fraction by another number you must multiply the numerator by that number. For instance:

$$2 \times \frac{3}{7} = \frac{6}{7}$$

You multiply the numerator, 3, by 2 and keep the same denominator, 7. In the problem at the top of the page all you have to do is multiply "*a*" by 1. The answer is "*a*," of course. This gives you $\frac{a}{c}$ as the result of your multiplication.

As you see, multiplying "*a*" by the reciprocal of *c* is the same as dividing by *c*. This is true of any number. Multiplying by the reciprocal of a number is the same as dividing by that number.

The reverse of this is true, also. Dividing one number by the reciprocal of another is the same as multiplying the two numbers together.

Now return to page 167 and choose the correct answer.

[*from page 174*]

YOUR ANSWER: The correct pair of reciprocals is: 3.57 and 0.320.

No, you made your reading on the wrong side of 3 on the CI scale. Note that the numbers are running the other way; they get larger from right to left. The hairline falls on the second large mark from 3, but as you see, this stands for 2.80 on the CI scale. Correctly stated, then, the reciprocals would be 3.57 and 0.280.

Let's review the method of reading reciprocals from the slide rule. As you can see, the C and the CI scales are already lined up, so it's best to read from them. Slide the hairline to a number on the C scale, and you will find the reciprocal of that number directly above it on the CI scale.

The reciprocal of a number, of course, is found by dividing that number into 1. The C and CI scales on the slide rule are set up to do this automatically. The distance from the left-hand index of the CI scale to the number 9 represents the log of the reciprocal of 9, and you may read the actual reciprocal on the C scale below: 0.111. Likewise, the distance from the left-hand index of the CI scale to 8 represents the log of the reciprocal of 8; below on the C scale you read 0.125.

Now return to page 174 and pick out the correct pair of reciprocals.

[*from page 167*]

YOUR ANSWER: I don't know whether or not $\frac{a}{c} = a \times \frac{1}{c}$.

Let's go back to the elementary rules for multiplying fractions. To multiply two fractions you simply multiply the numerators and the denominators:

$$\frac{2}{3} \times \frac{3}{4} = \frac{6}{12}$$

When a fraction is multiplied by a whole number, you keep the same denominator, because the denominator of the whole number is 1. For instance:

$$2 \times \frac{3}{7} = \frac{6}{7}$$

You multiply the numerator, 3, by 2 and keep the same denominator, 7. In the problem at the top of the page, all you have to do is multiply "a" by 1, and the answer is "a," of course. This gives you $\frac{a}{c}$ as the result of your multiplication when you multiply $a \times \frac{1}{c}$.

As you see, multiplying "a" by the reciprocal of c is the same as dividing by c. This is true of any number. Multiplying by the reciprocal of a number is the same as dividing by that number.

The reverse is true, also. Dividing one number by the reciprocal of another is the same as multiplying the two numbers together.

Now return to page 167 and choose the correct answer.

[*from page 183*]

YOUR ANSWER: The product of a number and its reciprocal is 1.

That's correct. When a number and its reciprocal are multiplied, the result is always 1: $6 \times \frac{1}{6} = 1$. In general form,

$$a \times \frac{1}{a} = 1$$

Now we're in a position to understand how the CI scale is constructed. Slide the left index of the CI scale to 2 on the D scale. Then slide the hairline indicator to 2 on the CI scale. The resulting setting looks like this:

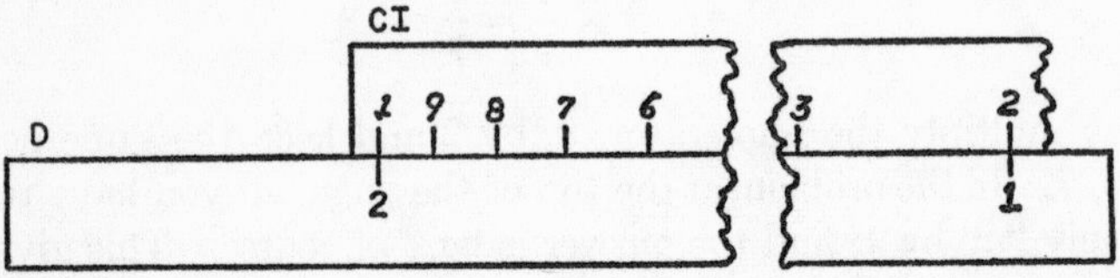

Now, what have we really done here? We've added the distance representing the log of 2 to the distance representing the log of the reciprocal of 2. The resulting log distance is the whole length of the D scale, because $2 \times \frac{1}{2} = 1$.

And we've seen something else (choose the correct statement):

The distance from the *right* end of the C or D scale to the 2 on that scale represents the log of the reciprocal of 2. **page 169**

The distance from the *right* end of the CI scale to 2 on that scale represents the log of the reciprocal of 2. **page 173**

I need some help. **page 185**

[*from page 172*]

YOUR ANSWER: The statement is true.

It certainly is. Multiplying by a number is the same as dividing by the reciprocal of the number. For example, $2 \times 4 = 2 \div \frac{1}{4}$. And this means that

$$\log (2 \times 4) = \log 2 - \log \frac{1}{4}$$

On the CI scale the distance from the left index to 4 represents the log of $\frac{1}{4}$, so we can use the CI scale to subtract the log of $\frac{1}{4}$ from that of 2:

1. Slide the hairline indicator to 2 on the D scale.
2. Shift 4 on the CI scale under the hairline.
3. Read the answer, 8, on the D scale at the index of the CI scale.

The setting will look like this:

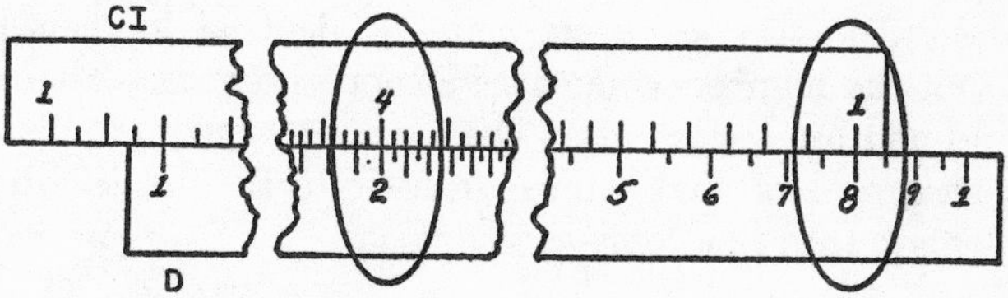

The real advantage to this kind of maneuver is in calculations requiring repeated multiplication or division, or both. With the aid of the CI scale we can often avoid re-indexing and minimize the number of necessary moves.

Try your hand at the problem below. If you use reciprocals and the CI scale, you can do it in two shifts of the sliding scale and two slides of the hairline indicator.

$$19.2 \times 546 \times 861 \times 2.33 = ?$$

(Hint: rewrite the second and fourth factors as reciprocals.)

2.32×10^7. **page 176**

1.30×10^7. **page 193**

2.10×10^7. **page 184**

1.75×10^7. **page 198**

[*from page 169*]

YOUR ANSWER: This statement is false: The CI scale is simply the C scale reversed.

No, this statement is all right. The numbers on the C scale run from left to right while those on the CI scale run from right to left. What's more important, though, the spatial relationship between the numbers on each scale is identical. That is, both are logarithmic scales.

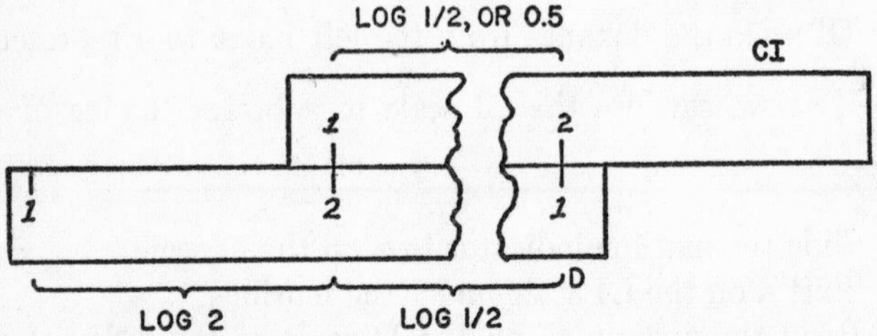

As you can see, the distance from the 2 on the D scale to the right index is the same as the distance from the 2 on the CI scale to the left index. The same would be true for every number on the C and CI scales. The two scales are actually identical in their layout, except that the numbers commence at opposite ends. This enables us to find and use reciprocals. The log of any number plus the log of the reciprocal of that number constitute the full length of the scale. This is the same thing as saying:

$$a \times \frac{1}{a} = 1$$

Now return to page 169 and pick out the statement that is false.

YOUR ANSWER: 2,578 and 0.000388 are reciprocals.

Right. The reciprocal of 2,578 is $\frac{1}{2,578}$. In approximation form,

$$\frac{1}{3.0 \times 10^3} = 0.333 \times 10^{-3} = 0.000333$$

Setting the hairline at 2.58 on the C scale, read 3.88 on the CI scale under the hairline. (Remember, on the CI scale the numbers increase from right to left, so 3.88 is to the left of 3.00 rather than the right.) Then $\frac{1}{2,578} = 0.388 \times 10^{-3} = 0.000388$.

We can reverse this procedure, of course, finding the reciprocal of 0.000388. In approximation form,

$$\frac{1}{4.0 \times 10^{-4}} = 0.25 \times 10^4 = 2,500$$

Setting the hairline at 3.88 on the C scale, we read 2.58 on the CI scale, so the reciprocal of 0.000388 is 2,580, to three figures of accuracy. It checks.

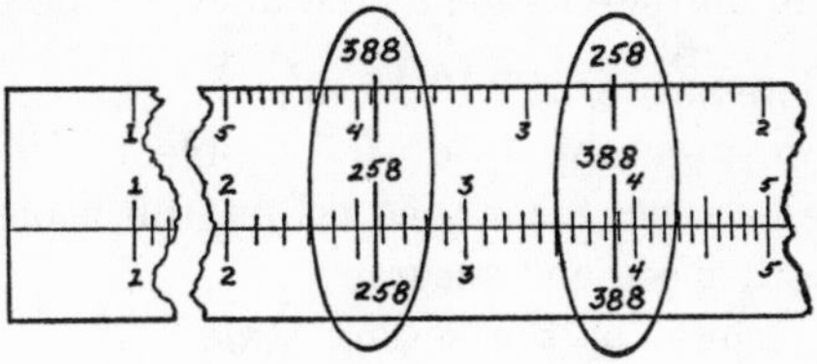

Which of the statements below is true?

The sum of a number and its reciprocal is equal to 1. **page 170**

The product of a number and its reciprocal is equal to 1. **page 180**

[*from page 181*]

YOUR ANSWER: $19.2 \times 546 \times 861 \times 2.33 = 2.10 \times 10^7$.

Right.

$19.2 \times 546 \times 861 \times 2.33 = 1.92 \times 5.46 \times 8.61 \times 2.33 \times 10^5$. In approximation form,

$$2 \times 5 \times 9 \times 2 \times 10^5 = 180 \times 10^5 = 1.80 \times 10^7$$

Rewriting the slide-rule part of the problem so that the second and fourth terms are reciprocals, we get

$$1.92 \div \frac{1}{5.46} \times 8.61 \div \frac{1}{2.33}$$

Writing the problem like this makes it possible to get the answer on the rule with a minimum number of moves. Here's the way it goes:

1. Slide the hairline indicator to 1.92 on the D scale.
2. Shift 5.46 on the CI scale under the hairline.
3. Slide the hairline to 8.61 on the C scale.
4. Shift 2.33 on the CI scale under the hairline.
5. Read 2.10 on the D scale at the index of the C scale.

Then the complete answer is 2.10×10^7.

Notice that we were able to do the problem without re-indexing the sliding scale. As was mentioned before, this is desirable from the standpoint of both speed and accuracy.

At least______shifts of the sliding scale and______slides of the hairline indicator are necessary to do this problem:

$$\frac{332 \times 759 \times 651}{912} = 1.80 \times 10^5$$

2 shifts, 1 slide. **page 188**

2 shifts, 2 slides. **page 191**

3 shifts, 3 slides. **page 195**

[*from page 180*]

YOUR ANSWER: I need some help.

Take a good look at the CI scale again. Beginning at the index on the right end and reading toward the left, you will see the numbers laid out in a logarithmic scale, with the intervals between the units becoming smaller and smaller until you reach the left index of the CI scale.

As we have explained, the CI scale is laid out like this because its spacing corresponds to the logs of the reciprocals of the numbers when measured from the *left-hand* index. The reciprocal of 2 is 0.5, so the distance from the left-hand index of the CI scale to 2 corresponds to the log of 0.5. You can see this is true, for the number 5 appears on the C scale just below the 2 on the CI scale.

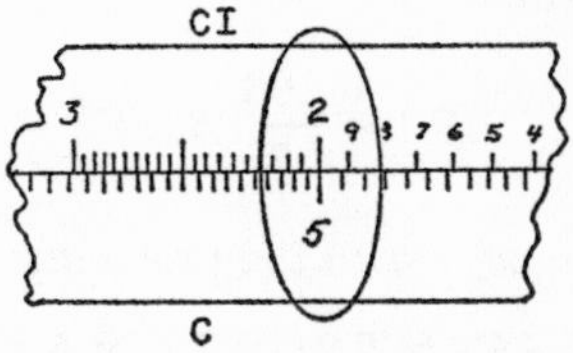

But the distance from the *right-hand* index to 2 on the CI scale represents the log of 2, just as the distance from the left-hand index to 2 on the C or D scale represents the log of 2. You can set the right-hand index of the CI scale on 2 of the D scale and check this, if you want.

Now return to page 180 and choose the correct answer.

[*from page 191*]

YOUR ANSWER: $$\frac{56.8 \times 23.1 \times 3.0 \times 0.00281 \times 0.532}{7.35 \times 48.0} = 0.01063.$$

No, there is an error somewhere in your calculations. It would seem that you got confused when you tried to read 2.81 on the CI scale; apparently you used 1.79 on the CI scale instead. Remember that the numbers on the CI scale run from right to left. Therefore, 2.81 will be on the *left* side of 2.00.

Let's go through the whole process and try to see where you went wrong. Reducing all the factors to scientific notation, we get

$$\frac{5.68 \times 2.31 \times 3.0 \times 2.81 \times 5.32}{7.35 \times 4.80} \times 10^{-3}$$

In approximation form:

$$\frac{6 \times 2 \times 3 \times 3 \times 5}{7 \times 5} \times 10^{-3} = \frac{108}{7} \times 10^{-3} = 15.4 \times 10^{-3} = 0.0154$$

For the slide rule we may write the problem:

$$\frac{5.68 \times 2.31 \times 3.0 \times 5.32}{7.35 \times 4.80 \times \dfrac{1}{2.81}}$$

We can do it this way because dividing by the reciprocal of 2.81 is the same as multiplying by 2.81.

Now set the hairline indicator to 5.68 on the D scale and shift 7.35 on the C scale under it. Then slide the hairline to 2.31 on the C scale. Shift 4.80 on the C scale under the hairline, and then slide the hairline to 3.0 on the C scale.

Now comes the timesaving use of the CI scale: Shift 2.81 on the CI scale under the hairline. (Be careful to count from the 2 on the CI scale toward the 3 on the left side of the 2.)

With the CI scale in this position you are dividing by the reciprocal of 2.81; this is the same as multiplying by 2.81.

Now slide the hairline to 5.32 on the C scale and read 1.67 on the D scale under the hairline. Your answer is 0.0167.

At this time it might be a good idea to go back to page 181 and do the problem there again; then proceed to work your way up to this problem.

[*from page 201*]

YOUR ANSWER: This figure shows one way of solving the problem:

$$\frac{368 \times 841}{927} = 334$$

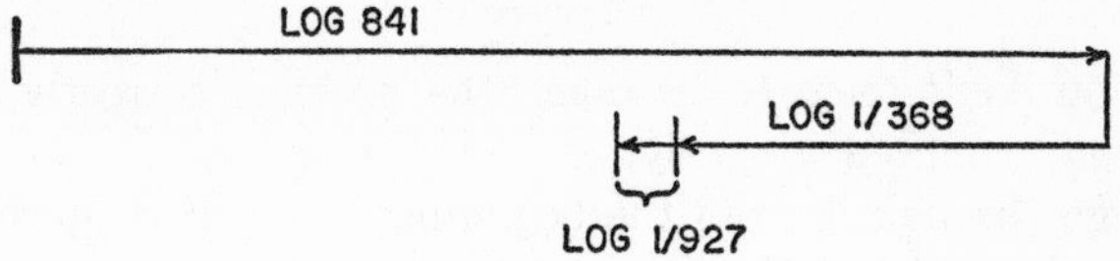

Well, it's partly right. Subtracting the log of the reciprocal of 368 from the log of 841 corresponds to dividing 841 by the reciprocal of 368. This is the same as multiplying the two numbers, of course.

But then you proceed to subtract the log of the reciprocal of 927, too. This is really a way of multiplying by 927, and you want to divide by 927.

Now turn back to page 201 and select a diagram that shows a workable solution to this problem. Note that we are not asking you to pick out a diagram that shows the simplest way of doing it. But there is a diagram there that shows one way the problem could be solved.

[*from page 184*]

YOUR ANSWER: At least 2 shifts of the sliding scale and 1 slide of the hairline indicator are necessary to do this problem:

$$\frac{332 \times 759 \times 651}{912} = 1.80 \times 10^5$$

No, you don't seem to be doing the problem correctly. Or else you haven't counted correctly.

Let's go through it from the beginning. It will be most efficient to set up the problem like this:

$$\frac{332 \times 759}{912 \times \dfrac{1}{651}}$$

Dividing by the reciprocal of 651 is the same as multiplying by 651, and this will enable us to use the CI scale, saving a step or two.

Now let's begin by setting the hairline indicator at 3.32 on the D scale (count 1 slide). Shift 9.12 on the C scale under the hairline. The partial answer for this division is on the D scale under the right-hand index of the C scale, but you don't need to read it yet. Instead, go ahead and multiply by 7.59: just slide the hairline to 7.59 on the C scale. Again, the partial answer for these two processes is on the D scale under the hairline, but you may go ahead and perform the last step before you read anything from the rule. The last step is multiplication by 6.51, but we have decided to save a little time and trouble by using the CI scale to divide by the reciprocal of 6.51. So shift 6.51 on the CI scale under the hairline and read the answer on the D scale at the left index of the CI scale.

Note that you do not have to re-index to do this problem. That is, you do not have to set the hairline on any partial answer and then put the index 1 under the hairline to continue the calculation. Count the shifts and slides in this process; then return to page 184 to choose another answer.

[*from page 172*]

YOUR ANSWER: This statement is false: To multiply 2 by 4 with the D and CI scales, set 4 on the CI scale opposite 2 on the D scale and read the answer on the D scale at the index of the CI scale.

Your answer is wrong. Did you actually try it? If you did it correctly, you can't help but find 8 on the D scale directly below the index of the CI scale. Go through the steps again if you found some other answer. Remember that you will have to use the hairline for this, and be sure that you are using the CI scale and not the C scale.

Perhaps you felt this answer must be wrong, since the manipulation of the rule reminds you of a division problem. You are being asked to multiply, of course. Actually, you *are* dividing when you use the CI scale like this. You are dividing by the reciprocal of 4, and this gives the same result as multiplying by 4. There will be times when it is to your advantage to divide by the reciprocal rather than multiply by the number itself, so you should learn how this works.

Just to be sure your mind is at ease regarding dividing by reciprocals:

$$\frac{a}{\frac{1}{b}} = a \times \frac{b}{1} = \frac{a \times b}{1} = a \times b$$

Now return to page 172 and choose the other answer.

[*from page 201*]

YOUR ANSWER: This diagram represents a workable solution:

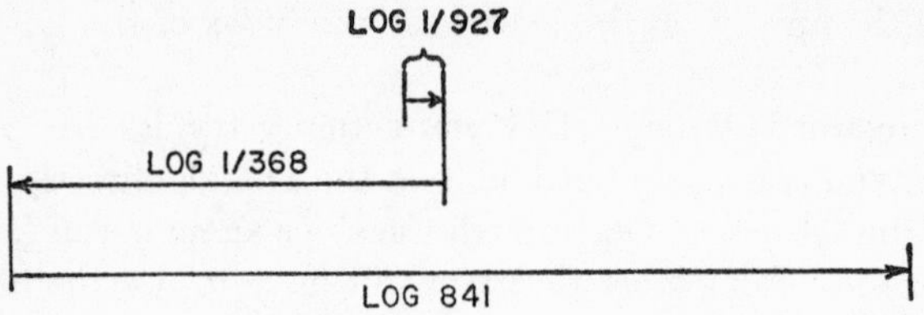

Right. The problem $\frac{368 \times 841}{927}$ can be rewritten as $\frac{1}{927} \div \frac{1}{368} \times$ 841. In this case we would subtract the log of $\frac{1}{368}$ from the log of $\frac{1}{927}$, and then add the log of 841. This is exactly what is shown in the diagram above. Furthermore, this procedure can be followed directly on the slide rule, even though it is not the way we would normally work the problem.

1. Align the CI and D scales, and set the hairline at 9.27 on the CI scale.
2. Shift 3.68 on the CI scale under the hairline.
3. Slide the hairline to 8.41 on the C scale.
4. Read 3.34 on the D scale under the hairline.

Let's try a slightly harder one. Look at the diagram below and then choose the correct statement.

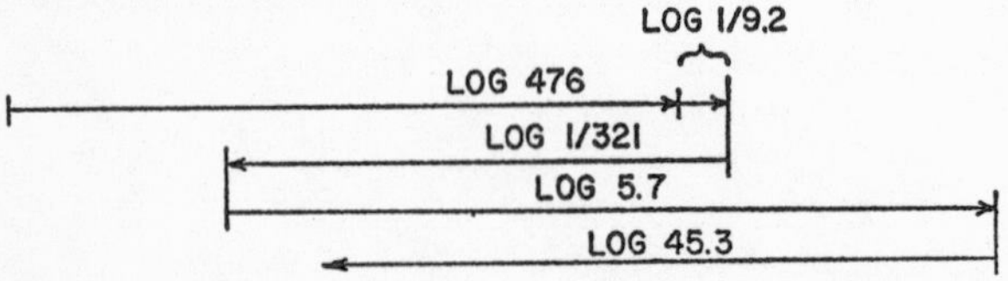

The diagram represents a workable solution to the problem: $\frac{476 \times 321 \times \frac{1}{9.2}}{45.3 \times \frac{1}{5.7}}$. **page 192**

The diagram represents a workable solution to the problem: $\frac{476 \times 5.7 \times 321}{9.2 \times 45.3}$. **page 197**

Both the above statements are true. **page 206**

[*from page 184*]

YOUR ANSWER: At least 2 shifts of the sliding scale and 2 slides of the hairline indicator are necessary.

Right. That's the minimum number of moves. Here's the problem again:

$$\frac{332 \times 759 \times 651}{912} = \frac{3.32 \times 7.59 \times 6.51}{9.12} \times 10^4$$

In estimating form,

$$\frac{3 \times 8 \times 7}{9} \times 10^4 = \frac{56}{3} \times 10^4 = 18.7 \times 10^4, \text{ or } 1.87 \times 10^5$$

The part of the problem to be dealt with on the slide rule can be rewritten as

$$\frac{3.32 \times 7.59}{9.12 \times \frac{1}{6.51}}$$

because dividing by the reciprocal of a number is the same as multiplying by the number itself. Then it's quite simple on the slide rule.

1. Slide the hairline indicator to 3.32 on the D scale.
2. Shift 9.12 on the C scale under the hairline.
3. Slide the hairline to 7.59 on the C scale.
4. Shift 6.51 on the CI scale under the hairline.
5. Read 1.80 on the D scale at the index of the CI scale.

Then the complete answer is 1.80×10^5.

You should be getting pretty good at this now. Try one more:

$$\frac{56.8 \times 23.1 \times 3.0 \times 0.00281 \times 0.532}{7.35 \times 48.0} = ?$$

0.01063. **page 186**

0.0211. **page 196**

0.0167. **page 200**

[*from page 190*]

YOUR ANSWER: This diagram represents a workable solution to the problem:

$$\frac{476 \times 321 \times \frac{1}{9.2}}{45.3 \times \frac{1}{5.7}}$$

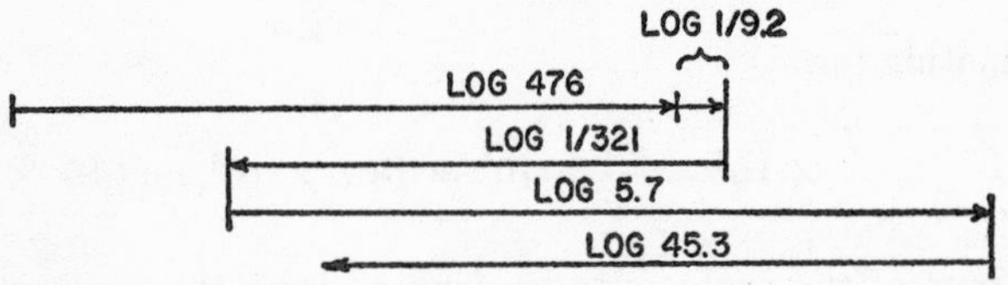

Yes, this is true, for this problem can be rewritten in the form:

$$476 \times \frac{1}{9.2} \div \frac{1}{321} \times 5.7 \div 45.3$$

To solve the problem we add the log of $\frac{1}{9.2}$ to that of 476, subtract the log of $\frac{1}{321}$, add the log of 5.7, and then subtract the log of 45.3.

When the arrows point to the right in the diagram we are adding logarithms, and when they point to the left we are subtracting logarithms. It's just the same on the slide rule. We move to the right to add logs and move to the left to subtract.

But let's take a closer look at the other problem:

$$\frac{476 \times 5.7 \times 321}{9.2 \times 45.3}$$

It's also true that it can be rewritten in the same form. Multiplying by the reciprocal of 9.2 is the same as dividing by 9.2. And dividing by the reciprocal of 5.7 is the same as multiplying by 5.7.

Now return to page 190 and choose the more complete answer.

[*from page 181*]

YOUR ANSWER: $19.2 \times 546 \times 861 \times 2.33 = 1.30 \times 10^7$.

No, apparently you multiplied with the CI scale instead of dividing. That is, you seem to have set the index of the CI scale at the number on the D scale you were multiplying by.

Remember, when you use the CI scale for multiplication, you are *dividing* by the reciprocal of the number. So don't use the index of the CI scale for multiplication of one number by another. Instead, set the hairline at one number on the D scale and find the other factor on the CI scale, placing it under the hairline. This is dividing by the reciprocal of the number on the CI scale, which is the same as multiplying by the number itself.

You could, of course, do the whole problem with the C and D scales. After multiplying 19.2 by 546, you will find the result at approximately 1.05 on the D scale. Then you could set the index at that point to multiply by the next number, 861, and so on. But every time you have to re-index you are increasing the chance for error.

The problem can be done much faster and more accurately by using the CI scale. Begin by setting the hairline at 1.92 on the D scale. Now shift 5.46 of the CI scale under the hairline. As you see, you are now *dividing* 1.92 by the reciprocal of 5.46, and this is the same as multiplying by 5.46. The answer is on the D scale at the left index of the C scale, though you don't need to read it yet.

Now proceed to multiply this partial result by 8.61, using the C scale in the normal manner. Just slide the hairline to 8.61 on the C scale. Don't read the answer here, either. Finally, divide by the reciprocal of 2.33. Simply slide 2.33 on the CI scale under the hairline.

You should now find the correct answer on the D scale under the left index of the C (or CI) scale. Return to page 181 and find the corresponding page reference.

[*from page 201*]

YOUR ANSWER: This figure shows one way of solving the problem:

$$\frac{368 \times 841}{927} = 334$$

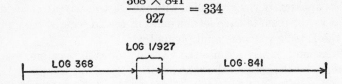

This method is all right in theory, for it shows a means of multiplying 368 by the reciprocal of 927. This is the same as dividing by 927, of course. Then adding the log of 841 is the slide rule method of multiplying this result by 841, and this is exactly what you want to do.

But the big difficulty is that your slide rule is not long enough to do the problem this way. The answer is going to appear far to the right of the scale, off the end of the rule.

Now turn back to page 201 and select a diagram that shows a *workable* solution to this problem. Note that we are not asking you to pick out a diagram that shows the simplest way of doing the problem. But there is a diagram there that shows one way the problem could be solved.

[*from page 184*]

YOUR ANSWER: At least 3 shifts of the sliding scale and 3 slides of the hairline indicator are necessary to do this problem:

$$\frac{332 \times 759 \times 651}{912} = 1.80 \times 10^5$$

No, apparently you did not use the CI scale.

Let's go through the problem from the beginning. It will be most efficient to set it up like this:

$$\frac{332 \times 759}{912 \times \frac{1}{651}}$$

Dividing by the reciprocal of 651 is the same as multiplying by 651, and this will enable us to use the CI scale, saving a step or two.

Now let's begin by setting the hairline indicator at 3.32 on the D scale (count 1 slide). Shift 9.12 on the C scale under the hairline. The partial answer for this division is on the D scale under the right-hand index of the C scale, but you don't need to read it yet. Instead, go ahead and multiply by 7.59: just slide the hairline to 7.59 on the C scale. Again, the partial answer for these two processes is on the D scale under the hairline, but you may go ahead and perform the last step before you read anything from the rule. The last step is multiplication by 6.51, but we have decided to save a little time and trouble by using the CI scale to divide by the reciprocal of 6.51. So shift 6.51 on the CI scale under the hairline and read the answer on the D scale at the left index of the CI scale.

Note that you do not have to re-index to do this problem. That is, you do not have to set the hairline on any partial answer and then put the index 1 under the hairline to continue the calculation.

Count the shifts and slides in this process; then return to page 184 to choose another answer.

[*from page 191*]

$$\text{YOUR ANSWER: } \frac{56.8 \times 23.1 \times 3.0 \times 0.00281 \times 0.532}{7.35 \times 48.0} = 0.0211.$$

No, there is an error somewhere in your calculations. It would seem that you multiplied by the reciprocal of 281 instead of dividing. Remember, multiplying by the reciprocal of a number is the same as dividing by that number; dividing by the reciprocal of a number is the same as multiplying by that number.

Let's go through the whole process and try to see where you went wrong. Reducing all the factors to scientific notation:

$$\frac{5.68 \times 2.31 \times 3.0 \times 2.81 \times 5.32}{7.35 \times 4.80} \times 10^{-3}$$

In approximation form:

$$\frac{6 \times 2 \times 3 \times 3 \times 5}{7 \times 5} \times 10^{-3} = \frac{108}{7} \times 10^{-3} = 15.4 \times 10^{-3} = 0.0154$$

For the slide rule we may write the problem:

$$\frac{5.68 \times 2.31 \times 3.0 \times 5.32}{7.35 \times 4.80 \times \dfrac{1}{2.81}}$$

We can do it this way because dividing by the reciprocal of 2.81 is the same as multiplying by 2.81.

Now set the hairline indicator to 5.68 on the D scale and shift 7.35 on the C scale under it. Then slide the hairline to 2.31 on the C scale. Shift 4.80 on the C scale under the hairline, and then slide the hairline to 3.0 on the C scale.

Now comes the timesaving use of the CI scale. Shift 2.81 on the CI scale under the hairline. (Note that you can do this without re-indexing as you seemed to have done to get your answer.)

With the CI scale in this position you are dividing by the reciprocal of 2.81; this is the same as multiplying by 2.81.

Now slide the hairline to 5.32 on the C scale and read 1.67 on the D scale under the hairline. Your answer is 0.0167.

At this time it might be a good idea to go back to page 181 and do the problem there again; then proceed to work your way up to this problem.

[*from page 190*]

YOUR ANSWER: This diagram represents a workable solution to the problem:

$$\frac{476 \times 5.7 \times 321}{9.2 \times 45.3}$$

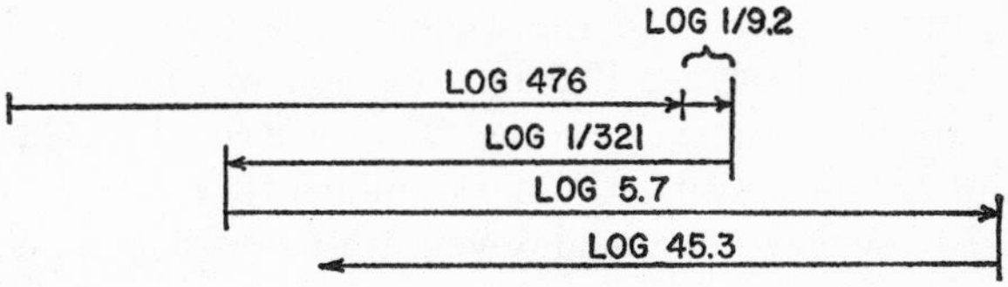

Yes, this is true, for this problem can be rewritten in the form:

$$476 \times \frac{1}{9.2} \div \frac{1}{321} \times 5.7 \div 45.3$$

To solve the problem we add the log of $\frac{1}{9.2}$ to that of 476, subtract the log of $\frac{1}{321}$, add the log of 5.7, and then subtract the log of 45.3.

When the arrows point to the right in the diagram we are adding logarithms, and when they point to the left we are subtracting logarithms. It's just the same on the slide rule. We move to the right to add logs and move to the left to subtract.

But let's take a closer look at the other problem:

$$\frac{476 \times 321 \times \frac{1}{9.2}}{45.3 \times \frac{1}{5.7}}$$

It's also true that it can be rewritten in the same form. Dividing by 9.2 is the same as multiplying by the reciprocal of 9.2. And multiplying by 5.7 is the same as dividing by the reciprocal of 5.7.

Now return to page 190 and choose the more complete answer.

[*from page 181*]

YOUR ANSWER: $19.2 \times 546 \times 861 \times 2.33 = 1.75 \times 10^7$.

No, you seem to have read 5.46 incorrectly on the CI scale. Note that since the CI scale is the reverse of the C scale, 5.46 will be on the *left* side of the 5.

You could, of course, do the whole problem with the C and D scales. After multiplying 19.2 by 546, you will find the result at approximately 1.05 on the D scale. Then you could set the index at that point to multiply by the next number, 861, and so on. But every time you have to re-index you are increasing the chance for error.

The problem can be done much faster and more accurately by using the CI scale. Begin by setting the hairline at 1.92 on the D scale. Now shift 5.46 of the CI scale under the hairline. As you see, you are now *dividing* 1.92 by the reciprocal of 5.46, and this is the same as multiplying by 5.46. The answer is on the D scale at the left index of the C scale, though you don't need to read it yet.

Now proceed to multiply this partial result by 8.61, using the C scale in the normal manner. Just slide the hairline to 8.61 on the C scale. Don't read the answer here, either. Finally, divide by the reciprocal of 2.33. Simply slide 2.33 on the CI scale under the hairline.

You should now find the correct answer on the D scale under the left index of the C (or CI) scale. Return to page 181 and find the corresponding page reference.

[*from page 206*]

YOUR ANSWER: 7.32 ft., 153.0 ft., and 5,000 ft.

No; you may be doing the operation correctly while reading the CI scale wrong. Look at this diagram of a portion of the CI scale:

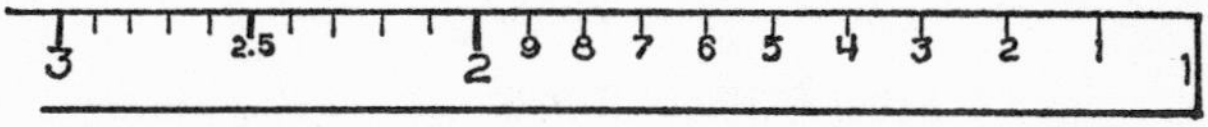

The readings get larger going from right to left, just the opposite of the other scales we have used. This is 2.77 on the CI scale:

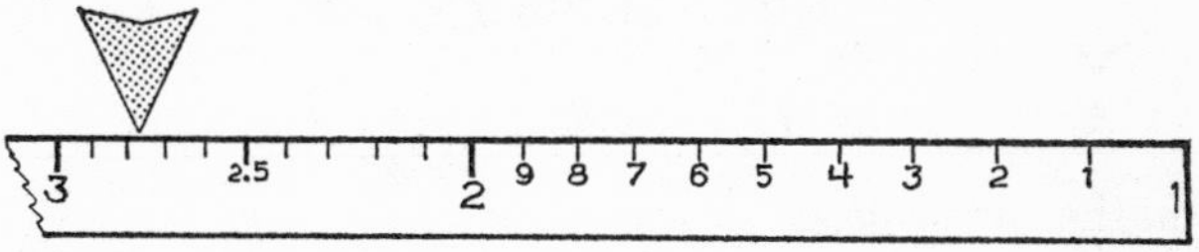

Not this:

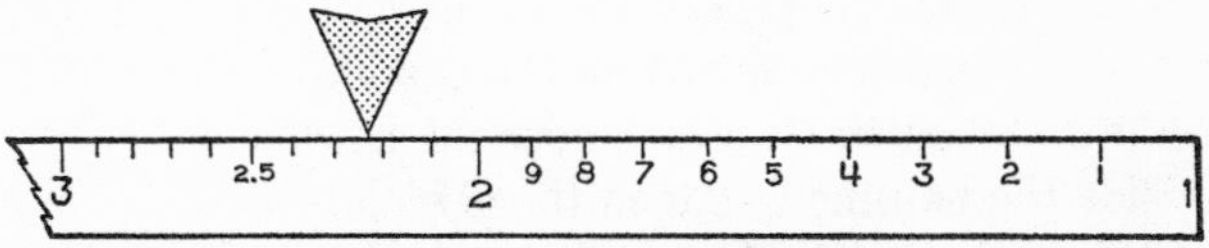

The figure above actually shows the setting 2.23.

Since there are 3.28 feet in one meter, we may convert meters to feet by multiplying the number of meters times 3.28. Begin by placing the hairline indicator at 3.28, the conversion factor, on the D scale. Now we can multiply this factor by 2.77, using the CI scale. Shift 2.77 on the CI scale under the hairline. Then you are dividing by the reciprocal of 2.77 which is the same as multiplying by 2.77. By the usual approximation method, you know that the answer must be about 9 ft., and since you read 9.10 on the D scale, the result must be 9.1 ft. Now do the same thing for 53.43 m. and 1,678 m., shifting these numbers on the CI scale until they are under the hairline and reading the answers on the D scale.

Now return to page 206 and choose the correct answer.

[*from page 191*]

YOUR ANSWER: 0.0167.

Right. Good. Here's the problem again:

$$\frac{56.8 \times 23.1 \times 3.0 \times 0.00281 \times 0.532}{7.35 \times 48.0}$$

In approximation form, $\dfrac{6 \times 2 \times 3 \times 3 \times 5}{7 \times 5} \times 10^{-3}$, or 0.0154.

The slide rule part of the problem can be rewritten to read:

$$\frac{5.68 \times 2.31 \times 3.0 \times 5.32}{7.35 \times 4.80 \times \dfrac{1}{2.81}}$$

Then, on the slide rule,

1. Slide the hairline indicator to 5.68 on the D scale.
2. Shift 7.35 on the C scale under the hairline.
3. Slide the hairline to 2.31 on the C scale.
4. Shift 4.80 on the C scale under the hairline.
5. Slide the hairline to 3.0 on the C scale.
6. Shift 2.81 on the CI scale under the hairline.
7. Slide the hairline to 5.32 on the C scale.
8. Read 1.67 on the D scale under the hairline.

Then the complete answer is 0.0167.

Incidentally, you will remember that some time back, when we were first learning to multiply with the C and D scales, we discussed the problem $3 \times 5 = 15$. We saw that setting the left index of the C scale over 3 on the D scale put 5 on the C scale clear off the end of the rule. Accordingly, we re-indexed, putting the right index of the C scale at 3 on the D scale. Then we were able to slide the hairline indicator to the left, to 5 on the C scale. This is all old stuff to you now. And now that you have a clearer understanding of reciprocals, you should be able to see *why* it works. We are multiplying by subtracting a logarithm, the logarithm of the reciprocal of 5. In other words, instead of multiplying by 5, we are dividing by $\frac{1}{5}$.

For a diagram of this solution, please go on to page 201.

[*from page 200*]

Here is the diagram of the solution to the problem just discussed ($3 \times 5 = 15$):

Diagrams like this one are helpful because they force us to visualize each move of the slide rule in terms of adding or subtracting a logarithm.

Below are three such diagrams. Which represents a workable solution of the problem $\frac{368 \times 841}{927} = 334$? (Remember that moving to the right on the rule corresponds to adding a logarithm, while moving to the left corresponds to subtracting a logarithm.)

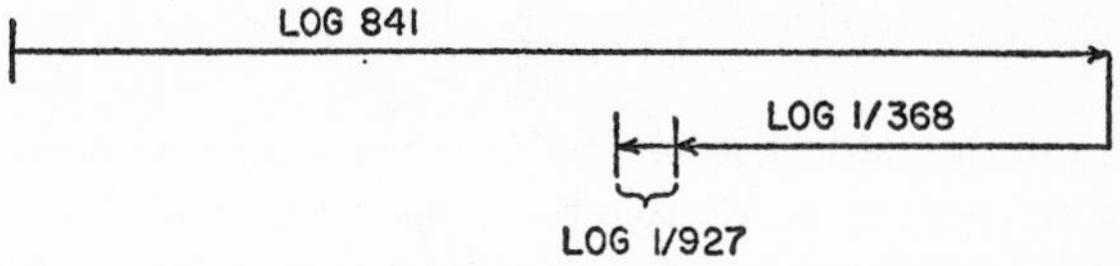

page 187

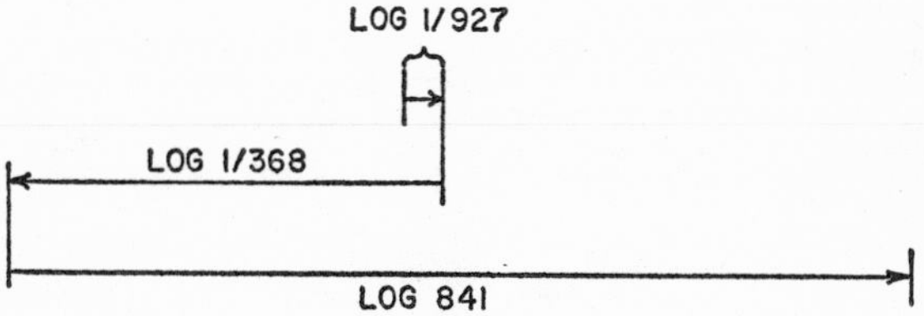

page 190

page 194

[*from page 208*]

YOUR ANSWER: 1 foot = 0.305 meters, 3 feet = 1 yard, and 1 rod = 5.03 meters; therefore, 1 rod = 5.12 yards.

No, apparently you used the wrong formula to make this conversion.

Here is one way to work the problem: To convert from rods to meters you must multiply the number of rods by 5.03, the number of meters in one rod. Now, to change 5.03 meters to feet you must know how many feet there are in one meter. But we have the conversion figure for the number of meters per foot instead: 1 foot = 0.305 meters. To find how many feet there are in one meter you must take the reciprocal of 0.305: 1 m. = $\frac{1}{0.305}$ ft. So if you multiply 5.03 by the reciprocal of 0.305,

$$5.03 \times \frac{1}{0.305}$$

you will have the number of feet in one rod.

Now all you have to do is divide this by 3, the number of feet in 1 yard, and you will have the number of yards in one rod:

$$\frac{5.03 \times \frac{1}{.305}}{3}$$

You can also write this:

$$\frac{5.03}{3 \times .305}$$

Dividing by a number is the same as multiplying by its reciprocal.

Apparently you used the formula

$$\frac{5.03 \times 0.305}{3.0}$$

This is saying that there are 0.305 feet in one meter, when it's actually the other way around.

Now return to page 208 and choose the correct answer.

[*from page 211*]

YOUR ANSWER: 1 gram = 15.4 grains, so

23.5 grains = 3.61 grams;

3,009 grains = 454 grams.

No, you have placed the hairline indicator at 1.54 on the D scale and multiplied this by 23.5 and 3,009. But this is the same as saying that 1 grain = 15.4 grams, i.e., that the grain is a much larger unit than the gram. Actually the reverse is true; 1 gram = 15.4 grains.

Let's start over.

Dividing both sides of the expression 1 gram = 15.4 grains by 15.4, we get

$$\frac{1}{15.4}\text{ gram} = 1\text{ grain}$$

In order to find the number of grams per grain, then, we must use the *reciprocal* of 15.4 as a multiplier.

1. Line up the CI and D scales, then slide the hairline indicator to 1.54 on the CI scale. Then the reciprocal of 1.54 is under the hairline on the D scale. (It happens to be at 6.5 on the D scale, but we don't need to read this figure.)
2. Then shift 2.35 on the CI scale under the hairline, and read the result on the D scale at the index of the CI scale.
3. Shift 3.009 on the CI scale under the hairline and read the result on the D scale at the index of the CI scale.

When you have done this, return to page 211 to choose the correct answer.

[*from page 210*]

YOUR ANSWER: This problem can be done with a minimum of 5 shifts of the sliding scale and 5 slides of the hairline indicator:

$$\frac{3.14 \times \sqrt{4.07} \times 786}{1.01 \times \sqrt{23.0} \times 373} = 2.76$$

No; unless you figured out the square roots separately and then miscounted, you must be guessing.

Let's go through the steps for a solution:

1. Slide the indicator to 3.14 on the D scale.
2. Shift 1.01 on the C scale under the hairline.
3. Slide the hairline indicator to 4.07 on the *left-hand* B scale. (Note that the square root of 4.07 is on the C scale at the hairline. This is actually what you are multiplying by.)
4. Shift 23.0 on the *right-hand* B scale under the hairline. (Note that on the C scale below the *right-hand* 23.0 of the B scale appears the square root of 23.0. Below the *left-hand* 2.30 of the B scale appears the square root of 2.30.)

At this point we see that 7.86 on the C scale is off the rule to the right. Rather than re-index we may simply rewrite the problem:

$$\frac{3.14 \times \sqrt{4.07} \times \frac{1}{373}}{1.01 \times \sqrt{23.0} \times \frac{1}{786}}$$

In other words, we divide by the reciprocal of 786 instead of multiplying by 786, and we multiply by the reciprocal of 373 instead of dividing by 373.

5. Slide the indicator to 3.73 on the CI scale.
6. Shift 7.86 on the CI scale under the hairline.
7. Read the answer, 2.76, on the D scale.

Now count the number of shifts of the center scale and slides of the indicator and return to page 210 to choose the correct answer.

[*from page 209*]

YOUR ANSWER: 1 pound = 0.454 kilogram, so

3.2 lb. = 1.45 kg.

353 lb. = 160 kg.

0.763 lb. = 0.0346 kg.

No, there's a mistake in this column. Apparently you have the method correct, however. Set the hairline indicator at the conversion factor, 4.54, on the D scale, and use the CI scale to multiply the other numbers by this factor. For instance, you shift 3.2 on the CI scale under the hairline and read the answer on the D scale. Then you are actually dividing by the reciprocal of 3.2, which is the same as multiplying by 3.2.

Everything is all right in this column of conversions until you get to the last one. If you had been careful with your approximations, you would not have missed this. The approximations in this case should be easy, for 1 pound equals just about one-half a kilogram. So you should have about half as many kilograms as pounds.

Or you can figure the last one this way:

$$0.454 \times 0.763 = 4.54 \times 7.63 \times 10^{-2}$$

This is about $4 \times 8 \times 10^{-2} = 32 \times 10^{-2} = 0.32$.

So the answer should be 0.346 kg., not 0.0346 kg.

Now return to page 209 and choose the correct answer.

[*from page 190*]

YOUR ANSWER: The given diagram represents a workable solution of the problems:

$$\frac{476 \times 321 \times \frac{1}{9.2}}{45.3 \times \frac{1}{5.7}} \quad \text{and} \quad \frac{476 \times 5.7 \times 321}{9.2 \times 45.3}$$

Right. Both the problems above can be rewritten in the form $476 \times \frac{1}{9.2} \div \frac{1}{321} \times 5.7 \div 45.3$. To solve this problem, we add the log of $\frac{1}{9.2}$ to that of 476, subtract the log of $\frac{1}{321}$, add the log of 5.7, and finally subtract the log of 45.3. This is exactly what is shown in the diagram.

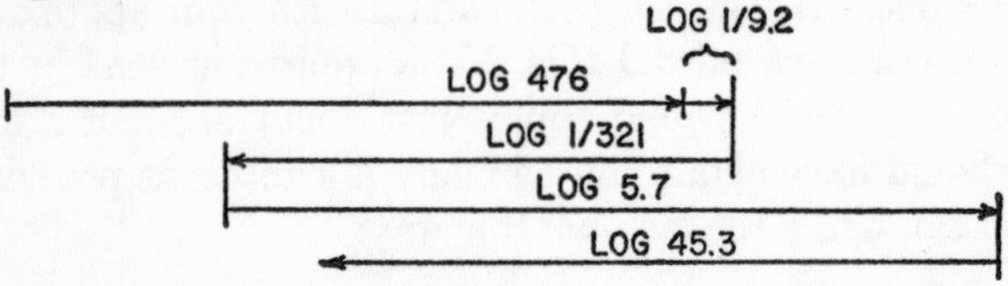

Remember, moving to the right on the slide rule represents adding a logarithm, while moving to the left constitutes subtracting a logarithm.

The CI scale is especially convenient when a series of figures are to be multiplied by the same factor. Simply slide the hairline to the given factor on the D scale and shift the CI scale until each of the figures to be multiplied is under the hairline. Then read each answer in turn on the D scale at the index of the CI scale. This is just another application of the principle that multiplying by a number in the same as dividing by its reciprocal.

For example, suppose that you are on the long-distance phone to Paris getting some measurements in meters. Knowing that there are 3.28 feet to a meter, you want to convert 2.77 m., 53.43 m., and 1,678 m. to feet. What are your results?

7.32 ft., 153.0 ft., and 5,000 ft. **page 199**

9.10 ft., 175.0 ft., and 5,500 ft. **page 209**

11.85 ft., 61.4 ft., and 19,550 ft. **page 213**

[*from page 210*]

YOUR ANSWER: This problem can be done with a minimum of 4 shifts of the sliding scale and 4 slides of the hairline indicator:

$$\frac{3.14 \times \sqrt{4.07} \times 786}{1.01 \times \sqrt{23.0} \times 373} = 2.76$$

No; you must not have used the CI scale to multiply by 786. Whenever you have to re-index, you make extra work for yourself and also give yourself additional chance for error.

Let's go through the steps for a solution:

1. Slide the indicator to 3.14 on the D scale.
2. Shift 1.01 on the C scale under the hairline.
3. Slide the hairline indicator to 4.07 on the *left-hand* B scale. (Note that the square root of 4.07 is on the C scale at the hairline. This is actually what you are multiplying by.)
4. Shift 23.0 on the *right-hand* B scale under the hairline. (Note that on the C scale below the *right-hand* 23.0 of the B scale appears the square root of 23.0. Below the *left-hand* 2.30 of the B scale appears the square root of 2.30.)

At this point we see that 7.86 on the C scale is off the rule to the right. Rather than re-index we may simply rewrite the problem:

$$\frac{3.14 \times \sqrt{4.07} \times \frac{1}{373}}{1.01 \times \sqrt{23.0} \times \frac{1}{786}}$$

In other words, we divide by the reciprocal of 786 instead of multiplying by 786, and we multiply by the reciprocal of 373 instead of dividing by 373.

5. So we slide the indicator to 3.73 on the CI scale.
6. Shift 7.86 on the CI scale under the hairline.
7. Read the answer, 2.76, on the D scale.

Now count the number of shifts of the center scale and slides of the indicator and return to page 210 to choose the correct answer.

[*from page 211*]

YOUR ANSWER: If 1 gram = 15.4 grains, then 23.5 grains = 1.53 grams; and 3,009 grains = 195 grams.

Right. If 1 gram = 15.4 grains, then

$$1 \text{ grain} = \frac{1}{15.4} \text{ grams} = \frac{1}{1.54} \times 10^{-1} \text{ grams,}$$

or roughly 0.667×10^{-1} grams. Going one step further, 1 grain is approximately 7×10^{-2} grams. Therefore, 23.5 grains is about $2 \times 10 \times 7 \times 10^{-2}$ grams, or 1.4 grams. 3,009 grains is about $3 \times 10^3 \times 7 \times 10^{-2}$ grams, or 210 grams.

On the slide rule,

1. Align the D and CI scales, and slide the hairline indicator to 1.54 on the CI scale. Then $\frac{1}{1.54}$ is under the hairline on the D scale.
2. Shift 2.35 on the CI scale under the hairline.
3. Read 1.53 on the D scale at the index of the CI scale. Then 23.5 grains = 1.53 grams.
4. Shift 3.01 on the CI scale under the hairline.
5. Read 1955 on the D scale at the index of the CI scale. Then 3,009 grains = 195 grams, to three figures of accuracy.

Try this one:

If 1 ft. = 0.305 meters, 3 ft. = 1 yard, and 1 rod = 5.03 meters, then

1 rod = 5.12 yd. **page 202**

1 rod = 5.50 yd. **page 210**

1 rod = 4.95 yd. **page 212**

[*from page 206*]

YOUR ANSWER: 9.10 ft., 175.0 ft., and 5,500 ft.

You are correct. There are 3.28 feet in 1 meter, and the given measurements were 2.77 m., 53.43 m., and 1,678 m. Then the values we want are given by

$$3.28 \text{ ft.} \times 2.77 \qquad 3.28 \text{ ft.} \times 53.43 \qquad 3.28 \text{ ft.} \times 1{,}678$$

With the usual approximation method, we find that our results should be roughly

$$9 \text{ ft.} \qquad 150 \text{ ft.} \qquad 6{,}000 \text{ ft.}$$

Rewriting the problem so that we can take advantage of the CI scale, we get

$$3.28 \text{ ft.} \div \frac{1}{2.77} \qquad 3.28 \text{ ft.} \div \frac{1}{53.43} \qquad 3.28 \text{ ft.} \div \frac{1}{1{,}678}$$

Then, on the slide rule,

1. Slide the hairline indicator to 3.28 on the D scale.
2. Shift 2.77 on the CI scale under the hairline.
3. Read 9.10 on the D scale at the index of the CI scale. Then the first value is 9.10 ft.
4. Shift 5.34 on the CI scale under the hairline.
5. Read 1.750 on the D scale at the index of the CI scale. Then the second value is 175.0 ft.
6. Shift 1.678 on the CI scale under the hairline.
7. Read 5.50 on the D scale at the index of the CI scale. Then the third value is 5,500 ft.

Check the conversions below. Then select the one group in which all are correct.

If 1 pound = 0.454 kilogram, then 3.2 lb. = 1.45 kg., 353 lb. = 160 kg., and 0.763 lb. = 0.0346 kg. **page 205**

If 1 inch = 2.54 centimeters, then 3.5 in. = 8.89 cm., 73.2 in. = 186 cm., and 1 ft. 7 in. = 48.2 cm. **page 211**

If 1 liter = 1.057 quarts, then 16 liters = 16.9 qts., 33.3 liters = 35.2 qts., and 0.00256 liters = 0.0271 qt. **page 214**

[*from page 208*]

YOUR ANSWER: 1 rod = 5.50 yards.

Right. We were given that 1 ft. = 0.305 meters, 3 ft. = 1 yd., and 1 rod = 5.03 meters. Here is one way to make the conversion:

Since 1 yd. = 3 ft., and 1 ft. = 0.305 meters, we know that

$$1 \text{ yd.} = 3 \times 0.305 \text{ meters}$$

Dividing both sides of this expression by 3 × 0.305,

$$1 \text{ meter} = \frac{1}{3 \times 0.305} \text{ yd.}$$

Then, since 1 rod = 5.03 meters,

$$1 \text{ rod} = 5.03 \times \frac{1}{3 \times 0.305} \text{ yd.} = \frac{5.03}{3 \times 3.05} \times 10 \text{ yd.},$$

which is approximately 5.56 yards.

The value of doing the problem this particular way is that we now have all the pertinent information in one equation. This simplifies the manipulation of the rule and reduces the risk of error.

1. Slide the hairline indicator to 5.03 on the D scale.
2. Shift 3.0 on the C scale under the hairline.
3. Slide the hairline to 3.05 on the CI scale.
4. Read 5.50 on the D scale under the hairline.

Then the complete answer is 1 rod = 5.50 yards.

To finish up this chapter on the CI scale, work the following problem in as few moves as possible. Remember that you also have A and B scales. Then select the correct answer at the bottom of the page.

$$\frac{3.14 \times \sqrt{4.07} \times 786}{1.01 \times \sqrt{23.0} \times 373} = 2.76$$

This problem can be done with a minimum of:

5 shifts of the sliding scale and 5 slides of the hairline. **page 204**

4 shifts of the sliding scale and 4 slides of the hairline. **page 207**

3 shifts of the sliding scale and 3 slides of the hairline. **page 215**

[*from page 209*]

YOUR ANSWER: All the conversions of the second series are correct.

That's right; they are. 1 inch = 2.54 centimeters, or, for estimating purposes, roughly 2.5 centimeters. Then 3.5 in. is roughly 3.5 × 2.5 cm., or 8.75 cm.; 73.2 in. is roughly 7 × 10 × 2.5 cm., or 175 cm.; and 1 ft. 7 in. = 19 in., roughly 2 × 10 × 2.5 cm., or 50 cm.

On the slide rule:

1. Slide the hairline indicator to 2.54 on the D scale.
2. Shift 3.5 on the CI scale under the hairline.
3. Read 8.89 on the D scale at the index of the CI scale. Then 3.5 in. = 8.89 cm.
4. Shift 7.32 on the CI scale under the hairline.
5. Read 1.86 on the D scale at the index of the CI scale. Then 73.2 in. = 186 cm.
6. Shift 1.9 on the CI scale under the hairline.
7. Read 4.82 on the D scale at the index of the CI scale. Then 1 ft. 7 in. (or 19 in.) = 48.2 cm.

If instead of being told that 1 in. = 2.54 cm., we are told that 1 cm. = 0.394 in., we can still perform these conversions with no difficulty. If 1 cm. = 0.394 in., we can divide both sides of this expression by 0.394 to find that

$$1 \text{ in.} = \frac{1}{0.394} \text{ cm.} = \frac{1}{394} \times 10$$

Now we need to locate $\frac{1}{394}$ on the D scale. The key is in remembering that a number on the CI scale is the reciprocal of the number directly below it on the D scale. Therefore, if we align the D and CI scales and slide the hairline indicator to 3.94 on the CI scale, $\frac{1}{394}$ is directly beneath the hairline on the D scale.

The rest of the problem is the same: shift 3.5 on the CI scale under the hairline, read 8.89 on the D scale, and so on.

Now you try one. If 1 gram = 15.4 grains, then

23.5 grains = 3.61 grams; and 3,009 grains = 454 grams. **page 203**

23.5 grains = 1.53 grams; and 3,009 grains = 195 grams. **page 208**

[*from page 208*]

YOUR ANSWER: 1 foot = 0.305 meters, 3 feet = 1 yard, and 1 rod = 5.03 meters; therefore, 1 rod = 4.95 yards.

No, apparently you used the wrong formula to make this conversion.

Here's one way to do the problem. To convert from rods to meters you must multiply the number of rods by 5.03, the number of meters in one rod. Now to change 5.03 meters to feet you must know how many feet there are in one meter. We have the conversion figure for the number of meters per foot instead; 1 foot = 0.305 meters. To find how many feet there are in one meter you must take the reciprocal of 0.305: 1 m. $= \frac{1}{0.305}$ ft. So if you multiply 5.03 by the reciprocal of 0.305:

$$5.03 \times \frac{1}{.305}$$

you will have the number of feet in one rod.

Now all you have to do is divide this by 3, the number of feet in 1 yard, and you will have the number of yards in one rod:

$$\frac{5.03 \times \frac{1}{.305}}{3}$$

You can also write this:

$$\frac{5.03}{3 \times .305}$$

Dividing by a number is the same as multiplying by its reciprocal.

Apparently you used the formula

$$\frac{5.03 \times 3}{0.305}$$

This is saying that there are 3 yards in one foot when it is the other way around, of course. Besides, this formula will give 49.5 yards for your answer.

Now return to page 208 and choose the correct answer.

[*from page 206*]

YOUR ANSWER: 11.85 ft., 61.4 ft., and 19,550 ft.

No; it would seem from this answer that you divided with the C scale instead of the CI scale. In other words, you divided by 2.77 m., 53.43 m., and 1,678 m., instead of dividing by their reciprocals. Remember that you can multiply two numbers together by using the CI scale to divide one of them by the reciprocal of the other.

As we have demonstrated before:

$$a \times b = a \div \frac{1}{b}$$

The CI scale is just a scale of reciprocals, of course. For instance, the distance from the left index to the number 2 on the CI scale corresponds to the log of the reciprocal of 2. The numerical equivalent of the reciprocal of 2 ($\frac{1}{2}$, or 0.5) appears on the C scale directly below the 2 on the CI scale:

CI

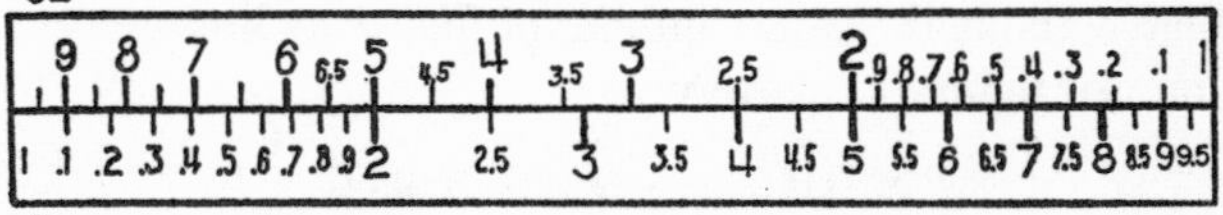

C

Since there are 3.28 feet in one meter, we may convert meters to feet by multiplying the number of meters times 3.28. To convert 2.77 meters to feet we should begin by placing the hairline indicator at 3.28, the conversion factor, on the D scale. Now we can multiply this factor by 2.77, using the CI scale. Shift 2.77 on the CI scale under the hairline. You are then dividing by the reciprocal of 2.77, which is the same as multiplying by 2.77. Read 9.10 on the D scale. With the usual estimating methods, you can see that the answer is about 9, so the result must be 9.1 ft. Now do the same thing for 53.43 m. and 1,678 m., shifting the CI scale until these numbers are under the hairline, and reading the answers on the D scale.

Now return to page 206 and choose the correct answer.

[*from page 209*]

YOUR ANSWER: 1 liter = 1.057 quarts, so

16 liters = 16.9 quarts

33.3 liters = 35.2 quarts

0.00256 liters = 0.0271 quarts

No, there's a mistake in this column. Apparently you have the method correct, however. Set the hairline indicator at the conversion factor, 1.057, on the D scale, and use the CI scale to multiply the other numbers by this factor. For instance, shift 1.6 on the CI scale under the hairline and read the answer on the D scale. Then you are actually dividing by the reciprocal of 1.6, which is the same as multiplying by 1.6.

Everything is all right in this column of conversions until you get to the last one. If you had been careful with your approximations, you would not have missed this. The approximations in this case should be easy, for 1 liter is just about the same as a quart. So you should have about the same number of quarts as liters.

Or you can figure it this way:

$$1.057 \times 0.00256 = 1.057 \times 2.56 \times 10^{-3}$$

This is about $1 \times 2.5 \times 10^{-3} = 0.0025$.

So the answer should be 0.00271 quarts, not 0.0271 quarts.

Now return to page 209 and choose the correct answer.

YOUR ANSWER: The problem can be done with a minimum of 3 shifts of the sliding scale and 3 slides of the hairline.

Right.

$$\frac{3.14 \times \sqrt{4.07} \times 768}{1.01 \times \sqrt{23.0} \times 373} = \frac{3.14 \times \sqrt{4.07} \times 7.86}{1.01 \times \sqrt{23.0} \times 3.73}$$

which is roughly 2.40. On the slide rule:

1. Slide the hairline indicator to 3.14 on the D scale.
2. Shift 1.01 on the C scale under the hairline.
3. Slide the hairline indicator to 4.07 on the *left-hand* B scale.
4. Shift 23.0 on the *right-hand* B scale under the hairline.

At this point, we see that 7.86 on the C scale is off the rule to the right. Rather than re-index, however, we simply rewrite the problem slightly:

$$\frac{3.14 \times \sqrt{4.07} \times 7.86}{1.01 \times \sqrt{23.0} \times 3.73} = \frac{3.14 \times \sqrt{4.07} \times \dfrac{1}{3.73}}{1.01 \times \sqrt{23.0} \times \dfrac{1}{7.86}}$$

Then we can go on:

5. Slide the hairline indicator to 3.73 on the CI scale.
6. Shift 7.86 on the CI scale under the hairline.
7. Read 2.76 on the D scale at the index of the CI scale.

Then the complete answer is 2.76.

This completes the chapter on the CI scale. We've seen that the CI scale, though not essential to the slide rule, increases the speed and accuracy with which many calculations can be made.

To learn about another useful scale, the L scale, go on to page 216.

CHAPTER 5

The L Scale

The L scale carries us all the way back to the fundamental idea of the slide rule. In the second lesson, we described how it was possible to multiply numbers by adding their logs. We demonstrated that fact with a hypothetical slide rule marked off evenly from 0 through 1. Those numbers were considered to be logarithms to the base 10. The logarithm of a number N is the power to which 10 must be raised to equal N. The logarithm of 100 with regard to the base 10 is 2, because 10 to the second power (10^2) is 100.

Knowing the logarithms of two numbers M and N, we are able to find the log of $M \times N$ by adding the logs of M and N. The slide rule is simply a device for performing such addition.

Once we discovered the principle of the logarithmic slide rule it was obvious that for most purposes it would be more convenient to put the numbers in the place of their logarithms. That way it wasn't necessary to have a table of logarithms around for reference. The logarithmic slide rule then became complete in itself.

But there comes a time when it is convenient to know the log of a number that you are working with, as you will see in the course of this chapter. The L scale is for that purpose. It is just a simple scale running from 0 to 1, on which it is possible by direct reading to find the log of a number. The reading is made from the C or D scale to the L scale. But the location of the scales varies on different slide rules. Let's find log 64.8 on two different rules.

On rules with only one face, the L scale sometimes appears on the back of the slide. Here is such a rule on which we have located 6.48 on the C scale above the right index of the D scale.

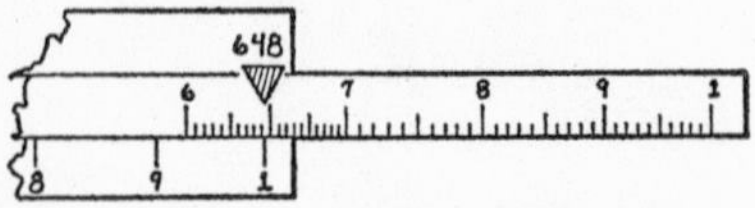

When we turn the rule over, we find an indicator on the back from which the log can be read on the L scale.

[*continued on page 217*]

[*from page 216*]

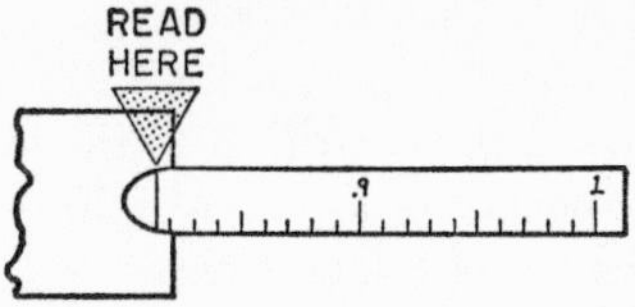

On other rules, the L scale is arranged on the back so that when the right index of the C scale is set opposite 6.48 on the D scale:

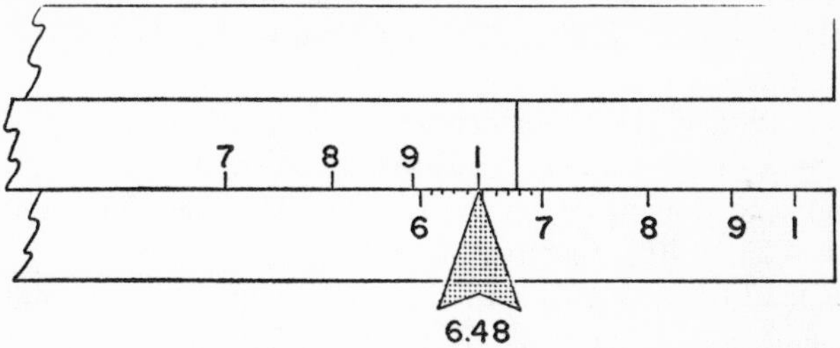

then log 6.48 appears under a hairline on the back of the slide.

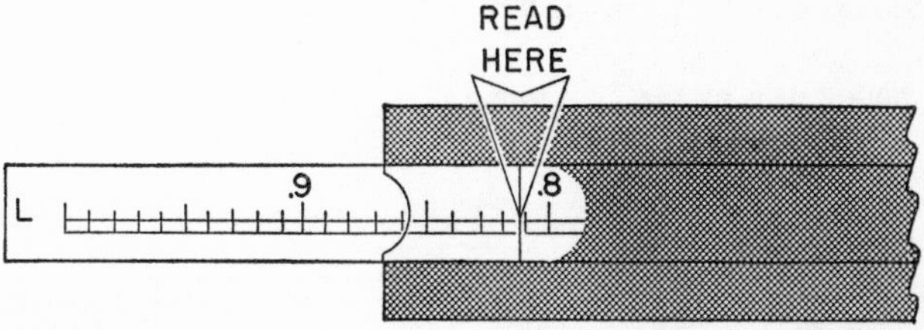

The reading is much simpler on a slide rule that has both the L and D scales on the face. Set the hairline over the number on the D scale. The log of that number is found under the hairline on the L scale.

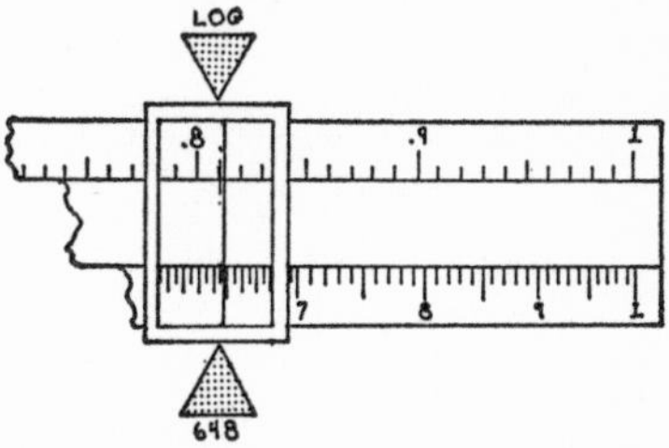

But how would you read that result? What is the log of 64.8?

1.812. **page 221** 8.12. **page 225**

I don't see how to begin. **page 228**

[*from page 221*]

YOUR ANSWER: 4.79×10^{12}.

Correct. The part of the logarithm to the left of the decimal can be considered the exponent of a power of 10. The part to the right of the decimal is the log of a factor between 1 and 10 by which the power of ten is to be multiplied.

To put this another way, the logarithm 12.68 may be considered the sum of the logarithm 12.00 *plus* the logarithm 0.68. So the number whose logarithm is 12.68 can be considered the product of the antilogs of 12.00 and 0.68.

The antilog of 12.00, of course, is 10^{12}. The antilog of 0.68 is found by a direct reading. Locate 0.68 on the L scale with the hairline and read the antilog on the D scale; it's 4.79. So the antilog of 12.68 is 4.79×10^{12}; therefore, $64.8^7 = 4.79 \times 10^{12}$.

If instead of raising 64.8 to the seventh power, you want to find the seventh root of 64.8 ($\sqrt[7]{64.8}$), what would you do first?

Divide log 64.8 by 7. **page 222**

Divide log 64.8 by log 7. **page 232**

[*from page 222*]

YOUR ANSWER: $0.0648^7 = 4.79$.

Not quite. You're forgetting about the -9 part of the logarithm. Let's backtrack a little.

We found that

$$\log 0.0648^7 = -9 + 0.68$$

Think about this expression for a moment. It means that the number 0.0648^7 can be considered the product of the antilogs of -9 and $+0.68$. So, we must find the antilogs of these two factors and multiply them.

The L scale is read from 0 to 1, and the corresponding numbers on the D scale are then read from 1 to 10. Sliding the hairline over 0.68 on the L scale, then, we read 4.79 on the D scale:

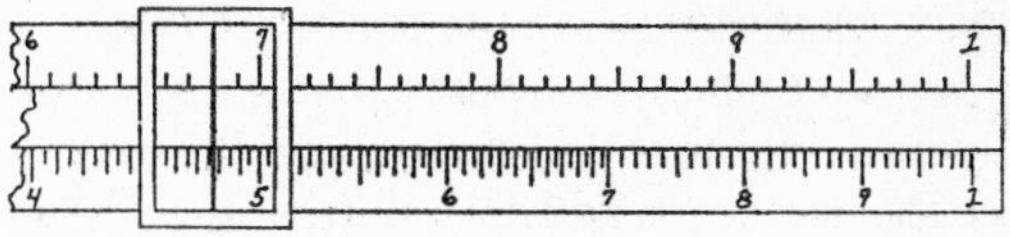

So one of the factors we are looking for is 4.79. The other one, of course, is 10^{-9}, the number whose logarithm is exactly -9. Therefore,

$$0.0648^7 = 4.79 \times 10^{-9} = 0.00000000479$$

When you understand how we arrived at this answer, return to page 222 to make the correct choice.

[*from page 231*]

YOUR ANSWER: Log $0.0648^{\frac{1}{7}} = 68.812 - 70$.

Not quite. You haven't done anything with that exponent, and you can't just ignore it. Let's go back a few steps.

Having found that the logarithm of 0.0648 is 0.812 − 2, or −1.188, we proceed according to this formula

$$\log A^{\frac{1}{n}} = \frac{\log A}{n}$$

$$\log 0.0648^{\frac{1}{7}} = \frac{\log 0.0648}{7} = \frac{-1.188}{7}$$

But we also saw that completing this division gives us a negative logarithm, which we can't find on the L scale. However, we can convert a negative logarithm to a more convenient form by adding and subtracting the same number. Since that amounts to adding zero, we are really doing nothing that will change the result.

We choose the number to add and subtract that will do the most to simplify calculations. In order to extract the seventh root, we are going to have to divide log 0.0648 by 7. To make this division easier, we add zero in the form 7.000 − 7.

$$\begin{array}{rl} 7.000 - 7 & \longleftarrow \text{this is equivalent to zero} \\ -1.188 & \longleftarrow \text{log } 0.0648 \\ \hline 5.812 - 7 & \longleftarrow \text{log } 0.0648 \text{ in new form.} \end{array}$$

So we can write

$$\log 0.0648 = 5.812 - 7 \quad (\textit{not} \log \sqrt[7]{0.0648} = 5.812 - 7)$$

then $$\log 0.0648^{\frac{1}{7}} = \frac{\log 0.0648}{7} = \frac{5.812 - 7}{7} = 0.830 - 1$$

Notice that this result is equal to −0.170, the negative log we're avoiding.

Now return to page 231 to choose the correct answer.

[*from page 217*]

YOUR ANSWER: The log of 64.8 is 1.812.

Yes. That is reasonable because log 10 = 1 and log 100 = 2, so the log of 64.8 will be somewhere between 1 and 2. This common-sense conclusion can be proved. Consider that the number 64.8 can be factored to 6.48×10^1; therefore $\log 64.8 = \log (6.48 \times 10^1)$. But, since the log of a product is the *sum* of the logs of its factors, $\log (6.48 \times 10^1) = \log 6.48 + \log 10^1$. So

$$\log 64.8 = \log 6.48 + \log 10^1$$

The log of 6.48 is 0.812 (found by direct reading from the D to the L scale) and the log of 10^1 is 1 (the exponent of the base 10 *is* the log), so:

$$\begin{aligned}\log 64.8 &= 0.812 + 1 \\ &= 1.812\end{aligned}$$

If you were asked to raise 64.8 to the seventh power $(64.8)^7$, you could do as you learned in the last chapter. However, that method has many opportunities for error, because of the number of steps required when you get much beyond the second and third powers. The L scale can be used to raise to powers in a manner that minimizes the error if the readings are made with care.

This is the way to set up the problem:

$$(64.8)^7 = (6.48 \times 10^1)^7$$

and since $\log (6.48 \times 10^1)^7 = 7 (\log 6.48) + \log 10^7$

$$\log (64.8)^7 = (7 \times \log 6.48) + 7$$

We find by reading from the D to the L scale that log 6.48 = 0.812. Then we multiply 0.812 by 7 on the C and D scales in the ordinary manner, getting the result 5.680. So

$$\begin{aligned}\log (64.8)^7 &= 5.68 + 7 \\ &= 12.68\end{aligned}$$

The number whose log is 12.68 is called the *antilog* of 12.68. What is the antilog of 12.68?

4.79×10^{12}. **page 218** 6.8×10^{12}. **page 229**

1,679. **page 224**

[*from page 218*]

YOUR ANSWER: To extract the seventh root of 64.8, first divide the log of 64.8 by 7.

Right. $$\log \sqrt[7]{64.8} = \frac{1}{7} \times \log 64.8$$

We've seen that the log of 64.8 was 1.812. Accordingly,

$$\log \sqrt[7]{64.8} = \frac{1}{7} \times 1.812 = 0.259$$

To find the value of $\sqrt[7]{64.8}$, we need only find the antilog of 0.259:

1. Slide the hairline indicator to 0.259 on the L scale.
2. Read 1.817 on the D scale under the hairline.

Then antilog $0.259 = \sqrt[7]{64.8} = 1.82$, to three figures of accuracy.

What about 0.0648^7? To raise 0.0648 to the seventh power, we first factor as follows:

$$\begin{aligned} 0.0648^7 &= (6.48 \times 10^{-2})^7 \\ \log 0.0648^7 &= 7 \times \log (6.48 \times 10^{-2}) \\ &= 7 \times (\log 6.48 + \log 10^{-2}) \\ &= 7 \times (0.812 - 2) \end{aligned}$$

So $$\log 0.0648^7 = 5.68 - 14$$

This may seem to be an unusual form and you may wonder why we do not simplify $5.68 - 14 = -8.32$. You will note that the slide rule does not have any negative logarithms on it. Further, it is more convenient to use logarithms in the form $5.68 - 14$ but we need to change the positive term (5.68) to a number between 0 and 1. This is done by noting that

$$5.68 - 14 = 5.00 + 0.68 - 14 = 0.68 - 9$$

It is easy to find the antilog of 0.68 and -9, but finding the antilog of -8.32 would present difficulties on the slide rule.

So we say that $\log 0.0648^7 = 0.68 - 9$, and we conclude that

$0.0648^7 = 4.79$. **page 219**

$0.0648^7 = 4.79 \times 10^{-3}$. **page 226**

$0.0648^7 = 4.79 \times 10^{-9}$. **page 231**

YOUR ANSWER: Log $0.0648^{\frac{1}{7}} = 0.830 - 1$.

Correct. Here's the way it goes:

$$\log 0.0648^{\frac{1}{7}} = \frac{\log 0.0648}{7}$$
$$= \frac{-2 + 0.812}{7}$$
$$= \frac{-1.188}{7}$$

Adding zero, in the form of 7.000 − 7, to −1.188,

$$\begin{array}{r} 7.000 - 7 \\ -1.188 \quad\;\; \\ \hline 5.812 - 7 \end{array}$$

So

$$\log 0.0648^{\frac{1}{7}} = \frac{5.812 - 7}{7} = 0.830 - 1$$

From the last expression we can find the result of $0.0648^{\frac{1}{7}}$. It's the product of the antilogs of 0.830 and −1. Sliding the hairline over 0.830 on the L scale, we read 6.76 on the D scale. So 6.76 is the antilog of 0.830. And since 10^{-1} is the antilog of −1, we find that

$$0.0648^{\frac{1}{7}}, \quad \text{or} \quad \sqrt[7]{0.0648} = 6.76 \times 10^{-1}$$
$$= 0.676$$

Now try one for yourself. Using the L scale, what is the value of the ninth root of 0.356 (that is, $0.356^{\frac{1}{9}}$)?

0.891. **page 227**

0.00891. **page 230**

0.960. **page 234**

9.95×10^{-10}. **page 237**

[*from page 221*]

YOUR ANSWER: 1,679 is the number whose log is 12.68.

No. Apparently you're not quite clear on how a number is determined from its log by means of the D and L scales.

First of all, you should be familiar with the general range of logarithms.

$$1 = 10^0 \qquad \log 1 = 0$$
$$10 = 10^1 \qquad \log 10 = 1$$
$$100 = 10^2 \qquad \log 100 = 2$$
$$1{,}000 = 10^3 \qquad \log 1{,}000 = 3$$
$$10{,}000 = 10^4 \qquad \log 10{,}000 = 4$$
$$100{,}000 = 10^5 \qquad \log 100{,}000 = 5,$$

and so on.

Any number between 1 and 10 will have a log of less than 1. Any number between 10 and 100 will have a log between 1 and 2; conversely, any log between 3 and 4 will represent a number between 1,000 (i.e., 10^3) and 10,000 (i.e., 10^4).

Our problem was to find the number between 10^{12} and 10^{13} represented by the logarithm 12.68. That is, we want the *antilog* of 12.68.

The logarithm 12.68 can be broken down to 12 *plus* 0.68. The antilogs of these two logs will be multiplied to give the antilog of 12.68.

The antilog of 12 is 10^{12}. The antilog of 0.68 can be found by reading from the L to the D scale; it is 4.79. The answer, then, is 4.79×10^{12}.

The easiest way to convert a log of more than one into a number is to consider that log as representing two factors. The part of the log to the left of the decimal is taken as the log of the power of 10. The part of the log to the right of the decimal is the log of the second factor, which is a number between 1 and 10.

	12 . 68		
↓		↓	log
10^{12}	$\times$	4.79	corresponding number

Now return to page 221 and select a better answer.

YOUR ANSWER: The log of 64.8 is 8.12.

Now, is 8.12 a reasonable answer? It should be clear by now that:

$$\log 10 = 1$$

$$\log 100 = 2$$

Since 64.8 is between 10 and 100, it stands to reason that the log of 64.8 should be between log 10 and log 100, i.e., between 1 and 2. Similarly, log 648 is between 2, the log of 100, and 3, the log of 1,000.

Let's look at the problem mathematically. 64.8 can be factored:

$$64.8 = 6.48 \times 10^1$$

The log of the product is the sum of the logs of the factors:

$$\log (M \times N) = \log M + \log N$$

Therefore,

$$\log 64.8 = \log 6.48 + \log 10^1$$

All we need do is find the logs of 6.48 and 10^1 and then add them. The log of 6.48 is found by:

1. sliding the hairline over 6.48 on the D scale, and
2. reading 0.812 on the L scale.

The log of 6.48 is 0.812 because the log scale is read from 0 to 1. And we know that the log of 10^1 is 1. So:

$$64.8 = 6.48 \times 10^1$$

$$\begin{aligned} \log 64.8 &= \log 6.48 + \log 10^1 \\ &= 0.812 + 1 \\ &= 1.812 \end{aligned}$$

We use the same steps to find the log of 648.

$$648 = 6.48 \times 10^2$$

$$\begin{aligned} \log 648 &= \log 6.48 + \log 10^2 \\ &= 0.812 + 2 \\ &= 2.812 \end{aligned}$$

By the same reasoning, log 6,480 = 3.812; log 64,800 = 4.812; and so on.

Return to page 217 to choose the correct answer.

[*from page 222*]

YOUR ANSWER: $0.0648^7 = 4.79 \times 10^{-3}$.

Evidently you tried to consider the -9 part of the logarithm, but couldn't decide just what to do with it. Let's backtrack a little.

We have found that

$$\log 0.0648^7 = -9 + 0.68$$

Think about this expression for a moment. What does it really mean? It means that the number 0.0648^7 can be considered the product of the antilog of -9 and $+0.68$. So, we must find these antilogs and multiply them.

The L scale is read from 0 to 1, and the corresponding numbers on the D scale are then read from 1 to 10. So, sliding the hairline over 0.68 on the L scale, we find that the number whose logarithm is 0.68 is 4.79, read from the D scale. One of the factors we are looking for, then, is 4.79. The other one is 10^{-9}, the only number whose logarithm is exactly -9. So

$$0.0648^7 = 4.79 \times 10^{-9} = 0.00000000479$$

The trick to all this, of course, is remembering that this rule is reversible. If

$$A \times B = N, \quad \text{then} \quad \log N = \log A + \log B$$

In other words, this is also true. If

$$\log N = \log A + \log B, \quad \text{then} \quad A \times B = N$$

This is the idea we used in order to get from $\log 0.0648^7 = -9 + 0.68$ to $0.0648^7 = 4.79 \times 10^{-9}$.

When you feel that you can perform the operation by yourself, return to page 222 to choose the right answer.

YOUR ANSWER: $0.356^{\frac{1}{9}} = 0.891$.

Right. 0.356 can be written as 3.56×10^{-1}, so

$$\begin{aligned}\log 0.356 &= \log 3.56 + \log 10^{-1}\\ &= 0.552 + (-1) \text{ (or } 0.552 - 1)\\ &= -0.448\end{aligned}$$

Adding zero in the form $9.000 - 9$,

$$\begin{array}{r} 9.000 - 9 \\ -0.448 \\ \hline 8.552 - 9 \end{array} \quad (\log 0.356 \text{ in new form})$$

Since, as we've seen, $\log A^{\frac{1}{N}} = \dfrac{\log A}{N}$,

$$\begin{aligned}\log 0.356^{\frac{1}{9}} &= \frac{8.552 - 9}{9}\\ &= 0.950 - 1\end{aligned}$$

The antilog of 0.950 (i.e., the number whose logarithm is 0.950) is 8.91. The antilog of -1 is 10^{-1}. And if $\log N = X + Y$, $N =$ (antilog X) $\times$ (antilog Y), so

$$\begin{aligned}0.356^{\frac{1}{9}} &= 8.91 \times 10^{-1}\\ &= 0.891\end{aligned}$$

Here are three problems. Use the L scale to solve them, and then pick the one with the wrong solution.

$\sqrt[4]{3.61} = 1.38$. **page 233**

$1{,}625^{\frac{2}{3}} = 138.2$. **page 236**

$84.9^5 = 9.21 \times 10^9$. **page 238**

[*from page 217*]

YOUR ANSWER: I don't see how to begin.

There is a little trick to the problem, but not a very difficult one. Since 64.8 is between 10 and 100, it stands to reason that the log of 64.8 should be between log 10 and log 100, i.e., between 1 and 2. Similarly, log 648 is between 2, the log of 100, and 3, the log of 1,000.

Let's look at the problem mathematically. 64.8 can be factored:

$$64.8 = 6.48 \times 10^1$$

The log of a product is the sum of the logs of the factors.

$$\log M \times N = \log M + \log N$$

Therefore,

$$\log 64.8 = \log 6.48 + \log 10^1$$

All we need do is find the logs of 6.48 and 10^1 and then add them. The log of 6.48 is found by:

1. sliding the hairline over 6.48 on the D scale, and
2. reading 0.812 on the L scale.

The log of 6.48 is 0.812 because the log scales are read from 0 to 1. And we know that the log of 10^1 is 1. So:

$$64.8 = 6.48 \times 10^1$$

$$\begin{aligned} \log 64.8 &= \log 6.48 + \log 10^1 \\ &= 0.812 + 1 \\ &= 1.812 \end{aligned}$$

We use the same steps to find the log of 648.

$$648 = 6.48 \times 10^2$$

$$\begin{aligned} \log 648 &= \log 6.48 + \log 10^2 \\ &= 0.812 + 2 \\ &= 2.812 \end{aligned}$$

By the same reasoning, log 6,480 = 3.812; log 64,800 = 4.812; and so on.

Return to page 217 to choose the correct answer.

YOUR ANSWER: 6.8×10^{12}.

No. Apparently you haven't got quite clear how a number is determined from its log by means of the D and L scales.

First of all, you should be familiar with the general range of logarithms.

$$1 = 10^0 \qquad \log 1 = 0$$

$$10 = 10^1 \qquad \log 10 = 1$$

$$100 = 10^2 \qquad \log 100 = 2$$

$$1{,}000 = 10^3 \qquad \log 1{,}000 = 3$$

$$10{,}000 = 10^4 \qquad \log 10{,}000 = 4$$

$$100{,}000 = 10^5 \qquad \log 100{,}000 = 5,$$

and so on.

Any number between 1 and 10 will have a log of less than 1. Any number between 10 and 100 will have a log between 1 and 2; conversely, any log between 3 and 4 will represent a number between 1,000 (i.e., 10^3) and 10,000 (i.e., 10^4).

Our problem was to find the number between 10^{12} and 10^{13} represented by the logarithm 12.68. That is, we want the *antilog* of 12.68.

The logarithm 12.68 can be broken down to 12 *plus* 0.68. The antilog of these two logs will be multiplied to give the antilog of 12.68.

The antilog of 12 is 10^{12}. The antilog of 0.68 can be found by reading from the L to the D scale; it is 4.79. The answer, then, is 4.79×10^{12}.

The easiest way to transfer a log of more than one into a number is to consider that log as representing two factors. The part of the log to the left of the decimal is taken as the log of a power of 10. The part of the log to the right of the decimal is the log of the second factor, which is a number between 1 and 10.

$$\begin{array}{ccccl} & & 12\,.\,68 & & \text{log} \\ \swarrow & & & \searrow & \\ 10^{12} & & \times & 4.79 & \text{corresponding number} \end{array}$$

Now, return to page 221 and select a better answer.

[*from page 223*]

YOUR ANSWER: $0.356^{\frac{1}{9}} = 0.00891$.

No, you've misplaced the decimal point. For the practice, let's rework the problem. To begin, we know that:

$$\log 0.356^{\frac{1}{9}} = \frac{\log 0.356}{9} = \frac{\log (3.56 \times 10^{-1})}{9}$$

Setting the hairline at 356 on the D scale, we find on the L scale that $\log 3.56 = 0.552$. The log of 10^{-1} is, of course, -1, so:

$$\log \sqrt[9]{0.356} = \frac{0.552 - 1}{9} = \frac{-0.448}{9}$$

Adding zero in the form $9.000 - 9$ (because we will have to divide by 9):

$$\begin{array}{r} 9.000 - 9 \\ -0.448 \quad\;\; \\ \hline 8.552 - 9 \end{array}$$

So

$$\log 0.356^{\frac{1}{9}} = \frac{8.552 - 9}{9} = 0.950 - 1$$

Therefore, the number we want is the *antilog* of $(0.950 - 1)$. Sliding the hairline over 0.950 on the L scale, we read its antilog, 8.91, on the D scale; and antilog $-1 = 10^{-1}$. So

$$0.356^{\frac{1}{9}} = 8.91 \times 10^{-1}$$

If you're still having trouble, it would be a good idea for you to review the entire chapter. It begins on page 216; otherwise, return to page 223 and select the correct answer.

[*from page 222*]

YOUR ANSWER: $0.0648^7 = 4.79 \times 10^{-9}$.

Right. We found that $\log 0.0648^7 = -9 + 0.68$. We read 4.79 as the antilog of 0.68, from L to the D scale. So, antilog $0.68 = 4.79$, and since we know that antilog $-9 = 10^{-9}$, the result above is correct.

The seventh root of 0.0648 would be found by much the same procedure as that used to find $64.8^{\frac{1}{7}}$:

$$\log \sqrt[7]{0.0648} = \frac{\log (6.48 \times 10^{-2})}{7} = \frac{-2 + 0.812}{7} = \frac{-1.188}{7}$$

At this point, we could complete the division $\left(\frac{-1.188}{7} = -0.170\right)$, but this doesn't help much, since we don't know how to find a negative logarithm on the L scale.

There is a way of avoiding the difficulty of negative logarithms. If we add 10 to -1.188, we have a positive number. Of course we can't add 10 without subtracting 10, too. We do so by setting a -10 over to one side. Then what we are doing, essentially, is adding 0, which will not change the actual value of the expression.

$$\begin{array}{r} 10.000 - 10 \\ -\ \ 1.188 \qquad \\ \hline 8.812 - 10 \end{array}$$

Notice that 0.812 is the log of 6.48, the sum of $+8$ and -10 is -2. Now we are on solid ground. Clearly, it doesn't matter which number we choose to add as long as we subtract the same one.

Where the seventh root is to be extracted, we must divide by 7, so it is most convenient to add zero in the form of $7.000 - 7$ rather than $10.000 - 10$. Then $\log 0.0648^{\frac{1}{7}} =$

$68.812 - 70$. **page 220**

$0.830 - 1$. **page 223**

-0.170. **page 235**

[*from page 218*]

YOUR ANSWER: To extract the seventh root of 64.8, first divide log 64.8 by log 7.

No. Perhaps a bit of review is in order. We have seen, in general terms, that

$$\log N^a = a \times \log N$$

For example,

$$\log 5^2 = 2 \times \log 5$$

$$\log 43^4 = 4 \times \log 43$$

We used this rule to find the seventh *power* of 64.8. We multiplied the log 64.8 by 7:

$$\log 64.8^7 = 7 \times \log 64.8$$

Actually, the same rule holds true when the exponent is a fraction, indicating a root:

$$\log N^{\frac{1}{b}} = \frac{1}{b} \times \log N, \quad \text{or} \quad \frac{\log N}{b}$$

You have already used this idea in dealing with square and cube roots. The others are no different.

$$\log \sqrt{3} = \log 3^{\frac{1}{2}} = \frac{1}{2} \times \log 3 = \frac{\log 3}{2}$$

$$\log \sqrt[4]{5} = \log 5^{\frac{1}{4}} = \frac{1}{4} \times \log 5 = \frac{\log 5}{4}$$

So we can find the log of the seventh root of 64.8 by dividing the *log of 64.8* by 7:

$$\log \sqrt[7]{64.8} = \log 64.8^{\frac{1}{7}} = \frac{1}{7} \times \log 64.8 = \frac{\log 64.8}{7}$$

Return to page 218 to answer the question correctly.

YOUR ANSWER: $\sqrt[4]{3.61} = 1.38$.

Sorry, but this problem is all right. Here is the correct solution:

$$\log 3.61^{\frac{1}{4}} = \frac{\log 3.61}{4}$$

Sliding the hairline over 3.61 on the D scale, we find its log, 0.558, on the L scale. So

$$\log 3.61^{\frac{1}{4}} = \frac{0.558}{4}$$

Using the C and D scales to complete the division, we get

$$\log 3.61^{\frac{1}{4}} = 0.139$$

Sliding the hairline over 0.139 on the L scale, we read its antilog as 1.38 on the D scale. Therefore,

$$3.61^{\frac{1}{4}} = 1.38$$

Since the fourth root is divisible by 2, this problem would have been easy to do on the A scale:

1. Slide the hairline to 3.61 on the A scale (that's between 1 and 10, remember), and read 1.902 on D. That's the square root.
2. Slide the hairline to 1.90 on the A scale, and read 1.38 on the D scale. And that's the fourth root because

$$\sqrt{\sqrt{N}} = \sqrt[4]{N}$$

Either way, you should get the same answer. In fact, doing the problem on the A scale is a good way to check the answer you got with the L scale.

Now return to page 227 to find the error.

[*from page 223*]

YOUR ANSWER: $0.356^{\frac{1}{9}} = 0.960$.

No. Apparently you made a relatively minor error in computing the log of 0.356. But a small error in a log can produce a big error in the final answer. Let's review the problem. To begin, we know that:

$$\log 0.356^{\frac{1}{9}} = \frac{\log 0.356}{9} = \frac{\log (3.56 \times 10^{-1})}{9}$$

Setting the hairline at 356 on the D scale, we find on the L scale that $\log 3.56 = 0.552$.

The log of 10^{-1} is, of course, -1, so:

$$\log \sqrt[9]{0.356} = \frac{0.552 - 1}{9} = \frac{-0.448}{9}$$

Adding zero in the form $9.000 - 9$ (because we'll have to divide by 9):

$$\begin{array}{r} 9.000 - 9 \\ -0.448 \quad\; \\ \hline 8.552 - 9 \end{array} \quad (\textit{not}\ 89.448 - 90)$$

So

$$\log 0.356^{\frac{1}{9}} = \frac{8.552 - 9}{9} = 0.950 - 1$$

Therefore, the number we want is the antilog of $(0.950 - 1)$. Sliding the hairline over 0.950 on the L scale, we read its antilog, 8.91, on the D scale; and antilog $-1 = 10^{-1}$. So

$$0.356^{\frac{1}{9}} = 8.91 \times 10^{-1}$$

If you're still having trouble, it would be a good idea for you to review the entire chapter.

If this was just a momentary lapse, return to page 223 and select the correct answer.

YOUR ANSWER: Log $0.0648^{\frac{1}{7}} = -0.170$.

Well, yes, but you've missed the point completely. The purpose behind adding zero in the form 10.000 − 10, or 7.000 − 7, is to *avoid* having to work with a negative logarithm.

Let's start over.

We have seen that log 0.0648 = −2 + 0.812, or −1.188. Adding zero in the form 7.000 − 7:

$$\begin{array}{r} 7.000 - 7 \\ -1.188 \\ \hline 5.812 - 7 \end{array}$$

Therefore,

$$\log 0.0648^{\frac{1}{7}} = \frac{\log 0.0648}{7}$$

$$= \frac{5.812 - 7}{7}$$

$$= \frac{5.812}{7} - \frac{7}{7}$$

$$= 0.830 - 1$$

And this is a form we can work with on the L scale, because it gives us a positive numerical factor between 0 and 1.

It should now be evident why we used 7.000 − 7 instead of 10.000 — 10. 7 is evenly divisible by 7, but 10 is not.

It's true, of course, that 0.830 − 1 = −0.170, but that puts us right back where we started. So the final form we want is

$$\log 0.0648^{\frac{1}{7}} = 0.830 - 1$$

Return to page 231 and select the correct answer.

[*from page 227*]

YOUR ANSWER: $1{,}625^{\frac{2}{3}} = 138.2$.

No, this problem is all right. Study the explanation below:

$$\log A^m = m \times \log A$$

$$\log A^{\frac{1}{n}} = \frac{\log A}{n}$$

$$\log A^{\frac{m}{n}} = \frac{m \times \log A}{n}$$

Therefore,

$$\log 1{,}625^{\frac{2}{3}} = \frac{2}{3} \times \log 1{,}625 = \frac{2 \times \log (1.625 \times 10^3)}{3}$$

Since $\log 1.625 = 0.211$ and $\log 10^3 = 3$,

$$\log 1{,}625 = 0.211 + 3$$

and $\log 1{,}625^{\frac{2}{3}} = \dfrac{2 \times (0.211 + 3)}{3} = \dfrac{0.422 + 6}{3} = 0.1406 + 2$

(Use the C and D scales to do the division.) Sliding the hairline over 0.1406 on the L scale, we read 1.382 on the D scale, so the antilog of 0.1406 + 2 (i.e., the number whose logarithm is 0.1406 + 2) is 1.382×10^2, or 138.2. That is the correct answer.

In Chapter 3, you learned that the problem could be done like this:

$$1{,}625^{\frac{2}{3}} = (1{,}625^{\frac{1}{3}})^2$$

We can say that a hairline reading from any number, N, on the K scale to the D scale, will give the cube root of N ($N^{\frac{1}{3}}$). The hairline reading from any number on the D scale to the A scale will give the square of that number. So, if the setting on the D scale is $N^{\frac{1}{3}}$, the reading on the A scale is $(N^{\frac{1}{3}})^2$. Therefore, a reading on the hairline directly from the K to the A scale should give an answer to the two-thirds power. If you set the hairline at 1,625 on the K scale you will read 1,382 on the A scale. And, if you estimate correctly, you will know that the result should be read as 138.2. That checks with what we got above.

Now, return to page 227 and see whether you can find the error.

YOUR ANSWER: $0.356^{\frac{1}{9}} = 9.95 \times 10^{-10}$.

No. Evidently you made a major error, after arriving at the logarithm of your answer.

Let's work the whole problem through.

To begin, we know that:

$$\log 0.356^{\frac{1}{9}} = \frac{\log 0.356}{9} = \frac{\log (3.56 \times 10^{-1})}{9}$$

Setting the hairline at 356 on the D scale, we find on the L scale that $\log 3.56 = 0.552$. The log of 10^{-1} is, of course, -1, so:

$$\log \sqrt[9]{0.356} = \frac{0.552 - 1}{9} = \frac{-0.448}{9}$$

Adding zero in the form $9.000 - 9$ (because we'll have to divide by 9):

$$\begin{array}{r} 9.000 - 9 \\ -0.448 \\ \hline 8.552 - 9 \end{array}$$

So

$$\log 0.356^{\frac{1}{9}} = \frac{8.552}{9} - 9 = 0.950 - 1$$

Sliding the hairline indicator to 0.950 on the L scale, we read 8.91 on the D scale. So the antilog of 0.950 is 8.91. The antilog of -1 is 10^{-1}, of course. So

$$0.356^{\frac{1}{9}} = 8.91 \times 10^{-1}$$

If you're having trouble, it might be a good idea to review this entire chapter. It begins on page 216.

If this was just a momentary lapse, return to page 223 and select the correct answer.

[*from page 227*]

YOUR ANSWER: This solution is incorrect: $84.9^5 = 9.21 \times 10^9$.

Yes, it is.

Here is the correct solution, step by step. First, we factor 84.9 as 8.49×10^1. Then reading from D to L scales, we find that the log of 8.49 is 0.929. Since the log of 10^1 is 1, the log of 84.9 is 0.929 + 1, or 1.929. Next, multiplying 1.929 by 5, using C and D, or CI and D scales, we get $\log (84.9)^5 = 9.645$. Now we need the antilog of 9.645, or 9.000 + 0.645. Sliding the hairline to 0.645 on the L scale, we read the antilog, 4.42, on the D scale. Since antilog $9.000 = 10^9$, $84.9^5 = 4.42 \times 10^9$.

The L scale can also be used as a means of checking problems involving combined operations. Remember, the slide rule is simply a device for physically adding and subtracting distances that represent logarithms. If you know the logs of the numbers in a problem, you can also add and subtract with paper and pencil. If you should want to check a problem that seems inaccurate, you can simply find the logs of all the factors and add or subtract them as appropriate. The result of these manipulations will be the log of the product.

Thus, the problem:

$$\frac{9.22 \times 0.465}{0.943}$$

could be solved, or checked, in the following manner:

$$\begin{array}{lll} \log 9.22 & = 0.965 & \\ +\log 0.465 & = \underline{.668} & \underline{-1} \\ =\log \text{sub-product} & = 1.633 & \\ -\log 0.943 & = \underline{0.975} & \underline{-1} \\ =\log \text{product} & = 0.658 & \end{array}$$

The antilog of 0.658 is 4.55.

The principal uses for the L scale, then, are the computation of problems involving powers not suitable for handling on the A and K scales, and the rough checking of problems solved in the normal manner.

The next chapter is a review in which you will be asked to apply the principles you've learned about slide rule computation to a series of problems. When you've completed the review, you will be introduced, in Chapter 7, to trigonometry.

Go on now to page 239.

CHAPTER 6

Applications

In this chapter, we are going to review the basic slide rule principles, and practice using the rule on some typical problems. So far, we have studied two basic principles:

The first is the notion that distance can be used to represent any measurable quantity, and that by combining distances properly, it is possible to add and subtract the values they represent.

The second principle is that multiplication and division of numbers can be accomplished by adding or subtracting their logarithms, or exponents, according to certain fundamental rules.

By joining these principles we can solve problems like this:

An engineer needs to know whether a certain roll of steel can be shipped on a plane that can accept only 1,600 pounds of additional freight. The specified steel weighs exactly 505 pounds per cubic foot. According to the mill foreman, the steel on the roll to be shipped measures 2,502 feet long, $36\frac{1}{8}$ inches wide, and 0.005 inches thick. Using his slide rule, and the expression

$$\frac{2{,}502 \times 12 \times 36.13 \times 0.005 \times 505}{12^3},$$

the engineer decides that the weight of the roll is under the 1,600 pound limit. Is this decision justified?

Yes, the roll weighs 1,587 pounds. **page 242**

No, the roll might be over the limit. **page 247**

[*from page 247*]

YOUR ANSWER: Yes, barely.

Right. 0.0050 has two figures of accuracy, so the engineer would know that the most the thickness could be is 0.00504 inch. The corresponding weight would be 1,595 pounds, just under the limit, with leeway for a heavy label and a few stamps.

As a general rule, when attacking a calculation like this one, it's best to rearrange the problem for alternate division and multiplication. This will usually eliminate re-indexing, and the opportunity it presents for error. Here is the solution in a minimum number of steps:

1. Rearrange the problem:

$$\frac{2.502 \times \frac{1}{1.44} \times 5.05}{\frac{1}{36.13} \times \frac{1}{5.04}}$$

2. Index the right end of the CI scale at 2.50 on the D scale.
3. Slide the hairline indicator to 1.44 on the CI scale.
4. Shift 3.61 on the CI scale under the hairline.
5. Slide the hairline to 5.05 on the C scale.
6. Shift 5.04 on the CI scale under the hairline. Read 1.595 on the D scale.

Try to rearrange each of the problems below so that it isn't necessary to re-index. Then choose the correct statement:

This problem can't be done without re-indexing:

$$\frac{2{,}470}{39.9 \times 402 \times 0.637} = 0.242.$$ **page 244**

This problem can't be done without re-indexing:

$$1.87 \times 0.743 \times 3{,}641 \times 19.2 \times 102 = 9.91 \times 10^6.$$ **page 248**

Both these problems can be done without re-indexing. **page 251**

YOUR ANSWER: The mass of an electron moving at 2.34×10^{10} cm/sec is 14.8×10^{-28} gm.

Very good indeed!
Substituting given values in the equation:

$$m = \frac{m_0}{\sqrt{1 - \frac{v^2}{c^2}}} = \frac{9.28 \times 10^{-28}}{\sqrt{1 - \frac{(2.34 \times 10^{10})^2}{(3.00 \times 10^{10})^2}}}$$

$$= \frac{9.28 \times 10^{-28}}{\sqrt{1 - \left(\frac{2.34 \times 10^{10}}{3.00 \times 10^{10}}\right)^2}} = \frac{9.28 \times 10^{-28}}{\sqrt{1 - \left(\frac{2.34}{3.00}\right)^2}}$$

1. Slide the hairline to 2.34 on the D scale.
2. Shift 3.00 on the C scale under the hairline.
3. Read 60.8 on the A scale at the index. Then $\left(\frac{2.34}{3.00}\right)^2 = 0.608$, and $m = \frac{9.28 \times 10^{-28}}{\sqrt{1 - 0.608}} = \frac{9.28 \times 10^{-28}}{\sqrt{0.392}}$
4. Slide the hairline to 9.28 on the D scale.
5. Shift 39.2 on the right-hand B scale under the hairline.
6. Read 1.482 on the D scale at the index of the sliding scale.

So the mass is 14.8×10^{-28} gm. Notice that proper use of the approximation methods we've learned was essential in order to place the decimal point correctly.

Here is a one-wrong series using the A and K scale. Which pair contains the error?

$0.452^3 = 0.0923$
$0.000369^2 = 1.36 \times 10^{-7}$ } **page 245**

$181{,}000^{\frac{1}{2}} = 4.25 \times 10^2$
$\sqrt[3]{0.00286} = 0.142$ } **page 249**

$(753 \times 10^8)^{\frac{1}{3}} = 9.10 \times 10^3$
$\sqrt[3]{3{,}970} = 15.83$ } **page 253**

[*from page 239*]

YOUR ANSWER: Yes, the roll weighs 1,587 pounds.

Your calculations are correct, but the roll still might be too heavy. Let's take another look at those measurements.

The roll was reported to be 2,502 feet long. Since it was measured to a precision of one foot, it could be only about 2,501.5 feet long. Or—and this is what we're interested in—it could be as much as 2,502.4 feet long. Similarly, the width of the roll was given as $36\frac{1}{8}$ inches, measured to an eighth of an inch. It might be almost $36\frac{3}{16}$, or, in decimal form, 36.19 inches. Finally, the thickness of the roll was measured as 0.005 inches, accurate to one-thousandth of an inch. It might be very close to 0.0054. This may seem like an error too small to be significant, but an error of 0.0004 inch spread out over the entire roll can make a sizable difference in the weight.

Using these maximum possible measurements to calculate the maximum possible weight of the roll, we find that

$$\frac{2{,}502.4 \times 12 \times 36.19 \times 0.0054 \times 505}{12^3} = 1{,}715$$

So the roll *might* weigh as much as 1,715 pounds, in which case it would be a full 115 pounds over the 1,600-pound limit.

Now, turn to page 239 to select the more appropriate answer.

YOUR ANSWER: Yes, this problem can be worked in two shifts of the sliding scales.

$$\frac{1.688 \times 7.75 \times 8{,}540^{\frac{1}{2}} \times 56.2^{\frac{1}{3}}}{26.5^{\frac{1}{2}}}$$

Good.

In all probability you could have worked this problem longhand in the time it took you to find a two-shift procedure.

Here is one solution requiring just two shifts:

In estimating form:

$$\frac{2 \times 8 \times 18 \times 4}{1} = 1{,}152.$$

Rewritten for alternate division and multiplication:

$$\frac{56.2^{\frac{1}{3}} \times 7.75 \times 8{,}540^{\frac{1}{2}}}{\frac{1}{1.688} \times 26.5^{\frac{1}{2}}} =$$

On the slide rule:

1. Slide the hairline to 56.2 on the center K scale.
2. Shift 1.688 on the CI scale under the hairline.
3. Slide the hairline to 7.75 on the C scale.
4. Shift 26.5 on the right-hand B scale under the hairline.
5. Slide the hairline to 85.4 on the right-hand B scale.
6. Read 9.00 on the D scale.

Then the answer is 900.

Which of these statements is correct? Be sure to read them very carefully.

To find the square root of 66 without the A scale, index 6.6 on the D scale with the left-hand index of the CI scale. Slide the hairline to the right, watching both D and CI scales. Stop at 8.125, the reading on *both* scales. 8.125 is the square root of 66. Similarly, $\sqrt{163} = 40.4$. **page 252**

Occasionally it is desirable to express a decimal fraction as a common fraction. For example, one setting is all that's needed to decide that 0.764 may be represented by $\frac{500}{655}$ or $\frac{378}{495}$ or $\frac{100}{131}$. **page 258**

[*from page 240*]

YOUR ANSWER: This problem can't be done without re-indexing:

$$\frac{2{,}470}{39.9 \times 402 \times 0.637} = 0.242$$

Yes it can.

$$\frac{2{,}470}{39.9 \times 402 \times 0.637} = \frac{2.470 \times 10^3}{3.99 \times 10^1 \times 4.02 \times 10^2 \times 6.37 \times 10^{-1}}$$

$$= \frac{2.470}{3.99 \times 4.02 \times 6.37} \times 10^1$$

In approximation form,

$$\frac{2}{4 \times 4 \times 6} \times 10^1 = \frac{2}{96} \times 10^1 = 0.02 \times 10^1 = 2.0 \times 10^{-1}$$

Rearranging the problem so that it can be done without re-indexing:

$$\frac{2.470}{3.99 \times 4.02 \times 6.37} = \frac{2.470 \times \frac{1}{4.02}}{3.99 \times 6.37}$$

On the slide rule:

1. Slide the hairline to 2.47 on the D scale.
2. Shift 3.99 on the C scale under the hairline.
3. Slide the hairline to 4.02 on the CI scale.
4. Shift 6.37 on the C scale under the hairline. Read 2.42 on the D scale at the index of the C scale.

The final answer is 2.42×10^{-1}, or 0.242.
Return to page 240 and try again.

[*from page 241*]

YOUR ANSWER: One of these solutions is wrong:

$$0.452^3 = 0.0923$$

$$0.000369^2 = 1.36 \times 10^{-7}$$

No, they're both right. Follow the explanations below:

$$0.452^3 = (4.52 \times 10^{-1})^3 = 4.52^3 \times 10^{-3}$$

The cube of 4.52 will be roughly halfway between 64, the cube of 4, and 125, the cube of 5. So the complete answer will be approximately 94×10^{-3}. To find it, set the hairline indicator at 4.52 on the D scale, and read 92.3 on the middle section of the K scale. The answer, then, is 92.3×10^{-3}, or 0.0923.

$$0.000369^2 = (3.69 \times 10^{-4})^2 = 3.69^2 \times 10^{-8}$$

In approximation form, $4^2 \times 10^{-8} = 16 \times 10^{-8}$. For the complete answer, set the hairline indicator at 3.69 on the D scale, and read 13.6 on the A scale. The square of 0.000369, then, is 13.6×10^{-8}, or 1.36×10^{-7}.

Actually, neither of these problems should have given you any trouble. Just remember that the A scale, which gives the squares of the numbers on the D scale, is divided into two identical sections. The first section is read from 1 to 10, and the second is read from 10 to 100. Similarly, the K scale gives the cubes of the numbers on the D scale, and is divided into three identical sections, read from 1 to 10, 10 to 100, and 100 to 1,000.

Now return to page 241 for another try.

[*from page 251*]

YOUR ANSWER: A cubic crate whose volume is 37 cubic feet will go through a door that is 40 inches wide.

No, there is a possibility that it won't. Consider the measurements again:

The volume of the crate is given as 37 cubic feet. Since a third significant figure is not given, we have to assume that it might be as large as 37.4 cubic feet, or as small as 36.6 cubic feet. By the same reasoning, the door might be 40.4 inches wide, or only 39.6 inches wide. We are concerned, of course, with what would happen if the volume of the crate should turn out to be 37.4 cubic feet, and the door only 39.6 inches wide.

If the volume of the crate is 37.4 cubic feet, its side, s, is given by

$$s = \sqrt[3]{V} = \sqrt[3]{37.4} \text{ cubic feet}$$

Setting the hairline indicator at 37.4 on the K scale, we read 3.34 on the D scale. So the length of one side of the crate could be as much as 3.34 feet.

The next step is to convert 39.6 inches, the minimum width of the door, to feet. Since there are 12 inches in a foot, we can write the proportion

$$\frac{39.6 \text{ inches}}{12 \text{ inches}} = \frac{x \text{ feet}}{1 \text{ foot}}$$

Setting 39.6 on the C scale over 12 on the D scale, we read 3.30 on the C scale at the index of the D scale. So 39.6 inches is equivalent to 3.30 feet.

Since the maximum possible length (3.34 feet) of one side of the crate is larger than the minimum possible width (3.30 feet) of the door, it is possible that the crate will not go through the door.

Return to page 251 and try again.

[*from page 239*]

YOUR ANSWER: No, the roll might weigh over 1,600 pounds.

And how!

Using his slide rule, and the values the foreman gave him, the engineer would compute the weight of the roll as 1,587 pounds. But let's look at the measurements he has to work with.

The roll was found to be 2,502 feet long. It was measured to a precision of one foot, so it could be anywhere from 2,501.5 to 2,502.4 feet long. The width was given as $36\frac{1}{8}$ inches, measured to an eighth of an inch. It could be almost $36\frac{3}{16}$ inches, or, in decimal form, 36.19 inches. The most significant difference, however, is in the thickness. It was measured as 0.005, accurate to a thousandth of an inch. It could be as much as 0.0054 inch. Using these maximum possible values to recalculate the weight of the roll,

$$\frac{2{,}502.4 \times 12 \times 36.19 \times 0.0054 \times 505}{12^3} = 1{,}715$$

You are probably wondering why the difference in the thickness should be the most significant. Here's the reason: The length and width were measured with little precision, but they were accurate to *more than three figures.* But the value given for the thickness, while relatively precise, was accurate to only *one* figure.

In general, the answer to a problem is never more accurate than the least accurate data. In this case, the calculated weight of the roll could have varied nearly 300 pounds due to the accuracy of the thickness measurement alone.

If the foreman had reported the thickness as 0.0050 inch, and all other measurements could be assumed accurate, would the engineer be justified in deciding that the roll weighs less than 1,600 pounds?

Yes, barely. **page 240**

No, he still can't be sure. **page 250**

[*from page 240*]

YOUR ANSWER: It is necessary to re-index this problem:

$$1.87 \times 0.743 \times 3{,}641 \times 19.2 \times 102 = 9.91 \times 10^6$$

No, it isn't.

$$1.87 \times 0.743 \times 3{,}641 \times 19.2 \times 102$$
$$= 1.87 \times 7.43 \times 10^{-1} \times 3.641 \times 10^3 \times 1.92 \times 10 \times 1.02 \times 10^2$$
$$= 1.87 \times 7.43 \times 3.641 \times 1.92 \times 1.02 \times 10^5$$

In approximation form,

$$2 \times 7 \times 4 \times 2 \times 1 \times 10^5 = 112 \times 10^5 = 11.2 \times 10^6$$

Rearranging for alternate multiplication and division,

$$\frac{1.87 \times 3.64 \times 1.92}{\dfrac{1}{1.02} \times \dfrac{1}{7.43}}$$

On the slide rule,

1. Index the CI scale at 1.87 on the D scale.
2. Slide the hairline to 3.64 on the C scale.
3. Shift 1.02 on the CI scale under the hairline.
4. Slide the hairline to 1.92 on the C scale.
5. Shift 7.43 on the CI scale under the hairline. Read 9.94 on the D scale at the index of the CI scale.

The complete answer is 9.94×10^6.

Return to page 240 for another try.

[*from page 241*]

YOUR ANSWER: One of these problems is wrong:

$$181{,}000^{\frac{1}{2}} = 4.25 \times 10^2$$

$$\sqrt[3]{0.00286} = 0.142$$

No, they're both all right. Here's the way they go:

$$181{,}000^{\frac{1}{2}} = (18.1 \times 10^4)^{\frac{1}{2}} = 18.1^{\frac{1}{2}} \times 10^2$$

The square root of 18.1 should be slightly more than 4, since $4^2 = 16$, and $5^2 = 25$. For the complete answer, set the hairline indicator at 18.1 on the A scale. (Remember that the A scale is divided into two identical sections. The first section is read from 1 to 10, and the second is read from 10 to 100.) Then 4.25, the square root of 18.1, is on the D scale, underneath the hairline. So the complete answer is 4.25×10^2, or 425.

$$\sqrt[3]{0.00286} = 0.00286^{\frac{1}{3}} = (2.86 \times 10^{-3})^{\frac{1}{3}} = 2.86^{\frac{1}{3}} \times 10^{-1}$$

The cube root of 2.86 will be more than 1, since $1^3 = 1$, but less than 2, since $2^3 = 8$. To find the actual answer, slide the hairline indicator to 2.86 on the K scale. (This position is in the left-hand section of the scale, since the three identical sections of the K scale are read from 1 to 10, 10 to 100, and 100 to 1,000.) Then 1.42, the cube root of 2.86, can be read on the D scale. So the cube root of 0.00286 is 1.42×10^{-1}, or 0.142.

Return to page 241 and try again.

[*from page 247*]

YOUR ANSWER: No, he still can't be sure.

Yes, he can, but not by much. If the thickness is measured at 0.0050 inch, then the most it can be is 0.00504 inch. Using this figure to recalculate the weight of the roll,

$$\frac{2{,}502 \times 12 \times 36.13 \times 0.00504 \times 505}{12^3}$$

$$= \frac{2.502 \times 3.613 \times 5.04 \times 5.05}{1.44} \times 10^1$$

In approximation form,

$$\frac{2 \times 4 \times 5 \times 5}{1} \times 10^1 = 200 \times 10^1 = 2.0 \times 10^3.$$

It is usually best to rearrange this kind of problem for alternate multiplication and division, in order to eliminate re-indexing and the accompanying opportunity for error:

$$\frac{2.502 \times 3.613 \times 5.04 \times 5.05}{1.44} = \frac{2.502 \times \dfrac{1}{1.44} \times 5.05}{\dfrac{1}{36.13} \times \dfrac{1}{5.04}}$$

1. Index the right end of the CI scale at 2.50 on the D scale.
2. Slide the hairline indicator to 1.44 on the CI scale.
3. Shift 3.61 on the CI scale under the hairline.
4. Slide the hairline to 5.05 on the C scale.
5. Shift 5.04 on the CI scale under the hairline. Read 1.595 on the D scale.

Then the answer is 1.595×10^3 pounds, or 1,595 pounds, just under the 1,600-pound limit.

Now turn to page 247 to select the correct answer.

[*from page 240*]

YOUR ANSWER: Both problems can be done without re-indexing.

Right you are. However, as you have probably figured out for yourself, rearranging a problem to avoid re-indexing isn't always worth the trouble. You have to use your own judgment: if you can do the problem, re-indexing just once or so, in half the time it would take you to find an arrangement that will eliminate re-indexing, go ahead. Just remember that, as a rule, avoiding re-indexing eliminates needless opportunity for error.

Now, here are two problems involving the use of the A and K scales. Only one of the two is strictly correct, although neither is grossly wrong. Which problem is correct?

The mass (m_0) of an electron at rest is 9.28×10^{-28} gm. If it is accelerated to a velocity (v) of 2.34×10^{10} cm/sec [the speed of light (c) is 3.00×10^{10} cm/sec], its mass increases to 14.8×10^{-28} gm. Use:

$$m = \frac{m_0}{\sqrt{1 - \frac{v^2}{c^2}}}.$$

page 241

A new washer is being shipped to you. The dealer states that its crate is a cube with a volume of 37 cu. ft. Your door measures 40 inches. Using your slide rule and the formula volume = side^3, you conclude that the machine can be uncrated indoors. **page 246**

[*from page 243*]

YOUR ANSWER: $\sqrt{163} = 40.4$.

This isn't a reasonable answer. If $\sqrt{163} = 40.4$, then 40.4^2 must be 163. But

$$40.4^2 = (4.04 \times 10)^2 = 4.04^2 \times 10^2 = 16.32 \times 10^2 = 1{,}632$$

And clearly $\sqrt{163}$ can't be 4.04, because, as we have just seen, the square of 4.04 is 16.32.

Let's see what went wrong.

You should remember that the first step in taking the square root of a number with the aid of a slide rule is to break the number down into two factors, one a power of 10 whose exponent is a multiple of 2 and the other a number between 1 and 100:

$$163 = 1.63 \times 10^2$$

Then: $$163^{\frac{1}{2}} = (1.63 \times 10^2)^{\frac{1}{2}} = 1.63^{\frac{1}{2}} \times 10$$

The square root of 1.63 must be more than 1, the square root of 1, but it must be less than 2, the square root of 4. The final answer, then, will be between 10 and 20.

Now, set the left index of the C scale at 1.63 on the D scale and start sliding the hairline to the right. Do you see what's happening? The hairline *passes 2* on the D scale without reaching a place where the reading is the same on both the D and CI scales. But we've said that $\sqrt{1.63}$ has to be *less* than 2. The logical conclusion, then, is that we're going in the wrong direction.

Accordingly, let's go to the left. Set the *right* index of the CI scale at 163 on the D scale. Slide the hairline to the *left*, stopping at 1.278, the reading on *both* scales. Then $\sqrt{1.63} = 1.278$, and $\sqrt{163} = 1.278 \times 10 = 12.78$.

This problem illustrates an important point: It's not enough just to follow directions. To come up with the right answer every time you have to understand the principles behind the method. With this in mind, return to page 243 to choose the right answer.

YOUR ANSWER: One of these problems is incorrect:

$$(753 \times 10^8)^{\frac{1}{3}} = 9.10 \times 10^3$$

$$\sqrt[3]{3{,}970} = 15.83$$

Yes. Here they are:
Rewrite 753×10^8 as 75.3×10^9. Then on the slide rule:

1. Slide the hairline indicator to 753 on the center K scale. Remember, it runs from 10 to 100.
2. Read 4.22 on the D scale under the hairline. Since the cube root of 10^9 is 10^3, the cube root of 753×10^8 is 4.22×10^3 not 9.10×10^3 as shown.

The second is correct:
Rewrite $\sqrt[3]{3{,}970}$ as 3.97×10^3. On the slide rule:

1. Slide the hairline to 397 on the left-hand K scale.
2. Read 1.583 on the D scale under the hairline.
   The cube root of 10^3 is 10^1, so the cube root of 3,970 is 1.583×10, or 15.83, as shown.

Finding roots is really pretty easy. But now try this problem:

$$\frac{1.688 \times 7.75 \times 8{,}540^{\frac{1}{2}} \times 56.2^{\frac{1}{3}}}{26.5^{\frac{1}{2}}}$$

Can you do it in two shifts of the sliding scales?

Yes. **page 243**

No. **page 257**

[*from page 258*]

YOUR ANSWER: The balloon will weigh 186 pounds.

No, you've misplaced the decimal point. Perhaps you misread the problem. The balloon is to be made of a plastic weighing 0.00411 pounds per *100 square feet* (not "per square foot").

If the diameter of the balloon is 120 feet, then its area (A) is given by

$$A = \pi \times (120 \text{ feet})^2$$

The weight of the balloon will be found by multiplying its surface area by the weight of the plastic, 0.00411 pounds per 100 square feet, or $\dfrac{0.00411 \text{ lb.}}{100 \text{ ft.}^2}$:

$$\text{wt.} = A \times \frac{0.00411 \text{ lb.}}{100 \text{ ft.}^2} = \pi \times (120 \text{ ft.})^2 \times \frac{0.00411 \text{ lb.}}{100 \text{ ft.}^2}$$

$$= \frac{\pi \times (120 \text{ ft.})^2 \times 0.00411 \text{ lb.}}{100 \text{ ft.}^2}$$

$$= \frac{\pi \times (1.2 \times 10^2 \text{ ft.})^2 \times 4.11 \times 10^{-3} \text{ lb.}}{10^2 \text{ ft.}^2}$$

The ft.^{2} may be canceled, so

$$= \frac{\pi \times 1.2^2 \times 10^4 \cancel{\text{ft.}^2} \times 4.11 \times 10^{-3} \text{ lb.}}{10^2 \cancel{\text{ft.}^2}}$$

$$\text{wt.} = \pi \times 1.2^2 \times 4.11 \times 10^{-1} \text{ lb.}$$

In approximation form,

$$\text{wt.} = 3 \times 1 \times 4 \times 10^{-1} \text{ lb.} = 12 \times 10^{-1} \text{ lb.} = 1.2 \text{ lb.}$$

Rework the problem on your slide rule, and then return to page 258 to choose the correct answer.

[*from page 261*]

YOUR ANSWER: Yes, the problem can be done without re-indexing.

Right. But it isn't as simple as it looks. In order to get the decimal point in the right place, we have to make some changes:

$$\text{wt.} = \pi \times 1.2^2 \times 4.11 \times 10^{-1} \text{ lb.} = \pi \times 0.12^2 \times 41.1 \times 10^0 \text{ lb.},$$

or just $\pi \times 0.12^2 \times 41.1$ lb.

Rearranging for alternate division and multiplication,

$$\text{wt.} = \frac{\pi \times 41.1}{\dfrac{1}{0.12^2}} \text{ lb.}$$

On the slide rule, slide the hairline to π on the A scale, shift 1.2 on the CI scale under the hairline, slide the hairline to 41.1 on the right half of the B scale, and read 1.86 on the A scale.

The conversion from 1.2^2 to $0.12^2 \times 10^2$ is necessary because of the limitations of the B scale. The B scale will not give the square of the reciprocal of a number on the CI scale directly unless the reciprocal is between 1 and 10. $\dfrac{1}{1.2^2}$ is *less* than 1, but $\dfrac{1}{0.12^2}$ is between 1 and 10.

Similarly, to locate 4.11 on the B scale, we must go to the left half of the scale, which in this particular problem turns out to be off the left end of the rule. 41.1, on the other hand, appears on the right half of the B scale, and so is accessible.

The problem below also deals with our hypothetical balloon:

The balloon goes into a circular orbit with an average height of 3,250 miles above the earth. If the diameter of the earth is 7,918 miles, how far does the balloon travel in each revolution? (Use the formula $c = \pi \times d$.)

35,100 miles. **page 259**

45,300 miles. **page 262**

453,000 miles. **page 265**

[*from page 262*]

YOUR ANSWER: This problem is not correctly solved: The formula for the volume of a sphere is $V = \frac{4}{3} \times \pi \times r^3$. If $r = 1.74$ inches, then the volume, V, is 22.1 cubic inches.

Let's check. If $r = 1.74$ inches, then

$$V = \tfrac{4}{3} \times \pi \times (1.74 \text{ inches})^3$$
$$= \tfrac{4}{3} \times \pi \times 1.74^3 \text{ cubic inches}$$

In approximation form,

$$\frac{4 \times \overset{1}{\cancel{3}} \times 2^3}{\underset{1}{\cancel{3}}} \text{ cu. in.} = 4 \times 8 \text{ cu. in.} = 32 \text{ cu. in.}$$

Here is one way to perform the calculation on the slide rule:

1. Slide the hairline indicator to 1.74 on the D scale. Read 5.29 on the left section of the K scale.
2. Index the B scale at 5.29 on the left section of the A scale. (529 on the right section would be 52.9, remember, not 5.29.)
3. Slide the hairline to π on the B scale.
4. Shift 3 on the B scale under the hairline.
5. Slide the hairline to 4 on the B scale. Read 22.1 on the right section of the A scale in line with the hairline.

The complete answer, then, is 22.1 cubic inches; the given solution is correct.

Study this explanation carefully. When you are sure you understand the why and wherefore of the outlined procedure, return to page 262 for another try.

[*from page 253*]

YOUR ANSWER: No, the problem can't be done in two shifts of the sliding scale.

Yes, it can. Let's start at the beginning:

$$\frac{1.688 \times 7.75 \times 8{,}540^{\frac{1}{2}} \times 56.2^{\frac{1}{3}}}{26.5^{\frac{1}{2}}}$$

$$= \frac{1.688 \times 7.75 \times (85.40 \times 10^2)^{\frac{1}{2}} \times 56.2^{\frac{1}{3}}}{26.5^{\frac{1}{2}}}$$

$$= \frac{1.688 \times 7.75 \times 85.4^{\frac{1}{2}} \times 56.2^{\frac{1}{3}}}{26.5^{\frac{1}{2}}} \times 10^1$$

In approximation form:

$$\frac{2 \times 8 \times 9 \times 4}{5} \times 10^1 = \frac{576}{5} \times 10^1 = 115.2 \times 10^1 = 1{,}152$$

Rearranged for alternate multiplication and division:

$$\frac{1.688 \times 7.75 \times 85.4^{\frac{1}{2}} \times 56.2^{\frac{1}{3}}}{26.5^{\frac{1}{2}}} \times 10^1 = \frac{56.2^{\frac{1}{3}} \times 7.75 \times 85.4^{\frac{1}{2}}}{\frac{1}{1.688} \times 26.5^{\frac{1}{2}}} \times 10^1$$

To do the problem in two shifts of the sliding scale:

1. Slide the hairline indicator to 56.2 on the center section of the K scale.
2. *Shift* 1.688 on the CI scale under the hairline.
3. Slide the hairline indicator to 7.75 on the C scale.
4. *Shift* 26.5 on the right-hand section of the B scale under the hairline.
5. Slide the hairline to 85.4 on the right-hand section of the B scale.
6. Read 9.0 on the D scale under the hairline.

The complete answer is 90×10^1, or 900.

When you can do the problem for yourself, return to page 253 to choose the correct answer.

[*from page 243*]

YOUR ANSWER: This statement is correct: One setting is all that's necessary to decide that 0.764 may be represented as $\frac{500}{655}$ or $\frac{378}{495}$ or $\frac{100}{131}$.

Yes, this is a problem in proportion.

Every rectangle whose width is 0.764 times its length is proportional to a rectangle with sides 100 × 131. For such similar rectangles, 0.764 is a constant.

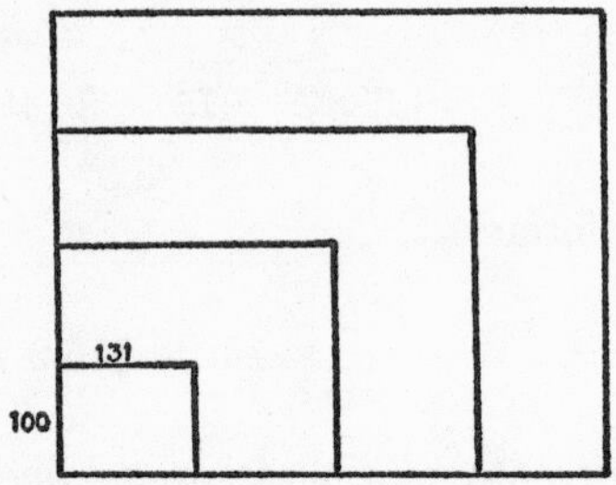

In similar fashion, because all squares are *similar*, the ratio of length to width is always 1: $\frac{\text{length}}{\text{width}} = 1.$

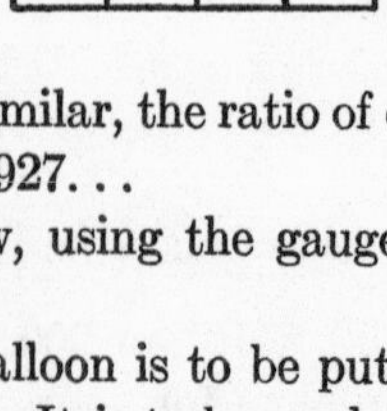

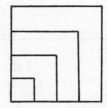

Because all circles are similar, the ratio of circumference to diameter is a constant, $\pi = 3.1415927\ldots$

Try the problem below, using the gauge points on the A and B scales.

An enormous plastic balloon is to be put into orbit and used as a reflector for radio signals. It is to be made of a plastic which weighs 0.00411 pounds per 100 square feet. It is to be 120 feet in diameter, and the formula for its surface area is $A = \pi \times d^2$. What will it weigh?

186 pounds. **page 254**

I need some help. **page 267**

1.86 pounds. **page 261**

[*from page 255*]

YOUR ANSWER: The balloon travels 35,100 miles in each revolution.

No, but your error was not in your slide rule calculations. Here is the problem again:

The balloon goes into a circular orbit with an average height of 3,250 miles above the earth. If the diameter of the earth is 7,918 miles, how far does the balloon travel in each revolution?

You were given the formula $c = \pi \times d$. In order to use this formula, you needed to determine the total diameter of the orbit of the balloon. This is where you made your mistake. Let's look at a diagram:

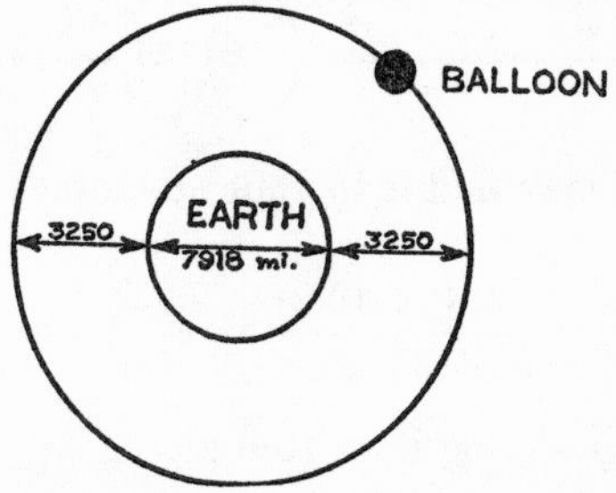

Clearly, the diameter of orbit of the balloon is equal to the diameter of the earth plus *twice* the average height above the earth:

$$d = 7{,}918 \text{ miles} + 3{,}250 \text{ miles} + 3{,}250 \text{ miles} = 14{,}418 \text{ miles}$$

So

$$c = \pi \times 14{,}418 \text{ miles} = \pi \times 1.4418 \times 10^4 \text{ miles}$$

In approximation form,

$$3 \times 1.5 \times 10^4 \text{ miles} = 4.5 \times 10^4 \text{ miles} = 45{,}000 \text{ miles}$$

Finish the problem for yourself, and then return to page 255 to choose the right answer.

[*from page 269*]

YOUR ANSWER: The maximum safe speed is 628 knots.

Yes. This can be done as a simple proportion. The expression is:

$$\frac{5280 \text{ kts.}}{6080 \text{ mph}} = \frac{x \text{ kts.}}{724 \text{ mph}}$$

Here is a sketch of the setting:

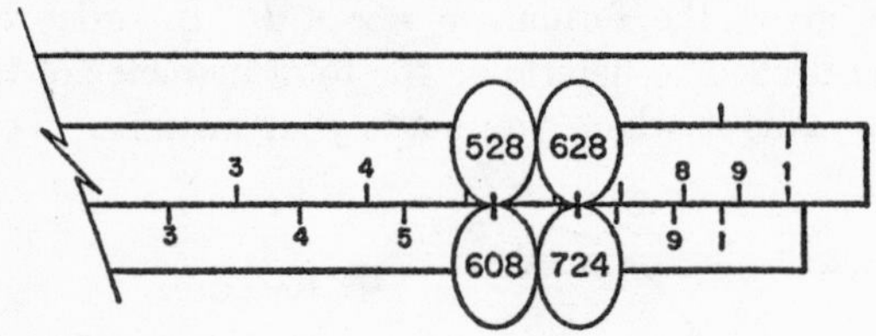

Many times you may find it to your advantage to work a problem like

$$\frac{86.4 \times 19.21}{63.4} = x$$

as a proportion, considering it written as:

$$\frac{x}{86.4} = \frac{19.21}{63.4}$$

Here is a sketch of the single setting required.

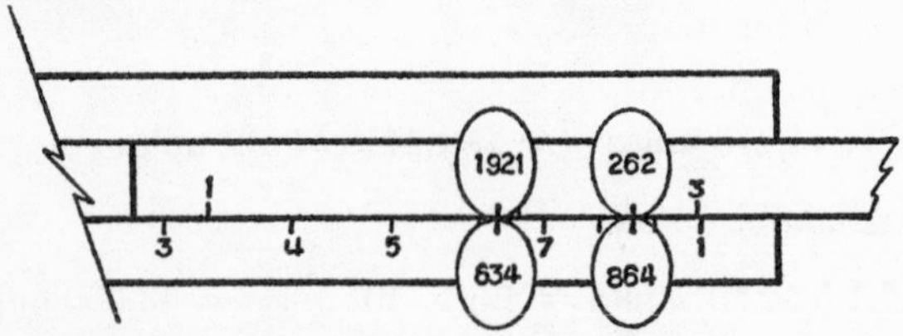

For comparison, here's the way you'd usually have done it:

1. Slide the hairline to 8.64 on the D scale.
2. Shift 6.34 on the C scale under the hairline.
3. Slide the hairline to 1.921 on the C scale.
4. Read 2.62 on the D scale. The answer is 26.2.

Is this also a solution by proportion?

Yes. **page 270** No. **page 276**

YOUR ANSWER: The balloon will weigh 1.86 pounds.

Right. You were given the formula $A = \pi \times d^2$ for the area of a sphere, or, in this case, a balloon. The designated diameter was 120 feet, so

$$A = \pi \times (120\text{ ft.})^2$$

To find the weight of the balloon, we multiply its surface area by the weight of the plastic, 0.00411 pounds per 100 square feet:

$$\text{wt.} = A \times \frac{0.00411\text{ lb.}}{100\text{ ft.}^2} = \pi \times (120\text{ ft.})^2 \times \frac{0.00411\text{ lb.}}{100\text{ ft.}^2}$$

$$= \frac{\pi \times 1.2^2 \times 10^4\text{ ft.}^2 \times 4.11 \times 10^{-3}\text{ lb.}}{10^2\text{ ft.}^2}$$

$$= \pi \times 1.2^2 \times 4.11 \times 10^{-1}\text{ lb.}$$

In approximation form:

$$\text{wt.} = 3 \times 1 \times 4 \times 10^{-1}\text{ lb.} = 12 \times 10^{-1}\text{ lb.} = 1.2\text{ lb.}$$

On the slide rule:

1. Index the B scale at π on the A scale.
2. Slide the hairline indicator to 1.2 on the C scale.
3. Re-index the B scale at the hairline.
4. Slide the hairline to 4.11 on the B scale. Read 18.6 on the A scale under the hairline.

So the complete answer is 18.6×10^{-1} lb., or 1.86 lb.

As we have seen before, it is usually advisable to avoid re-indexing. Can this problem be done without re-indexing?

Yes. **page 255**

No. **page 263**

[*from page 255*]

YOUR ANSWER: The balloon travels 45,300 miles in each revolution.

Of course. The diameter of the balloon's orbit is equal to the diameter of the earth plus twice the average distance above the earth:

$$d = 7{,}918 \text{ miles} + 3{,}250 \text{ miles} + 3{,}250 \text{ miles} = 14{,}418 \text{ miles.}$$

The distance traveled in one revolution is equal to the circumference of the orbit. The formula for the circumference of a circle is $c = \pi \times d$. In this case,

$$c = \pi \times 14{,}418 \text{ miles} = \pi \times 1.4418 \times 10^4 \text{ miles}$$

In approximation form,

$$3 \times 1.5 \times 10^4 \text{ miles} = 4.5 \times 10^4 \text{ miles}$$

Indexing the C scale at π on the D scale and sliding the hairline to 1.442 on the C scale, we read 4.53 on the D scale. So the distance traveled in each revolution is 4.53×10^4 miles, or 45,300 miles.

Below are three more problems in which π appears. Which of the solutions is *wrong?*

The formula for the volume of a sphere is $V = \frac{4}{3} \times \pi \times r^3$. If r is 1.74 inches, then the volume, V, is 22.1 cubic inches. **page 256**

The surface area of a sphere is given by the formula $A = \pi \times d^2$. If $d = 43.1$ inches, then $A = 1{,}858$ square inches. **page 266**

The volume of a cone is given by the formula $V = \frac{\pi}{3} \times r^2 \times h$. If $r = 10.5$ inches and $h = 6.26$ inches, then $V = 724$ cubic inches. **page 268**

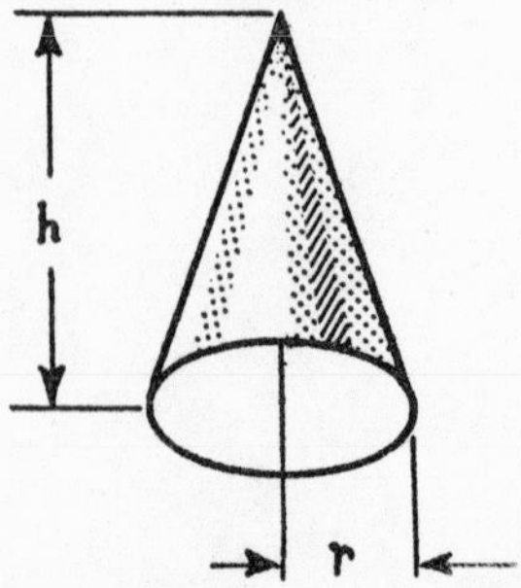

[*from page 261*]

YOUR ANSWER: No, the problem cannot be done without re-indexing.

Yes, it can, but we have to know exactly what we're doing. In its simplest form,

$$\text{wt.} = \pi \times 1.2^2 \times 4.11 \times 10^{-1} \text{ lb.}$$

This can be written as

$$\text{wt.} = \frac{\pi \times 4.11}{\frac{1}{1.2^2}} \times 10^{-1} \text{ lb.}$$

To do this problem on the slide rule, we would first slide the hairline to π on the A scale. Then we would probably shift 12 on the CI scale under the hairline, thinking that dividing by 1.2 on the CI scale would be equivalent to dividing by the reciprocal of 1.2^2 on the B scale. But there is a difficulty here. The B scale gives the square of the reciprocal of a CI number directly if the reciprocal is between 1 and 10. The value of $\frac{1}{1.2^2}$, on the other hand, is *less* than 1. However, we can change the form of the number so that the reciprocal is between 1 and 10:

$$1.2^2 = (0.12 \times 10)^2 = 0.12^2 \times 10^2,$$

so

$$\text{wt.} = \pi \times 0.12^2 \times 4.11 \times 10^1 \text{ lb.}$$

At this point, another problem comes into sight. After 1.2 on the CI scale is aligned with π on the A scale, we want to slide the hairline to 4.11 on the B scale. But 4.11 on the B scale is on the left section of the scale, which turns out to be off the left end of the rule. So we perform another trick: $4.11 = 41.1 \times 10^{-1}$, so

$$\text{wt.} = \pi \times 0.12^2 \times 41.1 \times 10^0 \text{ lb.} = \frac{\pi \times 41.1}{\frac{1}{0.12^2}} \times 1 \text{ lb.}$$

The answer, 1.86, can then be read on the left section of the A scale, with the decimal point in the right place.

Now return to page 261 to choose the correct answer.

[*from page 269*]

YOUR ANSWER: 854 knots is the maximum safe speed of the aircraft.

Sorry, it isn't.

Try this approach:

There is some speed in knots, say x knots, that is exactly the same as 724 miles per hour. That is:

$$x \text{ knots} = 724 \text{ mph}$$

Or, remembering that a knot is a nautical mile per hour,

$$\frac{x \text{ n. mi.}}{\text{hr.}} = \frac{724 \text{ mi.}}{\text{hr.}}$$

For this to be a proper equality, the units should be the same on both sides. Since nautical miles are not equal to statute miles, we must convert so that the same units appear on both sides.

There is no trick to this. You've already done it, in fact. A statute mile is shorter than a nautical mile:

$$\frac{1 \text{ mi.}}{1 \text{ n. mi.}} = \frac{5280 \text{ ft.}}{6080 \text{ ft.}}, \quad \text{so} \quad 1 \text{ mi.} = \frac{5280}{6080} \times 1 \text{ n. mi.}$$

Substituting this value for 1 mile in the previous expression, the result is both a proper equality, and an equation from which the answer can be readily found:

$$\frac{x \text{ n. mi.}}{\text{hr.}} = \frac{\frac{5280}{6080} \times 724 \text{ n. mi.}}{\text{hr.}}$$

or, since a knot is a nautical mile per hour,

$$x \text{ kts.} = \frac{5280}{6080} \times 724 \text{ kts.}$$

Complete this calculation, and if necessary, reread the explanation before returning to page 269 to choose the right answer.

YOUR ANSWER: The balloon travels 453,000 miles in each revolution.

Evidently you did realize that the diameter of the orbit of the balloon is equal to the diameter of the earth plus twice the average distance above the earth. That is,

$$d = 7{,}918 \text{ miles} + 3{,}250 \text{ miles} + 3{,}250 \text{ miles} = 14{,}418 \text{ miles}$$

But somewhere along the line you managed to acquire an extra power of 10. Follow the explanation below and try to see where you went wrong.

The given formula is $c = \pi \times d$, so the distance traveled by the balloon in one revolution is

$$c = \pi \times 14{,}418 \text{ miles} = \pi \times 1.4418 \times 10^4 \text{ miles}$$

In approximation form,

$$3 \times 1.5 \times 10^4 \text{ miles} = 4.5 \times 10^4 \text{ miles} = 45{,}000 \text{ miles}$$

So the answer should be roughly 45,000 miles, *not* 450,000 miles. For the complete answer:

1. Index the B scale at π on the D scale.
2. Slide the hairline indicator to 1.442 on the C scale.
3. Read 4.53 on the D scale in line with the hairline.

So the final answer is 4.53×10^4 miles, or 45,300 miles.

When you are sure you understand your error, return to page 255 to select the correct answer.

[*from page 262*]

YOUR ANSWER: This problem is incorrectly solved: The surface area of a sphere is given by the formula $A = \pi \times d^2$. If $d = 43.1$ inches, then $A = 1{,}858$ square inches.

You're right; the solution is wrong. Here's the way it should have gone:

$$A = \pi \times (43.1 \text{ in.})^2 = \pi \times (4.31 \times 10 \text{ in.})^2 = \pi \times 4.31^2 \times 10^2 \text{ in.}$$

Since

$$3 \times 4^2 \times 10^2 \text{ in.} = 3 \times 16 \times 10^2 \text{ in.} = 48 \times 10^2 \text{ in.},$$

the complete answer should be roughly 48×10^2 sq. in., or 4,800 sq. in.

On the slide rule:

1. Shift the left-hand B scale index to π on the A scale.
2. Slide the hairline to 4.31 on the C scale.
3. Read 58.4 on the A scale.

Then $A = 5{,}840$ sq. in.

The answer given, 1,858, is simply d^2; π was omitted from the computation.

Quite often you will find it necessary to convert a figure in one system of units into another system of units, or to different units in a given system.

Here is the area of the sphere found above, 5,840 square inches, expressed in terms of square feet and square centimeters. Check each for accuracy. Remember, there are 12 inches to a foot and 1 inch is equivalent to 2.54 centimeters.

$$5{,}840 \text{ square inches} = 40.6 \text{ sq. ft.} = 37{,}600 \text{ cm}^2.$$

These are both correct. **page 269**

There is at least one error. **page 275**

[*from page 258*]

YOUR ANSWER: I need some help.

Let's work it out logically. Here's the problem again:

An enormous plastic balloon is to be put into orbit. It is to be made of a plastic which weighs 0.00411 pound per 100 square feet. It is to be 120 feet in diameter, and the formula for its surface area is: $A = \pi \times d^2$. What will be its weight?

If the diameter of the balloon is 120 feet, then its area is

$$A = \pi \times (120 \text{ feet})^2$$

The weight of the balloon will be found by multiplying its surface area by the weight of the plastic, 0.00411 pound per 100 square feet:

$$\text{wt.} = A \times \frac{0.00411 \text{ lb.}}{100 \text{ ft.}^2} = \pi \times (120 \text{ ft.})^2 \times \frac{0.00411 \text{ lb.}}{100 \text{ ft.}^2}$$

$$= \frac{\pi \times (120 \text{ ft.})^2 \times 0.00411 \text{ lb.}}{100 \text{ ft.}^2}$$

$$= \frac{\pi \times (1.2 \times 10^2 \text{ ft.})^2 \times 4.11 \times 10^{-3} \text{ lb.}}{10^2 \text{ ft.}^2}$$

The ft.^{2} may be canceled, so

$$= \frac{\pi \times 1.2^2 \times 10^4 \cancel{\text{ft.}^2} \times 4.11 \times 10^{-3} \text{ lb.}}{10^2 \cancel{\text{ft.}^2}}$$

$$\text{wt.} = \pi \times 1.2^2 \times 4.11 \times 10^{-1} \text{ lb.}$$

In approximation form:

$$\text{wt.} = 3 \times 1 \times 4 \times 10^{-1} \text{ lb.} = 12 \times 10^{-1} \text{ lb.} = 1.2 \text{ lb.}$$

Try to work the rest of the problem for yourself. Then return to page 258 to choose the correct answer.

[*from page 262*]

YOUR ANSWER: This problem is incorrectly solved: The volume of a cone is given by the formula $V = \frac{\pi}{3} \times r^2 \times h$. If $r = 10.5$ inches and $h = 6.26$ inches, then $V = 724$ cubic inches.

Let's work the problem from the beginning. If $r = 10.5$ in., and $h = 6.26$ in., then

$$V = \frac{\pi}{3} \times (10.5 \text{ in.})^2 \times 6.26 \text{ in.}$$

$$= \frac{\pi}{3} \times (1.05 \times 10 \text{ in.})^2 \times 6.26 \text{ in.}$$

$$= \frac{\pi}{3} \times 1.05^2 \times 6.26 \times 10^2 \text{ cu. in.}$$

In approximation form:

$$\frac{\overset{1}{\cancel{3}}}{\underset{1}{\cancel{3}}} \times 1 \times 6 \times 10^2 \text{ cu. in.} = 6 \times 10^2 \text{ cu. in.} = 600 \text{ cu. in.}$$

On the slide rule:

1. Index the B scale at π on the A scale.
2. Slide the hairline indicator to 1.05 on the C scale.
3. Shift 3 on the B scale (3 is on the left section of the scale) under the hairline.
4. Slide the hairline to 6.26 on the B scale (6.26 will be on the left section of the scale). Read 7.24 on the A scale.

So the complete answer is 7.24×10^2 cu. in., or 724 cu. in. And this, of course, is the answer that was given.

When you understand the procedure that was used to get the answer, return to page 262 for another try.

YOUR ANSWER: These are both correct:

$$5{,}840 \text{ square inches} = 40.5 \text{ ft.}^2 = 37{,}600 \text{ cm.}^2$$

Very good.

While conversion of units is only partly a slide rule problem, it is important enough to justify practice whenever possible.

Let's assume the sphere we've been dealing with is a newly discovered planetoid, and the Department of Agriculture is interested in recording its acreage.

Reference to a list of conversion factors discloses that 1 acre equals 4.3560×10^4 square feet. The area of the sphere is 5,840 square inches, so it must first be converted to square feet. There are 144 square inches per square foot, so it will be necessary to divide:

$$\text{in.}^2 \div \frac{\text{in.}^2}{\text{ft.}^2} = \overset{1}{\cancel{\text{in.}^2}} \times \frac{\text{ft.}^2}{\underset{1}{\cancel{\text{in.}^2}}} = \text{ft.}^2$$

Once again, to get acres:

$$\text{ft.}^2 \div \frac{\text{ft.}^2}{\text{acres}} = \overset{1}{\cancel{\text{ft.}^2}} \times \frac{\text{acres}}{\underset{1}{\cancel{\text{ft.}^2}}} = \text{acres}$$

Combined in a single expression, here is the solution:

$$\overset{1}{5{,}840 \text{ in.}^2} \times \frac{1\,\overset{1}{\cancel{\text{ft.}^2}}}{144\,\underset{1}{\cancel{\text{in.}^2}}} \times \frac{1 \text{ acre}}{4.36 \times 10^4\,\underset{1}{\cancel{\text{ft.}^2}}} = 9.31 \times 10^{-4} \text{ acres}$$

The knot is a unit of speed equal to *one nautical mile per hour*. The nautical mile is 6,080 feet instead of 5,280 feet, which is a statute mile. If the maximum safe speed an aircraft is built to attain is 724 miles per hour, and its indicators read in knots, what figure in knots should be used?

628 knots. **page 260**

854 knots. **page 264**

Neither of these; the answer should be in knots per hour. **page 272**

I'm not sure how to start. **page 279**

[*from page 260*]

YOUR ANSWER: Yes, this is also a solution by proportion.

That's right.

In a sense, every solution can be considered a proportion.

In this case the proportion is:

$$\frac{63.4}{86.4} = \frac{19.21}{x}; \qquad x = 26.2$$

The principal difference is that in a proportion solution, the answer appears most frequently on the C scale, while the method of alternate division and multiplication usually gives the answer on the D scale. Obviously this is immaterial.

The L scale has been introduced primarily as an aid in checking calculations using tables of logarithms. It can also be used to find roots of equations of the sort represented by this example:

$$x^5 = 8.46$$

Solving for log x:

$$\log x = \tfrac{1}{5} \log 8.46$$

From the L scale, the log of 8.46 is 0.927. Taking one-fifth of this,

$$\log x = 0.1854$$

Again referring to the L scale, we find that the antilog of 0.1854 (i.e., the number whose log is 0.1854) is 1.53. So

$$x = 8.46^{\frac{1}{5}} = 1.53$$

Equations of this sort are not frequently found in most fields. However, should you find that they do crop up with regularity, you might consider the purchase of a log-log slide rule, which has scales especially designed for such operations.

How about this? If $x^6 = 75{,}300{,}000$, then $x = 13.6$.

This is correct. **page 274**

This is not correct. **page 277**

I don't know where to start. **page 282**

[*from page 277*]

YOUR ANSWER: $\log 8.7018 = 0.939574$.

Hold it! You don't quite have the idea. Let's start over.

Knowing that $\qquad \log 8.7010 = 0.93957,$

and $\qquad \log 8.7020 = 0.93962,$

we want to determine the log of 8.7018. Now, the 8 in the fifth figure of 8.7018 is eight-tenths of 10, the difference between 10 and 20. So the fifth figure of the logarithm we want will be eight-tenths of the way between 57 and 62. Perhaps you can see it more clearly like this:

$$\left.\begin{array}{l}\left.\begin{array}{l}8.7010\\ 8.7018\end{array}\right\}8\\ 8.7020\end{array}\right\}10 \qquad \left.\begin{array}{l}\log 8.7010 = 0.93957\\ \\ \log 8.7020 = 0.93962\end{array}\right\}5$$

In other words, we need to add some number to the fifth figure of 0.93957, the logarithm of 8.7010. Let's call the number to be added x. Then we can write the proportion

$$\frac{8}{10} = \frac{x}{5}$$

from which we see that $x = 4$. *Adding* 4 to the fifth figure of 0.93957 (*not* tacking 4 on to the end of the logarithm, as you did), or, more precisely, adding 0.00004 to the logarithm, we get:

$$\begin{array}{r}0.93957\\ +\ \underline{0.00004}\\ 0.93961\end{array}$$

So the log of 8.7018 is 0.93961.

Study this explanation until you feel reasonably sure you know what's happening. Then return to page 277 to choose the right answer.

[*from page 269*]

YOUR ANSWER: Neither of these; the answer should be in knots per hour.

No, it shouldn't. A knot is defined as *a nautical mile per hour*. Five knots, for example, means *5 nautical miles per hour*, not just *5 nautical miles.*

With this in mind, let's tackle the problem again.

We are looking for the speed in knots—call it x knots—that is equivalent to 724 miles per hour. In other words, x knots = 724 miles per hour, or

$$\frac{x\text{ n. mi.}}{\text{hr.}} = \frac{724\text{ mi.}}{\text{hr.}}$$

Now, since 1 mi. = 5,280 ft., and 1 n. mi. = 6,080 ft.,

$$\frac{1\text{ mi.}}{1\text{ n. mi.}} = \frac{5{,}280\text{ ft.}}{6{,}080\text{ ft.}},$$

which becomes

$$1\text{ mi.} = \frac{5{,}280}{6{,}080} \times 1\text{ n. mi.}$$

So we can substitute $\frac{5{,}280}{6{,}080} \times 1$ n. mi. for 1 mile in the expression $\frac{x\text{ n. mi.}}{\text{hr.}} = \frac{724\text{ mi.}}{\text{hr.}}$, getting

$$\frac{x\text{ n. mi.}}{\text{hr.}} = \frac{\frac{5{,}280}{6{,}080} \times 724\text{ n. mi.}}{\text{hr.}}$$

or, more simply,

$$x\text{ knots} = \frac{5{,}280}{6{,}080} \times 724\text{ knots.}$$

Complete the calculation. Then return to page 269 to select the right answer.

YOUR ANSWER: Log 8.7018 = 0.93961.

Good.

Here again, the principle of proportion is the key.

$$10\left\{\begin{matrix} 8\left\{\begin{matrix}\log 8.7010 = 0.93957\\ \log 8.7018 = 0.93961\end{matrix}\right\}4 \\ \\ \log 8.7020 = 0.93962\end{matrix}\right\}5$$

Since the number given, 8.7018, is eight-tenths of the way between the last figures of the table values, its logarithm is also at about eight-tenths of the interval between the logs of these values.

$$\frac{x}{5} = \frac{8}{10}$$

A similar example from the other end of the tables will give you an idea of the value of the slide rule in interpolation: Find log 1.2157.

From the tables:

$$\log 1.2150 = 0.08458$$

$$\log 1.2160 = 0.08493$$

The difference is found to be 0.00035, or 35 in the fifth figure. Multiplying 35 by 0.7, the proportional increase is 24.5 or 25. Then

$$\log 1.2157 = 0.08458 + 0.00025 = 0.08483$$

Frequently the problem is reversed: given the log of a number, find the number.

As an example of this sort of problem, what is the antilog of 0.08467?

Antilog 0.08467 = 1.2153. **page 278**

Antilog 0.08467 = 1.2157. **page 280**

I don't understand. **page 283**

[*from page 270*]

YOUR ANSWER: It's correct that if $x^6 = 75{,}300{,}000$, then $x = 13.6$.

No, it's wrong. Follow the procedure below, and try to discover where you got lost.

If $x^6 = 75{,}300{,}000$, then

$$\log x^6 = \log 75{,}300{,}000$$

$$6 \times \log x = \log 75{,}300{,}000$$

$$\log x = \frac{\log 75{,}300{,}000}{6}$$

$$\log x = \frac{\log 7.53 + \log 10^7}{6}$$

Setting the hairline at 7.53 on the D scale, we read 0.877 on the L scale, so

$$\log x = \frac{0.877 + 7}{6}$$

$$\log x = \frac{7.877}{6}$$

$$\log x = 1.313$$

Therefore, $x = \text{antilog } 1.313$

If this confuses you, remember that the *antilog* of 1.313 is simply the number whose logarithm is 1.313. $1.313 = 0.313 + 1$, so we know that

$$x = 10 \times \text{antilog } 0.313.$$

This should make sense to you, because 10 is the number whose logarithm is 1, and antilog 0.313 is the number whose logarithm is 0.313. To find the antilog of 0.313, just set the hairline at 0.313 on the L scale, and read the antilog on the D scale.

Complete the problem and then return to page 270 to choose the right answer.

[*from page 266*]

YOUR ANSWER: There is at least one error in the expression

$$5{,}840 \text{ sq. in.} = 40.6 \text{ sq. ft.} = 37{,}600 \text{ sq. cm.}$$

Sorry, but both of these relationships are right. Let's check them out.

First, there are 12 inches to 1 foot, which means that 1 square foot, or 1 ft.^{2}, is equal to 12 in. $\times$ 12 in., or 144 in.^{2}. Therefore, if we divide 5,840 in.^{2} by 144 in.^{2}, the result will be the number of square feet in 5,840 square inches.

In proportion form, $\dfrac{5{,}840 \text{ in.}^2}{144 \text{ in.}^2} = \dfrac{x \text{ ft.}^2}{1 \text{ ft.}^2}$

Estimating the answer, $\dfrac{6 \times 10^3}{1.5 \times 10^2} = 4.0 \times 10^1 = 40$

On the slide rule,

1. Slide the hairline indicator to 1.44 on the D scale.
2. Shift 5.84 on the C scale under the hairline, and read 4.06 on the C scale at the index of the D scale.

So the complete answer is 40.6 ft.^{2}, as given.

Similarly, there are 2.54 centimeters to an inch, so 1 in.^{2} is equivalent to (2.54 cm.)^2, or 2.54^2 cm.^{2}. The ratio of 5,840 in.^{2} to 1 in.^{2} must be equal to the ratio of the number of centimeters in 5,840 in.^{2} to 2.54^2 cm.^{2}, the number of square centimeters in 1 in.^{2}:

$$\frac{5{,}840 \text{ in.}^2}{1 \text{ in.}^2} = \frac{x \text{ cm.}^2}{2.54^2 \text{ cm.}^2}, \quad \text{or} \quad x \text{ cm.}^2 = 5{,}840 \times 2.54^2 \text{ cm.}^2$$

Complete this operation on your slide rule. Then return to page 266 to choose the correct answer.

[*from page 260*]

YOUR ANSWER: **No, this is not a solution by proportion.**

Isn't it? Let's review the directions given:

1. Slide the hairline to 8.64 on the D scale.
2. Shift 6.34 on the C scale under the hairline.
3. Slide the hairline to 1.921 on the C scale. Read 2.62 on the D scale.

Now look at a diagram showing the setting that is the result of this procedure:

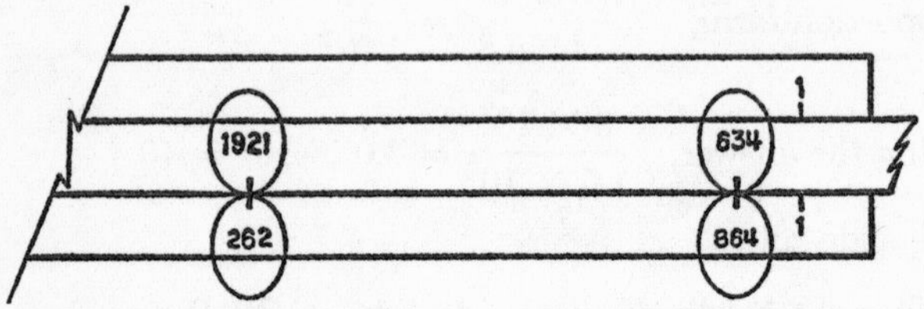

In this setting, 6.34 on the C scale is over 8.64 on the D scale, and 1.921 on the C scale is over 2.62 on the D scale. Compare this setting with the first one we looked at:

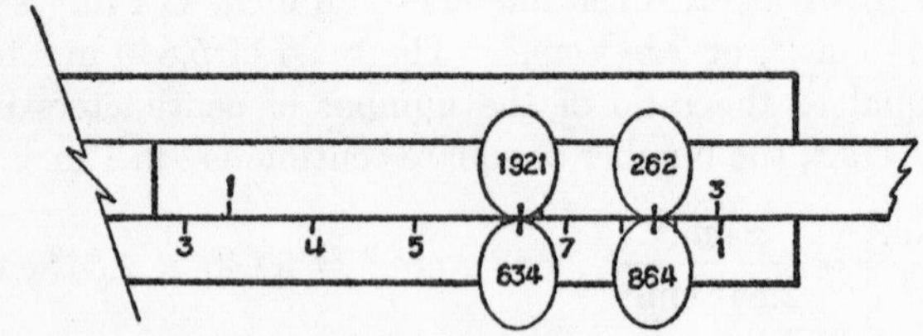

You should be able to see that the top setting is essentially the same as the bottom one, but with the roles of the C and D scales reversed. So the procedure you were asked about can be considered a solution by proportion.

Study the diagrams until you're sure you understand the relationship between them. Then return to page 260 to choose the correct answer.

[*from page 270*]

YOUR ANSWER: $(13.6)^6 \neq 75{,}300{,}000$.

Yes, there is an error.
Writing $x^6 = 75{,}300{,}000$ in terms of logs:

$$6 \times \log x = \log 75{,}300{,}000$$

$$\log x = \tfrac{1}{6} \log 75{,}300{,}000$$

From the L scale, log (7.53×10^7) is 7.876. Dividing by 6:

$$\log x = 1.313$$

Looking up 0.313 on the L scale, we read 2.055, or, to three figures, 2.06, on the D scale. So $x = 2.06 \times 10$, or 20.6, and

$$20.6^6 = 75{,}300{,}000$$

Most tables of logarithms used are printed to five-figure accuracy; the logarithms are called five-place logarithms. Data which is itself given to five figures can be operated on with no significant loss of accuracy, although it is necessary to *interpolate* to arrive at the fifth figure.

Interpolate is virtually synonymous with *estimate* in the sense we've used the term. With the slide rule, you've had to estimate the third figure by mentally dividing the space between marks and gauging where the hairline lies in relation to them.

A similar procedure is used with log tables. For instance, suppose we want to find the log of 8.7018. From a log table, we find:

$$\log 8.7010 = 0.93957$$

$$\log 8.7020 = 0.93962$$

Bearing in mind that the difference in the logs is 5 in the fifth figure, and that the number whose log you are trying to find is eight-tenths of the way between the given values, 8.7010 and 8.7020, what is its log?

log 8.7018 = 0.939574. **page 271**

log 8.7018 = 0.93961. **page 273**

I need some help. **page 281**

[*from page 273*]

YOUR ANSWER: The antilog of 0.08467 is 1.2153.

Yes.

This log differs from the preceding value by 9 in the fifth figure. Since the interval is 35, its antilog will be $\frac{9}{35}$ of the distance between 1.2150 and 1.2160. The proportion is:

$$\frac{x}{10} = \frac{9}{35}$$

Solving this gives $x = 2.6$ or 3 in the fifth figure. Adding this amount, the antilog of 0.08467 is 1.2153.

$$\log 1.2150 = 0.08458$$

$$\log 1.2153 = 0.08467$$

$$\log 1.2160 = 0.08493$$

By now, you should have an excellent grasp of the principles on which the slide rule is based, and considerable practice in the use of the primary scales as well. In addition, you have used the slide rule in applications similar to those which are likely to arise in the course of your studies or work.

The remainder of this book concerns itself with the application of the basic slide rule principles to trigonometry, for which the rule is admirably suited.

Again, no previous experience with the subject matter is assumed. The very fact that you've come this far is enough to assure you that trigonometry will hold no terrors for you. Even though you may never again use the slide rule in similar situations, the practice the concluding chapters will afford is sufficient justification to continue. After all, practice is now the only limiting factor in your mastery of the slide rule.

Chapter 7 begins on page 284.

[*from page 269*]

YOUR ANSWER: I'm not sure how to start.

Try this approach:

There is some speed in knots, say x knots, that is exactly the same as 724 miles per hour. That is:

$$x \text{ knots} = 724 \text{ mph}$$

Or, remembering that a knot is a nautical mile per hour,

$$\frac{x \text{ n. mi.}}{\text{hr.}} = \frac{724 \text{ mi.}}{\text{hr.}}$$

For this to be a proper equality, the units should be the same on both sides. Since nautical miles are not equal to statute miles, we must convert so that the same units appear on both sides.

There is no trick to this. You've already done it, in fact. A statute mile is shorter than a nautical mile:

$$\frac{1 \text{ mi.}}{1 \text{ n. mi.}} = \frac{5{,}280 \text{ ft.}}{6{,}080 \text{ ft.}}, \quad \text{so} \quad 1 \text{ mi.} = \frac{5{,}280}{6{,}080} \times 1 \text{ n. mi.}$$

Substituting this value for 1 mile in the previous expression, the result is both a proper equality, and an equation from which the answer can be readily found:

$$\frac{x \text{ n. mi.}}{\text{hr.}} = \frac{\frac{5{,}280}{6{,}080} \times 724 \text{ n. mi.}}{\text{hr.}}$$

or, since a knot is a nautical mile per hour,

$$x \text{ kts.} = \frac{5{,}280}{6{,}080} \times 724 \text{ kts.}$$

Complete this calculation, and if necessary, reread the explanation before returning to page 269 to choose the right answer.

[*from page 273*]

YOUR ANSWER: The antilog of 0.08467 is 1.2157.

No, you made a slip. Here is the whole procedure.

Knowing that $\log 1.2150 = 0.08558,$

and $\log 1.2160 = 0.08493,$

we want to find the number whose logarithm is 0.08467.

Since $93 - 58 = 35,$

and $67 - 58 = 9,$

the number will be $\frac{9}{35}$ of the way between 1.2150 and 1.2160. The proportion we need is:

$$\frac{x}{10} = \frac{9}{35}$$

From this we see that $x = 2.57$, or, rounded off to two figures, $x = 2.6$. So we should add 2.6 to the fifth figure of 1.2150 (not subtract it from the fifth figure of 1.2160). What we are really doing, of course, is adding 0.00026 to the entire number:

$$\begin{array}{r} 1.2150 \\ +\ 0.00026 \\ \hline 1.21526 \end{array}$$

So the antilog of 0.08467 is 1.2153, rounded off to five-figure accuracy.

Study this explanation carefully before you return to page 273 to answer the question correctly.

YOUR ANSWER: I need some help.

Well, let's start at the beginning.

Knowing that $\log 8.7010 = 0.93957,$

and $\log 8.7020 = 0.93962,$

we want to determine the log of 8.7018. Now, the 8 in the fifth figure of 8.7018 is eight-tenths of 10, the difference between 10 and 20. So the fifth figure of the logarithm we want will be eight-tenths of the way between 57 and 62. Perhaps you can see it more clearly like this:

$$\left.\begin{array}{l} \left.\begin{array}{l} 8.7010 \\ 8.7018 \end{array}\right\} 8 \\ 8.7020 \end{array}\right\} 10 \qquad \left.\begin{array}{l} \log 8.7010 = 0.93957 \\ \\ \log 8.7020 = 0.93962 \end{array}\right\} 5$$

In other words, we need to add some number to the fifth figure of 0.93957, the logarithm of 8.7010. Let's call the number to be added x. Then we can write the proportion

$$\frac{8}{10} = \frac{x}{5}$$

from which we see that $x = 4$. *Adding* 4 to the fifth figure of 0.93957 or, more precisely, adding 0.00004 to the logarithm, we get:

$$\begin{array}{r} 0.93957 \\ +\ \underline{0.00004} \\ 0.93961 \end{array}$$

So the log of 8.7018 is 0.93961.

Study this explanation until you feel reasonably sure you know what's happening. Then return to page 277 to choose the right answer.

[*from page 270*]

YOUR ANSWER: I don't know where to start.

If $x^6 = 75{,}300{,}000$, then

$$\log x^6 = \log 75{,}300{,}000$$

$$6 \times \log x = \log 75{,}300{,}000$$

$$\log x = \frac{\log 75{,}300{,}000}{6}$$

$$\log x = \frac{\log 7.53 + \log 10^7}{6}$$

Setting the hairline at 7.53 on the D scale, we read 0.877 on the L scale, so

$$\log x = \frac{0.877 + 7}{6}$$

$$\log x = \frac{7.877}{6}$$

$$\log x = 1.313$$

Therefore, $x = \text{antilog } 1.313$

If this confuses you, remember that the *antilog* of 1.313 is simply the number whose logarithm is 1.313. $1.313 = 0.313 + 1$, so we know that

$$x = 10 \times \text{antilog } 0.313.$$

This makes sense, because 10 is the number whose logarithm is 1, and antilog 0.313 is the number whose logarithm is 0.313. To find the antilog of 0.313, just set the hairline at 0.313 on the L scale, and read the antilog on the D scale.

Complete the problem and then return to page 270 to choose the right answer.

[*from page 273*]

YOUR ANSWER: I don't understand.

Let's begin by restating the problem.

We know that $\log 1.2150 = 0.08458$,

and $\log 1.2160 = 0.08493$.

We want to find the antilog of 0.08467. That is, we want to find the number whose logarithm is 0.08467.

Looking at the given numbers and their corresponding logarithms, we can see that the number we want must be between 1.2150 and 1.2160. In fact, it must be $\frac{9}{35}$ of the way between them, because

$$0.08493 - 0.08458 = 35,$$

and

$$0.08467 - 0.08458 = 9$$

The difference between 1.2150 and 1.2160 is 10 in the fifth place. So, letting x represent the value we need to add to 1.2150 to arrive at the desired antilog,

$$\frac{x}{10} = \frac{9}{35}$$

$$x = \frac{90}{35}$$

$$x = 2.57,$$

or, to two figures,

$$x = 2.6.$$

Therefore, we want to add 2.6 to the fifth figure of 1.2150. More precisely, we want to add 0.00026 to the number 1.2150:

$$\begin{array}{r} 1.2150 \\ +\ 0.00026 \\ \hline 1.21526 \end{array}$$

The antilog of 0.08467 is 1.21526, or rounding off to five figures of accuracy, 1.2153.

Study this solution carefully. Then, if you feel you understand the method that was used, return to page 273 to choose the right answer. If you still feel uncertain, return to page 277 for some review.

CHAPTER 7

Trigonometry

As the name implies, trigonometry is a specialized branch of geometry which has to do with triangles. Trigonometry can be used to find whose lot a fence is on, how far it is to Mars, the speed and location of ships at sea, or the stress on a girder in the Brooklyn Bridge.

While the problems we will deal with in this chapter are necessarily straightforward, the techniques you will learn can be extended to more complex and even apparently unrelated situations. The following is a typical problem in practical trigonometry.

Two ocean liners passed at sea, one headed south and the other east. The captain of the southbound vessel—which was making 14 knots—wanted to know the speed of his competitor. From compass readings that showed the second ship was maintaining a constant bearing of 36° off his stern, the captain was able to determine that the other ship was making 10.2 knots. (See diagram below, left.)

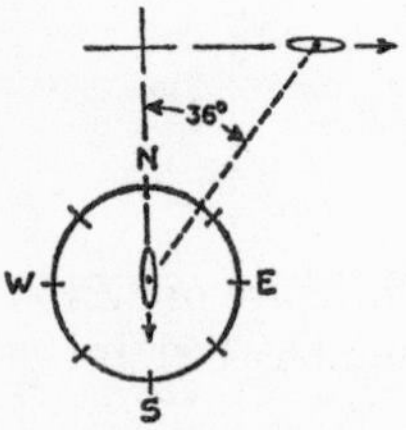

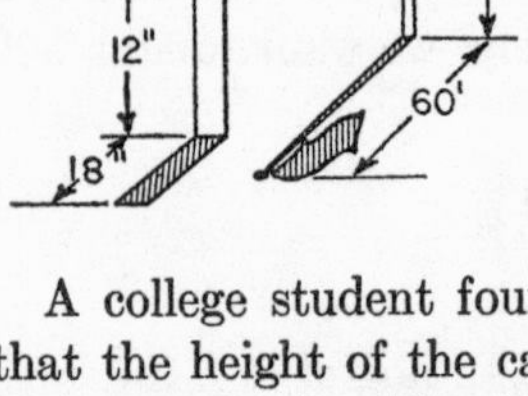

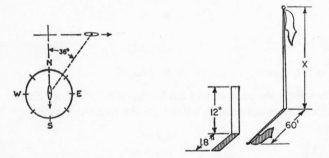

But let's begin with a simple one! A college student found an acquaintance who was willing to bet that the height of the campus flagpole couldn't be determined without measuring it. The student paced off the shadow of the flagpole, finding it to be 60 feet long. He stood a 12-inch ruler on end and found its shadow to be 18 inches long. How high is the flagpole? (See diagram above, right.)

40 feet. **page 288** 70 feet. **page 291** 90 feet. **page 294**

[*from page 288*]

YOUR ANSWER: The hypotenuse of the smaller triangle is 21.6 inches.

Yes. Letting the hypotenuse of the smaller triangle be labeled c_1, you could have used either of two proportions:

$$\frac{c_1}{12\text{ in.}} = \frac{72.1\text{ ft.}}{40\text{ ft.}} \quad \text{or} \quad \frac{c_1}{18\text{ in.}} = \frac{72.1\text{ ft.}}{60\text{ ft.}}$$

The answer comes out the same:

$$c_1 = 21.6\text{ inches.}$$

In any group of similar triangles, the ratio of corresponding sides remains *constant,* i.e., the same. The three triangles below are similar. Notice that the ratio of the *a* side to the *b* side is the same in all three cases.

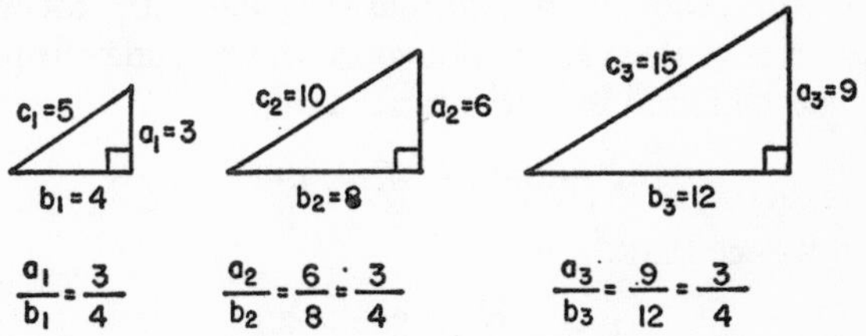

However, we can't say that every triangle is similar to every other triangle. In fact, not even all *right* triangles are similar. It's a little more complicated than that.

So before we go any further, let's make sure we're clear on some basic ideas and definitions from geometry. As a start, choose the one incorrect statement below:

The sum of the angles of a triangle is 180°. **page 289**

An acute angle is an angle of less than 90°; an obtuse angle is an angle of more than 90°. **page 293**

A right triangle contains one 90° angle, one acute angle, and one obtuse angle. **page 296**

There are 360° in a complete circle, 60 minutes in a degree, and 60 seconds in a minute. **page 299**

[*from page 289*]

YOUR ANSWER: Angle $x = 30°$.

No, you missed the boat. Let's attack the problem logically.

First, we know that the sum of the angles of any triangle is 180°. With this in mind, look at the triangle again:

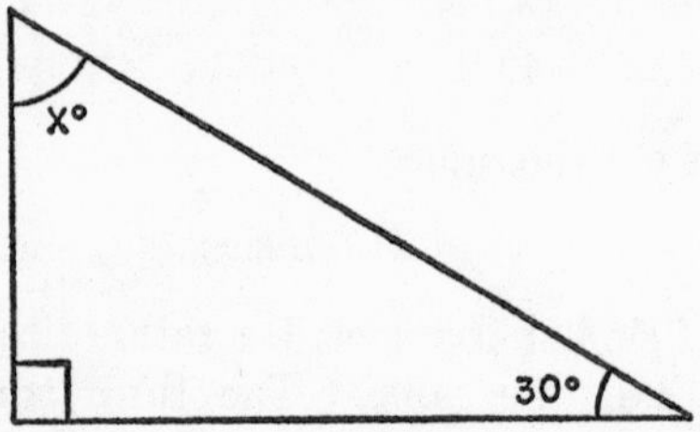

The boxlike symbol in the lower left angle signifies a *right* angle—an angle of 90°. And we are also told that one of the other angles is 30°. So we know the values of two of the triangle's three angles. The third can be found from the relationship

$$x + 30° + 90° = 180°$$

from which we see that

$$x = 180° - 90° - 30°$$

When you have completed the indicated subtraction, you can check your answer by adding it to the two known angles. The sum, of course, should be 180°. If you had checked your first answer this way, you would have found that

$$30° + 30° + 90° = 150°$$

instead of the desired 180°.

Now complete the calculation, check your answer, and then return to page 289 to make the correct choice.

[*from page 293*]

YOUR ANSWER: Angle $x = 30°$.

No, you missed the boat. Let's attack the problem logically.

First, we know that the sum of the angles of any triangle is 180°. With this in mind, look at the triangle again:

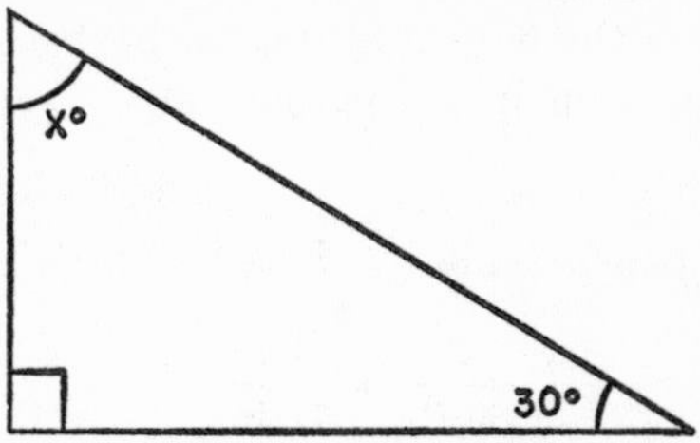

The boxlike symbol in the lower right angle signifies a *right* angle—an angle of 90°. And we are also told that one of the other angles is 30°. So we know the values of two of the triangle's three angles. The third can be found from the relationship

$$x + 30° + 90° = 180°$$

from which we see that

$$x = 180° - 90° - 30°$$

When you have completed the indicated subtraction, you can check your answer by adding it to the two known angles. The sum, of course, should be 180°. If you had checked your first answer this way, you would have found that

$$30° + 30° + 90° = 150°$$

instead of the desired 180°.

Now complete the calculation, check your answer, and then return to page 293 to make the correct choice.

[*from page 284*]

YOUR ANSWER: The flagpole is 40 feet high.

Very good.

Because the shadow of the rule is just half again as long as the rule, the student concluded that the shadow of the flagpole is half again its height. Though he found the solution mentally by multiplying the length of the flagpole's shadow by two-thirds, essentially he was applying the principle of proportion:

$$\frac{\text{length of pole}}{\text{length of pole's shadow}} = \frac{\text{length of ruler}}{\text{length of ruler's shadow}},$$

or

$$\frac{x}{60 \text{ ft.}} = \frac{12 \text{ in.}}{18 \text{ in.}},$$

where x is the length (or *height*) of the flagpole.

If a line is drawn from the top of the ruler to the end of its shadow, and the same is done with the flagpole and its shadow, two triangles are formed. These triangles are called *right* triangles because one angle of each is a "square corner," an angle of exactly 90 degrees.

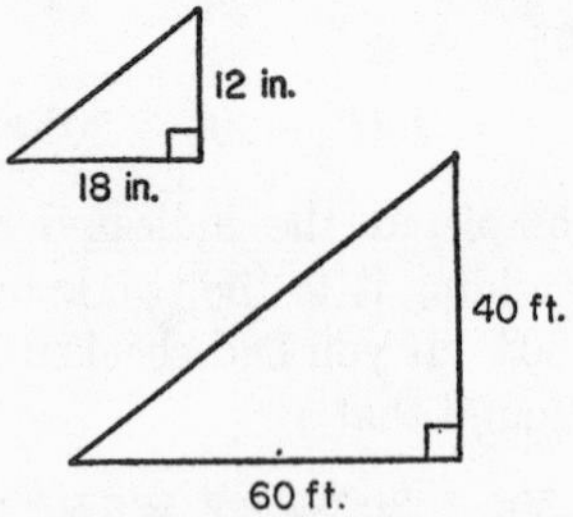

Looking at these triangles, we see that they are *similar*. In terms of geometry this means that their sides are proportional. In ordinary language, the triangles are of the same shape, though not of the same size. As you probably recall, the side of a right triangle that is opposite the right angle is called the *hypotenuse* of the triangle.

Use the proportion principle (and your slide rule, of course) to find the length of the hypotenuse of the smaller triangle if that of the larger is 72.1 feet.

21.6 inches. **page 285** 27 inches. **page 292** 150 inches. **page 297**

[*from page 285*]

YOUR ANSWER: This statement is incorrect: The sum of the angles of a triangle is 180 degrees.

No, the statement is right. Let's make sure you're familiar with all the terms involved.

First, angles are measured in terms of degrees (°), minutes (′), and seconds (″). There are 360 degrees in a full circle, 60 minutes in a degree, and 60 seconds in a minute. An angle labeled 52° 16′ 31″, for instance, is an angle of 52 degrees, 16 minutes, and 31 seconds.

An acute angle is an angle of *less* than 90 degrees; and an obtuse angle is an angle of *more* than 90 degrees:

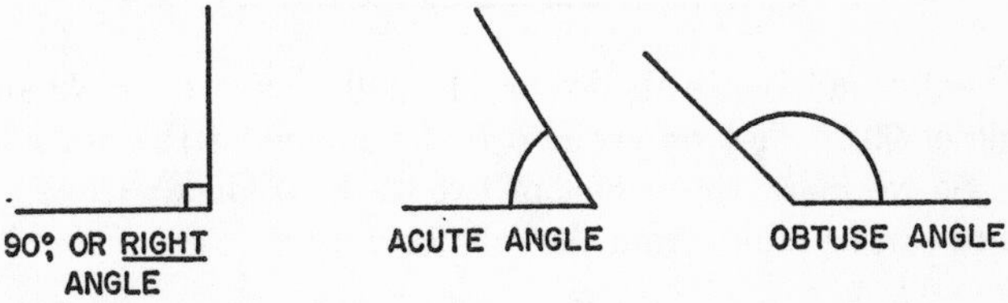

Though we will not take the time to do it here, it can be proved that if we measure all three angles of any triangle, and add these three measurements together, the resulting sum will be 180°. This is a very useful relationship. For example, what is the size of angle x of this triangle?

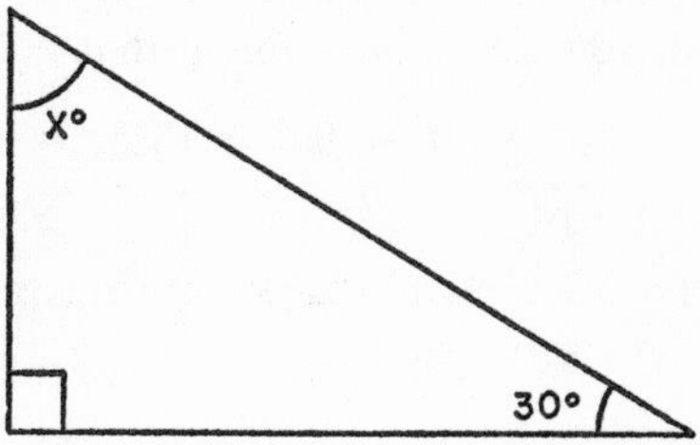

$x = 30°$. **page 286**

$x = 45°$. **page 295**

$x = 60°$. **page 298**

[*from page 293*]

YOUR ANSWER: Angle $x = 45°$.

No, you missed the boat. Let's attack the problem logically.

First, we know that the sum of the angles of any triangle is 180°. With this in mind, look at the triangle again:

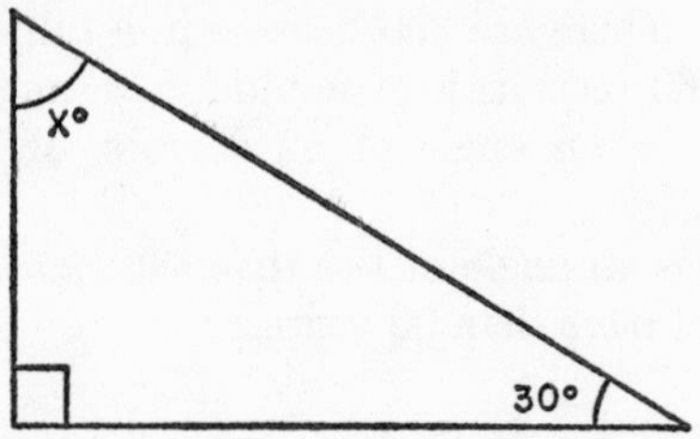

The boxlike symbol in the lower left angle signifies a *right* angle—an angle of 90°. And we are also told that one of the other angles is 30°. So we know the values of two of the triangle's three angles. The third can be found from the relationship

$$x + 30° + 90° = 180°$$

from which we see that

$$x = 180° - 90° - 30°$$

When you have completed the indicated subtraction, you can check your answer by adding your result to the two known angles. The sum, of course, should be 180°. If you had done this with the answer you selected, you would have found that

$$45° + 30° + 90° = 165°$$

instead of the desired 180°.

Now complete the calculation, check your answer, and return to page 293 to make the correct choice.

[*from page 284*]

YOUR ANSWER: The flagpole is 70 feet high.

No. And this looks like a guess. Here is the diagram again:

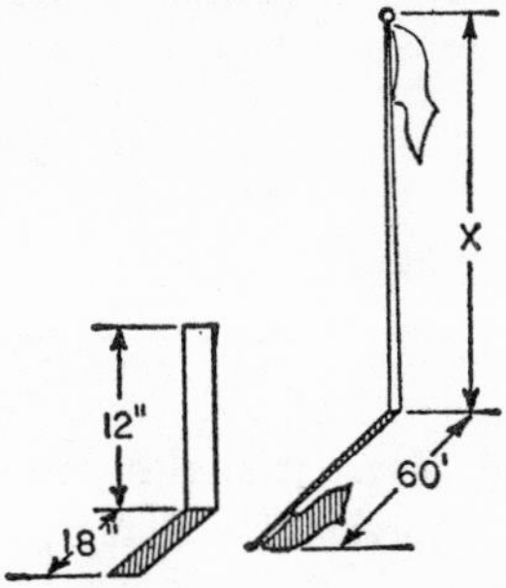

Clearly, the ruler's shadow is one and a half times as long as the ruler. The logical conclusion, then, is that the flagpole's shadow is one and a half times the height of the flagpole. Letting x stand for the height of the flagpole, then,

$$\frac{60 \text{ ft.}}{x} = \frac{18 \text{ in.}}{12 \text{ in.}}$$

And since $\frac{18 \text{ in.}}{12 \text{ in.}} = \frac{3}{2}$ (which is just $1\frac{1}{2}$, of course),

$$\frac{60 \text{ ft.}}{x} = \frac{3}{2}$$

$$x = \frac{2 \times 60 \text{ ft.}}{3}$$

The relationship between the rule and its shadow might also be expressed this way: The ruler is two-thirds as long as its shadow. Then the appropriate proportion would look like this:

$$\frac{x}{60 \text{ ft.}} = \frac{2}{3}$$

$$x = \frac{2 \times 60 \text{ ft.}}{3}$$

Either way, the final answer will be the same. Complete the calculation and then return to page 284 to choose the correct answer.

[*from page 288*]

YOUR ANSWER: The hypotenuse of the smaller triangle is 27 inches.

No, you're way off the track. Let's label the sides of the triangles for easy identification and examine them more closely.

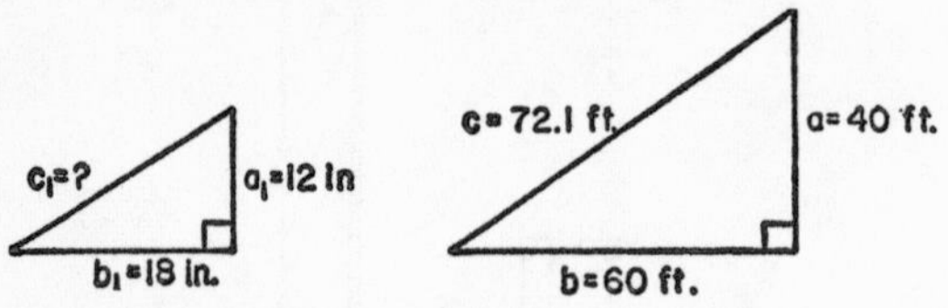

As we've seen before, these triangles are similar because their sides are known to be proportional. That is,

$$\frac{40 \text{ ft.}}{60 \text{ ft.}} = \frac{12 \text{ in.}}{18 \text{ in.}}, \quad \text{or} \quad \frac{a}{b} = \frac{a_1}{b_1}$$

To put it another way, similar triangles are triangles in which the ratios of *corresponding sides* are the same. Corresponding sides, of course, are sides that occupy the same relative position. In the given triangles, side a (the flagpole) corresponds to side a_1 (the ruler), and side b (the flagpole's shadow) corresponds to side b_1 (the ruler's shadow). Extending this reasoning a little further, we see that side c, the hypotenuse of the larger triangle, corresponds to side c_1, the hypotenuse of the smaller triangle.

In terms of the labels we've assigned, then,

$$\frac{c}{b} = \frac{c_1}{b_1}, \quad \text{and also} \quad \frac{c}{a} = \frac{c_1}{a_1}$$

Using the second of these proportions, and inserting the known values, we get

$$\frac{72.1 \text{ ft.}}{40 \text{ ft.}} = \frac{c_1}{12 \text{ in.}}, \quad \text{so that} \quad c_1 = \frac{72.1 \times 12 \text{ in.}}{40}$$

Study the explanation, complete the calculation, and then return to page 288 to choose the correct answer.

YOUR ANSWER: This statement is not correct: An acute angle is an angle of less than 90 degrees; an obtuse angle is an angle of more than 90 degrees.

No, the statement is right. Let's make sure you're familiar with all the terms involved.

First, angles are measured in terms of degrees (°), minutes (′), and seconds (″). There are 360 degrees in a full circle, 60 minutes in a degree, and 60 seconds in a minute. An angle labeled 52° 16′ 31″, for instance, is an angle of 52 degrees, 16 minutes, and 31 seconds.

An acute angle is an angle of *less* than 90 degrees; and an obtuse angle is an angle of *more* than 90 degrees:

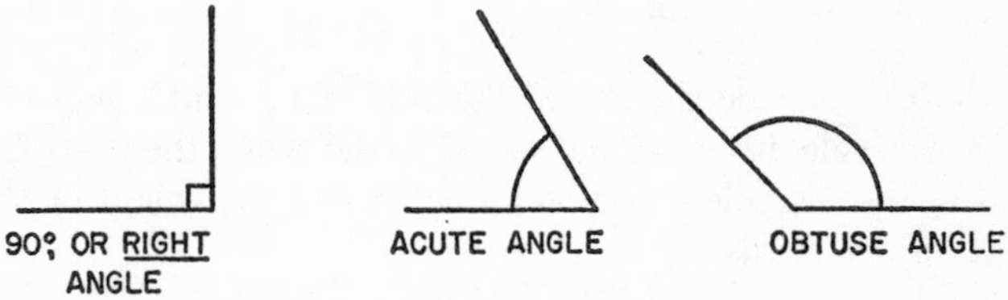

Though we will not take the time to do it here, it can be proved that if we measure all three angles of any triangle, and add these three measurements together, the resulting sum will be 180°. This is a very useful relationship. For example, what is the size of angle x of this triangle?

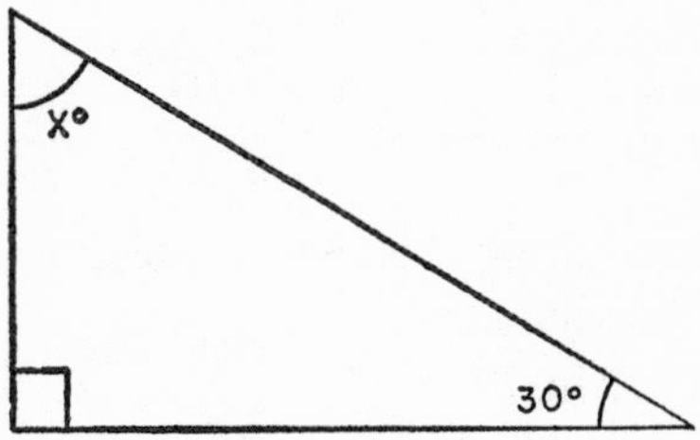

$x = 30°$. **page 287**

$x = 45°$. **page 290**

$x = 60°$. **page 300**

[*from page 284*]

YOUR ANSWER: The flagpole is 90 feet high.

No, it isn't. Look at the diagram again:

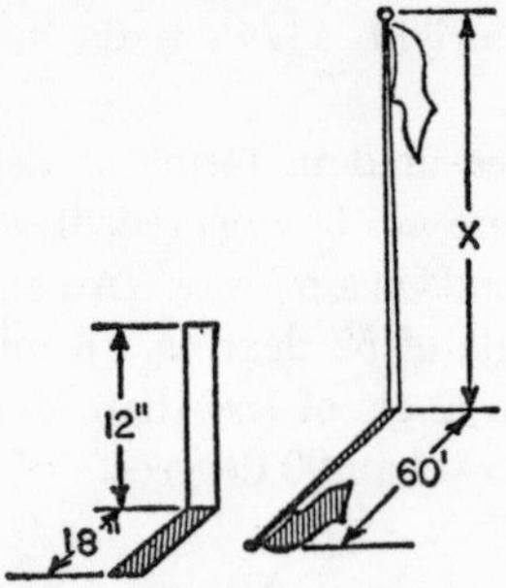

We notice that the shadow of the rule is one and a half times as long as the rule itself. The logical conclusion, then, is that the shadow of the flagpole is one and a half times the height of the flagpole. In other words,

$$\frac{60 \text{ ft.}}{x} = \frac{18 \text{ in.}}{12 \text{ in.}}$$

where x represents the height of the flagpole. Then, since $\frac{18 \text{ in.}}{12 \text{ in.}} = \frac{3}{2}$ (which is just $1\frac{1}{2}$, of course),

$$\frac{60 \text{ ft.}}{x} = \frac{3}{2}$$

$$x = \frac{2 \times 60 \text{ ft.}}{3}$$

Evidently you reversed this relationship, using the incorrect proportion $\frac{x}{60 \text{ ft.}} = \frac{18 \text{ in.}}{12 \text{ in.}}$. But plain old horse sense should have told you that your answer was wrong. Since the ruler is shorter than its shadow, it stands to reason that the flagpole must be shorter than its shadow, not longer.

Complete the calculation with the correct proportion. Then return to page 284 to choose the right answer.

[*from page 289*]

YOUR ANSWER: Angle $x = 45°$.

No, you missed the boat. Let's attack the problem logically.

First, we know that the sum of the angles of any triangle is 180°. With this in mind, look at the triangle again:

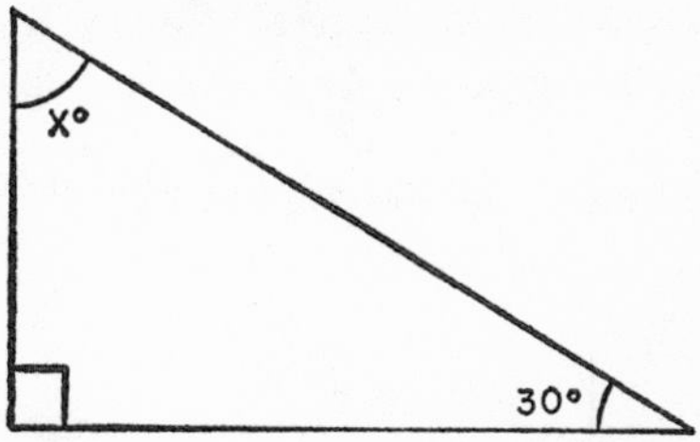

The boxlike symbol in the lower left angle signifies a *right* angle—an angle of 90°. And we are also told that one of the other angles is 30°. So we know the values of two of the triangle's three angles. The third can be found from the relationship

$$x + 30° + 90° = 180°$$

from which we see that

$$x = 180° - 90° - 30°$$

When you have completed the indicated subtraction, you can check your answer by adding your result to the two known angles. The sum, of course, should be 180°. If you had done this with the answer you selected, you would have found that

$$45° + 30° + 90° = 165°$$

instead of the desired 180°.

Now complete the calculation, check your answer, and return to page 289 to make the correct choice.

[*from page 285*]

YOUR ANSWER: This statement is incorrect: A right triangle contains one 90° angle, one acute angle, and one obtuse angle.

Of course it's wrong. The sum of the angles of any triangle is 180 degrees. A right triangle is defined as a triangle in which one of the angles is 90 degrees, so the sum of the other two angles must be 180 degrees minus 90 degrees, or 90 degrees. Each of the two angles, then, must be *less* than 90 degrees. Angles of less than 90 degrees are called *acute* angles, so both must be acute. (An *obtuse* angle, as you recall, is an angle of *more* than 90 degrees.)

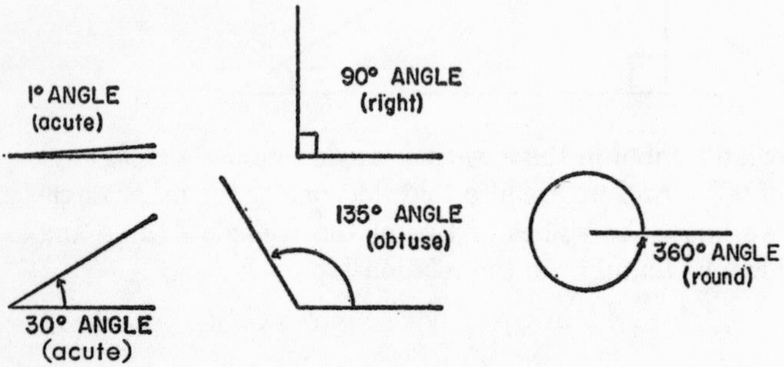

You should also remember that there are 360° (*degrees*) in a complete circle, 60′ (*minutes*) in a degree, and 60″ (*seconds*) in a minute. Circles have been marked off into 360 equal parts since ancient times, when the solar year was thought to be 360 days, and calendars were made in circular form.

Sometimes it is more convenient to deal with fractions of degrees in decimal form. Any portion of a degree expressed in minutes and seconds has its decimal equivalent. For example, 32° 12′ is equivalent to 32.2°.

How would you write 51° 50′, expressing 50′ as a decimal fraction of a degree?

51° 50′ = 51.5°. **page 301**

51° 50′ = 51.64°. **page 303**

51° 50′ = 51.83°. **page 307**

[*from page 288*]

YOUR ANSWER: The hypotenuse of the smaller triangle is 150 inches.

No, it isn't. Let's label the sides of the triangles for easy identification and examine them more closely.

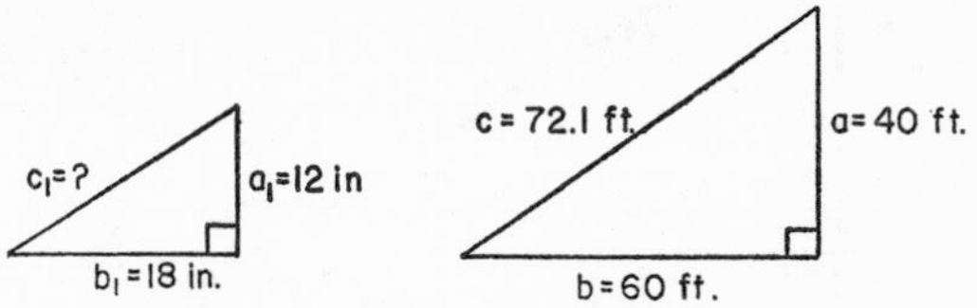

As we've seen before, these triangles are similar because their sides are known to be proportional. That is,

$$\frac{40 \text{ ft.}}{60 \text{ ft.}} = \frac{12 \text{ in.}}{18 \text{ in.}}, \quad \text{or} \quad \frac{a}{b} = \frac{a_1}{b_1}$$

To put it another way, similar triangles are triangles in which the ratios of *corresponding sides* are the same. Corresponding sides, of course, are sides that occupy the same relative position. In the given triangles, side a (the flagpole) corresponds to side a_1 (the ruler), and side b (the flagpole's shadow) corresponds to side b_1 (the ruler's shadow). Extending this reasoning a little further, we see that side c, the hypotenuse of the larger triangle, corresponds to side c_1, the hypotenuse of the smaller triangle.

In terms of the labels we've assigned, then,

$$\frac{c}{b} = \frac{c_1}{b_1}, \quad \text{and also} \quad \frac{c}{a} = \frac{c_1}{a_1}$$

Using the second of these proportions, and inserting the known values, we get

$$\frac{72.1 \text{ ft.}}{40 \text{ ft.}} = \frac{c_1}{12 \text{ in.}}, \quad \text{so that} \quad c_1 = \frac{72.1 \times 12 \text{ in.}}{40}$$

Study the explanation, complete the calculation, and then return to page 288 to choose the correct answer.

[*from page 289*]

YOUR ANSWER: Angle $x = 60°$.

Right. Here is the given triangle again:

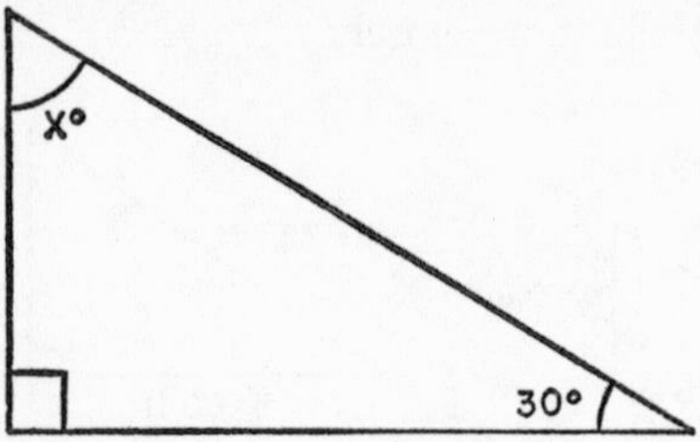

Two of the angles are known: 90° and 30°. Since the sum of the angles of any triangle is 180°, the value of angle x must be given by the expression

$$x + 90° + 30° = 180°$$

from which we see that

$$x = 180° - 90° - 30°$$

$$x = 60°$$

And this answer checks:

$$60° + 90° + 30° = 180°$$

Actually, as you may have noticed, the value of angle x could be found by subtracting 30° from 90°, because $180° - 90° = 90°$. In any *right* triangle the value of either of the two non-right angles may be found by subtracting the other from 90°.

Now, remembering that an acute angle is less than 90° and an obtuse angle is more than 90°, return to page 285 for another try.

[*from page 285*]

YOUR ANSWER: This statement is not correct: There are 360 degrees in a complete circle, 60 minutes in a degree, and 60 seconds in a minute.

No. Since ancient times (when the solar year was thought to be 360 days and calendars were made in circular form), for measuring purposes circles have been divided into 360 equal parts which we now call degrees. When we measure an angle, we consider its vertex to be at the center of a circle. We extend its sides so that they cross the circumference, and say that the measure of the angle is the number of degrees in the arc cut by the sides.

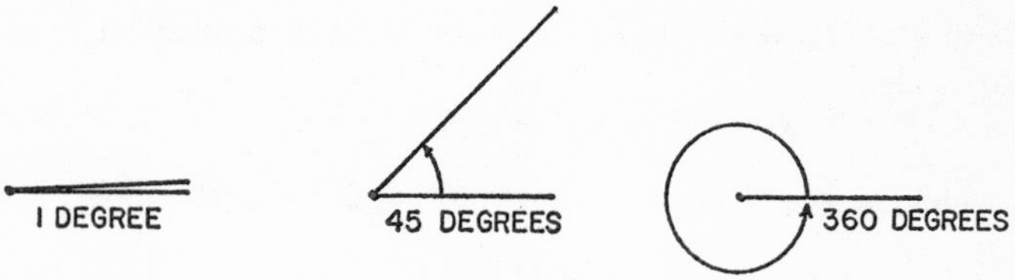

Notice that the size of the circle makes no difference. A one-degree angle will intersect $\frac{1}{360}$ of the circumference of any circle with the same center.

For greater accuracy in measuring angles, the degree is divided into sixtieths. One-sixtieth of a degree is called a *minute*. Consequently, there are 60 minutes in a degree. Similarly, the minute is also divided into sixtieths. One-sixtieth of a minute is called a *second*. So there are 60 seconds in a minute.

The symbol for degree is $^\circ$; the symbol for minute is $'$, and the symbol for second is $''$. For instance, an angle labeled $31^\circ\ 52'\ 17''$ is read as an angle of 31 degrees, 52 minutes, and 17 seconds.

Study the diagrams and explanation carefully. Then return to page 285 for another try.

[*from page 293*]

YOUR ANSWER: Angle $x = 60°$.

Right. Here is the given triangle again:

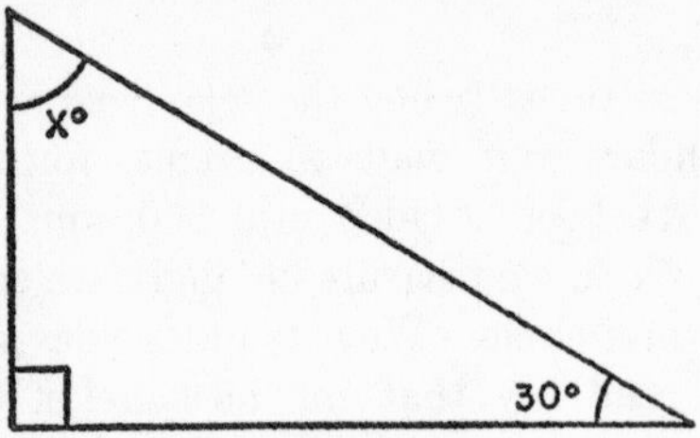

Two of the angles are known: 90° and 30°. Since the sum of the angles of any triangle is 180°, the value of angle x must be given by the expression

$$x + 90° + 30° = 180°$$

from which we see that

$$x = 180° - 90° - 30°$$

$$x = 60°$$

And this answer checks:

$$60° + 90° + 30° = 180°$$

Actually, as you may have noticed, the value of angle x could be found by subtracting 30° from 90°, because $180° - 90° = 90°$. In any *right* triangle the value of either of the two non-right angles may be found by subtracting the other from 90°.

Now, remembering that an acute angle is less than 90° and an obtuse angle is more than 90°, return to page 285 for another try.

[*from page 296*]

YOUR ANSWER: $51° \, 50' = 51.5°$.

No. Let's begin by analyzing the example given on the last page:

$$32° \, 12' = 32.2°$$

This means, of course, that 12 minutes (or $12'$) is equivalent to two-tenths of a degree (or $0.2°$).

Now, we know that 60 minutes (not 100 minutes) equal 1 degree. In symbols, $60' = 1°$. Considering the conversion in terms of proportion, then, we can write

$$\frac{12'}{60'} = \frac{0.2°}{1.0°}$$

$0.2°$ ⟵ decimal fraction of a degree equivalent to 12 minutes
$1.0°$ ⟵ equivalent, in degrees, of 60 minutes

We can use this same kind of relationship to find the decimal fraction of a degree equivalent to $50'$:

$$\frac{50'}{60'} = \frac{x}{1.0°}$$

x ⟵ the desired decimal fraction of a degree

Solving for x:

$$x = \frac{5}{6} \times 1.0°$$

$$x = 0.8333333\ldots°$$

Rounding off to two figures,

$$x = 0.83°$$

In other words, $50' = 0.83°$, so that

$$51° \, 50' = 51.83° \quad (\textit{not } 51.5°)$$

Study this conversion carefully. Then return to page 296 to choose the correct answer.

[*from page 305*]

YOUR ANSWER: This statement is incorrect: If you were asked to find the side adjacent to the 33.7° angle in a right triangle, and only the side opposite the angle were specified, it would be necessary for you to find the hypotenuse first.

Right. The proportion principle can be used directly.

Here is the proportion you need to find the opposite side of a triangle in which the adjacent side is known.

$$\frac{a}{81.4} = \frac{0.555}{0.832}$$

$$a = \frac{0.555}{0.832} \times 81.4$$

$$a = 0.667 \times 81.4 = 54.2$$

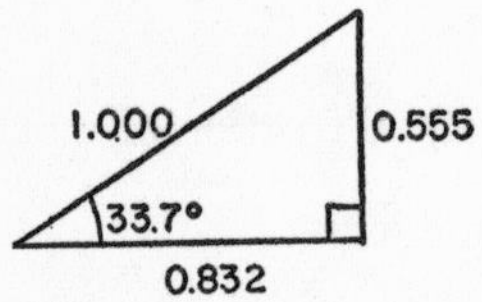

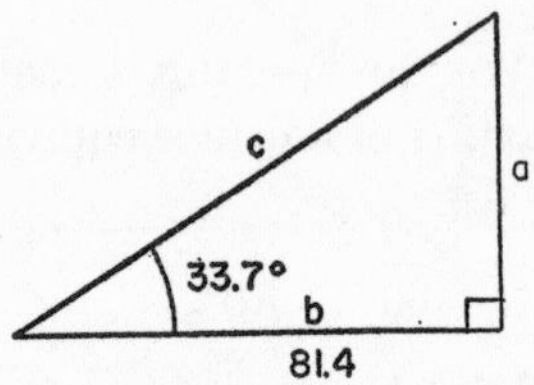

This adds another constant to our collection, 0.667, the ratio of the side opposite the 33.7° angle to the side adjacent to that angle.

$$\frac{a}{b} = \frac{0.555}{0.832} = 0.667$$

We have quite a bit of information about one kind of triangle. Specifically, we know three basic ratios which will be true of all right triangles having either a 33.7° or a 56.3° acute angle.

1. The ratio of the side a opposite the 33.7° angle to the hypotenuse c will always be 0.555.
2. The ratio of the side b adjacent to the 33.7° angle to the hypotenuse c will always be 0.832.
3. The ratio of the side a opposite the 33.7° angle to the side b adjacent to this angle will always be 0.667.

In a given right triangle, one of the sides is 35.8 inches, and another is 28 inches. Is one of the acute angles of the triangle 33.7°?

Yes. **page 306**   No. **page 312**

[*from page 296*]

YOUR ANSWER: $51^\circ\,50' = 51.64^\circ$.

Wrong. And this looks like a guess. We'd better start over. Let's begin by analyzing the example given on the last page:

$$32^\circ\,12' = 32.2^\circ$$

This means, of course, that 12 minutes (or 12′) is equivalent to two-tenths of a degree (or 0.2°).

Now, we know that 60 minutes (not 100 minutes) equal 1 degree. In symbols, $60' = 1^\circ$. Considering the conversion in terms of proportion, then, we can write

$$\frac{12'}{60'} = \frac{0.2^\circ \longleftarrow \text{decimal fraction of a degree equivalent to 12 minutes}}{1.0^\circ \longleftarrow \text{equivalent, in degrees, of 60 minutes}}$$

We can use this same kind of relationship to find the decimal fraction of a degree equivalent to 50′:

$$\frac{50'}{60'} = \frac{x}{1.0^\circ}$$

where x is the desired decimal fraction of a degree.

Solving for x:

$$x = \frac{5}{6} \times 1.0^\circ$$

$$x = 0.8333333\ldots^\circ$$

Rounding off to two figures,

$$x = 0.83^\circ$$

In other words, $\quad 50' = 0.83^\circ$,

so that $\quad 51^\circ\,50' = 51.83^\circ \quad$ (*not* 51.64°)

Study this conversion carefully. Then return to page 296 to choose the correct answer.

[*from page 307*]

YOUR ANSWER: $a = 0.555$ in., and $b = 0.832$ in.

Correct. The proportions are:

$$\frac{a}{1.000 \text{ in.}} = \frac{40}{72.1}, \quad \text{so} \quad a = \frac{40}{72.1} \times 1.000 \text{ in.} = 0.555 \text{ in.}$$

$$\frac{b}{1.000 \text{ in.}} = \frac{60}{72.1}, \quad \text{so} \quad b = \frac{60}{72.1} \times 1.000 \text{ in.} = 0.832 \text{ in.}$$

As you can see, using a triangle with a hypotenuse of 1.000 makes it a simple matter to determine the unknown sides of similar triangles. (This is called *solving* the triangles.)

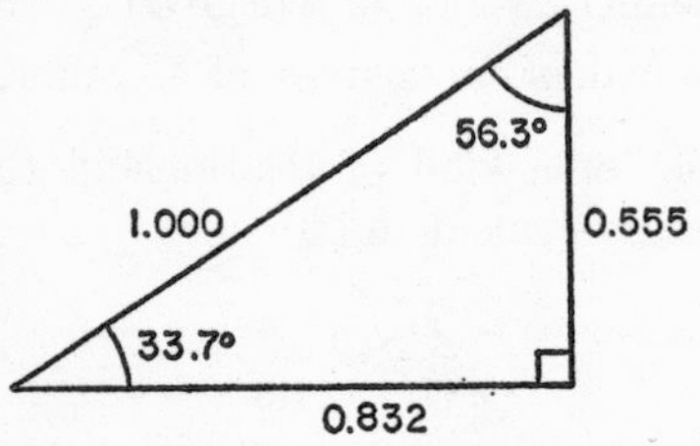

Let's apply the information from the triangle above to the similar one below. The hypotenuse of this triangle is 163. (The units in which the two triangles are measured really don't matter for now, since they cancel out.)

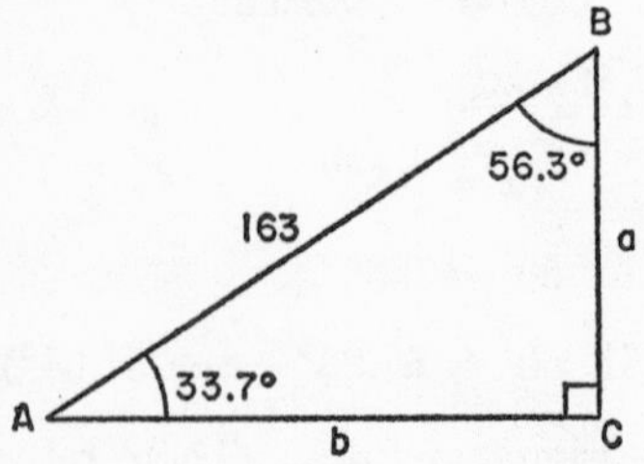

Then

$$\frac{a}{163} = \frac{0.555}{1.000}, \quad \text{so that} \quad a = \frac{0.555}{1.000} \times 163 = 90.5$$

$$\frac{b}{163} = \frac{0.832}{1.000}, \quad \text{so that} \quad b = \frac{0.832}{1.000} \times 163 = 135.5$$

[*from page 304*]

The advantage in choosing a triangle with a hypotenuse of 1.000, or *unit* hypotenuse, is evident when you consider that $\frac{0.555}{1.000}$ is really just 0.555, and $\frac{0.832}{1.000}$ is just 0.832. We may call the numbers 0.555 and 0.832 the *constants* of any 33.7° right triangle. In other words, for any 33.7° right triangle, the ratio of the side opposite the 33.7° angle to the hypotenuse is equal to the constant 0.555, and the ratio of the adjacent side (the side next to the 33.7° angle) to the hypotenuse is equal to the constant 0.832. Generally speaking, the units in which the sides of the triangle are measured don't matter, since they cancel out in the ratios.

Which of the three statements below is false?

If you were asked to find the side adjacent to the 33.7° angle (side b) of a right triangle, and knew the side opposite (side a), you would first have to find the hypotenuse to use the proportion principle. **page 302**

If you were shown a 56.3° right triangle, you could determine the two unknown sides from any one given side by using the constants of a 33.7° right triangle. **page 308**

Knowing side a and side c (the hypotenuse) of a certain right triangle, you can determine whether or not one of the acute angles of the triangle is 33.7°. **page 311**

[*from page 302*]

YOUR ANSWER: Yes, one of the acute angles of the triangle is 33.7°.

No, it isn't. Here is the question again:

In a given right triangle, one of the sides is 35.8 inches and another is 28 inches. Is one acute angle of the triangle 33.7°?

Let's see what we have to work with. We know that for *any* 33.7° right triangle:

1. The ratio of the side opposite the 33.7° angle to the hypotenuse is 0.555.
2. The ratio of the side adjacent to the 33.7° angle to the hypotenuse is 0.832.
3. The ratio of the side opposite the 33.7° angle to the side adjacent is 0.667.

(Notice that all these ratios are less than 1. And the ratio of 28 inches to 35.8 inches will be less than 1, because dividing a number by a larger number produces a result of less than 1. The ratio of 35.8 to 28, of course, would be more than 1.)

If 28 inches and 35.8 inches are sides of a 33.7° right triangle, then $\frac{28}{35.8}$ must be equal either to 0.555, to 0.832, or to 0.667, the constant ratios for a 33.7° right triangle. However, if we divide on the slide rule, we find that:

$$\frac{28}{35.8} = 0.782$$

Since 0.782 is not one of the constants for a 33.7° right triangle, a triangle in which two sides are known as 35.8 and 28 inches cannot be a similar triangle in this class.

Now, return to page 302 and select the correct answer.

YOUR ANSWER: $51° 50' = 51.83°$.

That's correct. There are 60 minutes to a degree, so

$$\frac{x}{1.0°} = \frac{50'}{60'}$$

where x is the desired decimal fraction of a degree equivalent to 50 minutes.

Then $$x = \frac{5}{6} \times 1.0° = 0.8333333\ldots°$$

Rounding off to two figures, $x = 0.83°$

So $$51° 50' = 51.83°$$

Now let's go back to the larger of the two triangles we were working with some time ago. It looked like this:

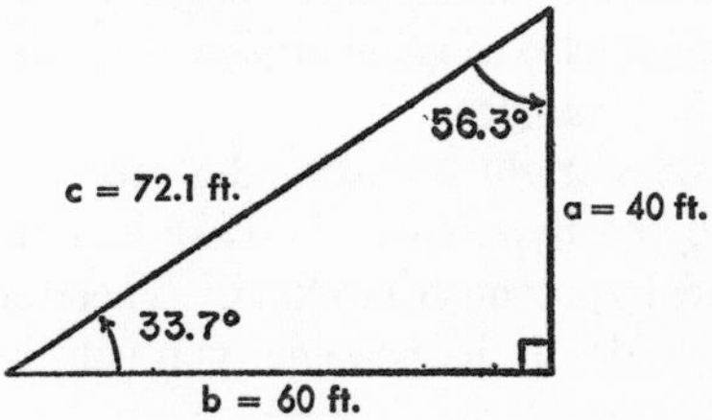

The acute angles of this triangle are 33.7° and 56.3°, as indicated in the illustration (notice that 33.7° + 56.3° = 90°). Clearly, any other right triangle containing an angle of 33.7° also contains one of 56.3°, and vice versa. Furthermore, any other right triangle in which the acute angles are 33.7° and 56.3° has sides proportional to those of this one; in other words, it's similar.

Consider the triangle below. What are its remaining sides?

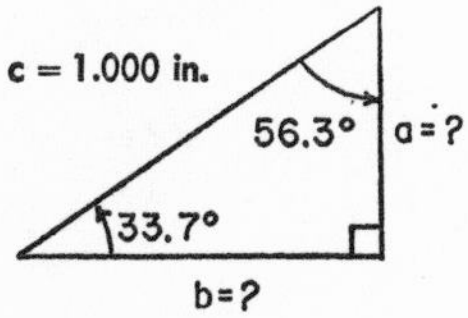

$a = 0.555$ in., $b = 0.832$ in. **page 304**

$a = 0.832$ in., $b = 0.555$ in. **page 310**

$a = 1.803$ in., $b = 1.202$ in. **page 313**

[*from page 305*]

YOUR ANSWER: This statement is false: If you were shown a 56.3° right triangle, you could determine two unknown sides from any one given side by using the constants of a 33.7° right triangle.

No, that's true, because the third angle of a 56.3° right triangle is 33.7°. You can prove this for yourself:

Call this third angle x. Then $x + 56.3° + 90° = 180°$, so $x = 180° - 56.3° - 90°$ and $x = 33.7°$.

Similarly, the third angle of a 33.7° right triangle has to be 56.3°. Call this third angle y. Then we know that $y + 33.7° + 90° = 180°$, so $y = 180° - 33.7° - 90° = 56.3°$.

Therefore, any 56.3° right triangle is similar to any 33.7° right triangle. (If the angles of two triangles are the same, then the triangles are similar. Remember that from plane geometry?) This means that the constants of a 56.3° right triangle are the same as those of a 33.7° right triangle. The only thing you need remember is that the side adjacent to the 33.7° angle is the side opposite the 56.3° angle and, similarly, the side adjacent to the 56.3° angle is the side opposite the 33.7° angle.

Thus, for any 56.3° right triangle, the ratio of the side opposite the 56.3° angle to the hypotenuse is 0.832 and the ratio of the adjacent side to the hypotenuse is 0.555. Therefore, knowing these constants and one side of the triangle, you can determine the other sides.

Now, return to page 305 and select the correct answer.

[*from page 312*]

YOUR ANSWER: This is a correct representation of a 30° right triangle.

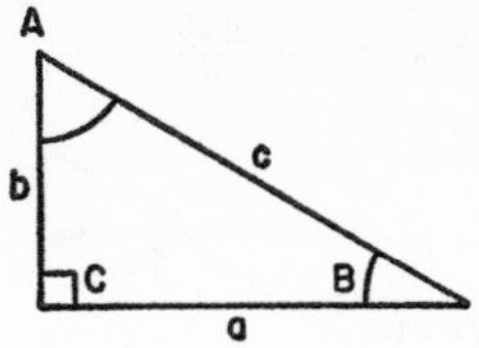

No, it isn't.

The identifying angle of a triangle should be labeled *A*. In the case of a 30° right triangle, the identifying angle is the 30° angle. If we are to lable the triangle correctly, then, we need to know whether the 30° angle is the larger or the smaller of the two acute angles. The value of the other acute angle, *B*, is given by the expression

$$B = 180° - C - A$$

Or, since angle *C* in any right triangle is 90°,

$$\begin{aligned} B &= 90° - A \\ &= 90° - 30° \\ &= 60° \end{aligned}$$

So angle *B*, the complementary angle, is actually larger than angle *A*, the identifying angle. In the diagram you selected, this relationship is reversed, with the larger angle labeled *A* and the smaller angle labeled *B*.

Return to page 312 to select the correct diagram.

[*from page 307*]

YOUR ANSWER: $a = 0.832$ in., $b = 0.555$ in.

Hold it! It's the ratios of *corresponding* sides that remain the same. Look at the two figures again:

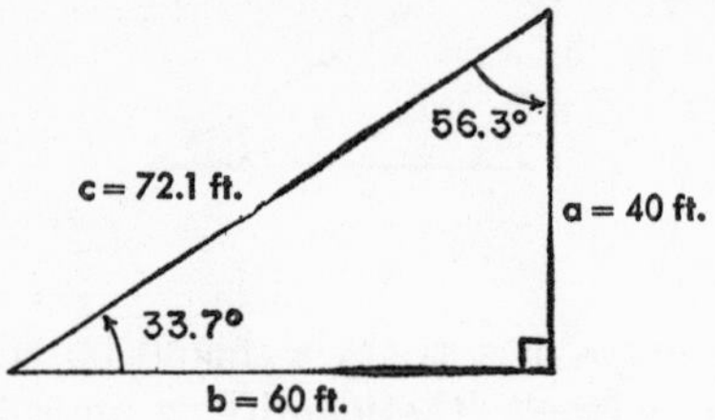

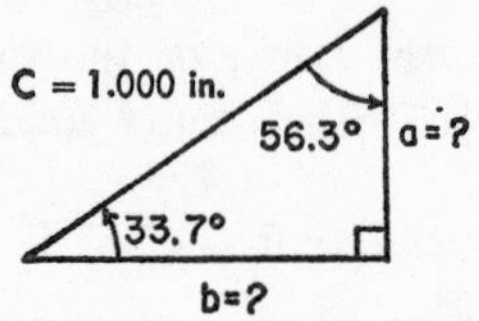

The hypotenuse (the side opposite the right angle) of the smaller triangle (c) corresponds to the hypotenuse of the larger triangle (C). Side a in the smaller triangle corresponds to side A in the larger triangle (both are opposite 33.7° angles). And side b in the smaller triangle corresponds to side B in the larger triangle (both are opposite the 56.3° angles). Since the triangles are similar,

$$\frac{a}{c} = \frac{A}{C} \quad \text{and} \quad \frac{b}{c} = \frac{B}{C}$$

Note that these relationships are *not* interchangeable. That is:

$$\frac{a}{c} \neq \frac{B}{C} \quad \text{and} \quad \frac{b}{c} \neq \frac{A}{C}$$

The *correct* proportions, then, are:

$$\frac{a}{1.000 \text{ in.}} = \frac{40}{72.1} \quad \text{and} \quad \frac{b}{1.000 \text{ in.}} = \frac{60}{72.1}$$

Solve these proportions for a and b, and then return to page 307 to choose the correct answer.

[*from page 305*]

YOUR ANSWER: This statement is false: Knowing side *a* and side *c* (the hypotenuse) of a certain right triangle, you can determine whether or not one of the acute angles of the triangle is 33.7°.

Sorry, but it's true.

For example, suppose you are told that in a given right triangle, side $a = 1.2$ inches and side c (the hypotenuse) $= 4.8$ inches.

Now, we know that in a 33.7° right triangle, the ratio of the side opposite the 33.7° angle to the hypotenuse is 0.555. And the ratio of the side adjacent to the 33.7° angle to the hypotenuse is 0.832. Accordingly, if one of the angles in the given triangle is 33.7°, then the ratio of side *a* to side *c* must be either 0.555 or 0.832. But

$$\frac{a}{c} = \frac{1.2 \text{ inches}}{4.8 \text{ inches}}$$
$$= 0.250$$

So we have to conclude that side *a* is neither adjacent to nor opposite a 33.7° angle, i.e., that there is no 33.7° angle in the given triangle.

Of course, if the ratio of side *a* to side *c* happened to be 0.555, then we could assert that angle $A = 33.7°$. Similarly, if $\frac{a}{c}$ happened to be 0.832, we could conclude that angle $B = 33.7°$.

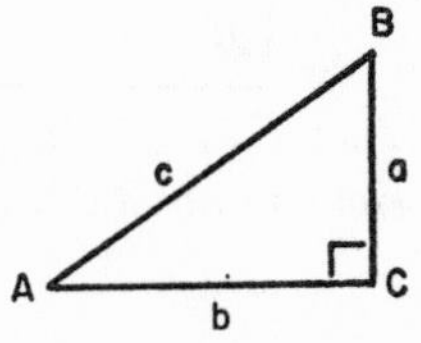

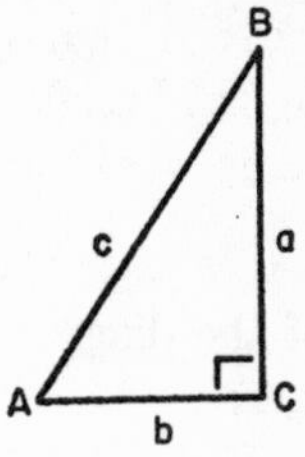

When you're sure you understand why these conclusions are justified, return to page 305 to try again.

[*from page 302*]

YOUR ANSWER: If in a given right triangle, one of the sides is 35.8 inches and another is 28 inches, then the triangle does not contain an acute angle of 33.7°.

That's right. Since $\frac{28.0}{35.8}$ does not equal 0.555, 0.832, or 0.667, a triangle with sides of 35.8 inches and 28 inches has none of the constant ratios of all 33.7° right triangles.

All 33.7° right triangles make up just one set of similar right triangles. There are, however, limitless numbers of possible sets of similar right triangles, each set with a different combination of acute angles. There is no reason why the procedure used to find the constants of 33.7° right triangles wouldn't work to find constants for every other set of similar right triangles.

As you should suspect by now, for every set of similar right triangles (those with the same combination of angles) there are three basic constant ratios. But before we identify these ratios in general terms, we need to be familiar with a standard notation used in dealing with right triangles. The angles are labeled with the capital letters A, B, and C, C being the right angle. Each side is labeled with the small letter corresponding to the capital letter of the opposite angle (the hypotenuse is c). The identifying angle, the one by which the whole set is named, will be A. The other acute angle, B, is called the complementary angle.

In the 33.7° triangles we've been discussing, the 33.7° angle would be A, and the 56.3° angle would be B.

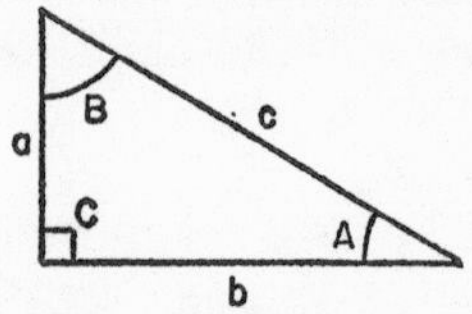

Which of the diagrams below is a correct representation of a 30° right triangle?

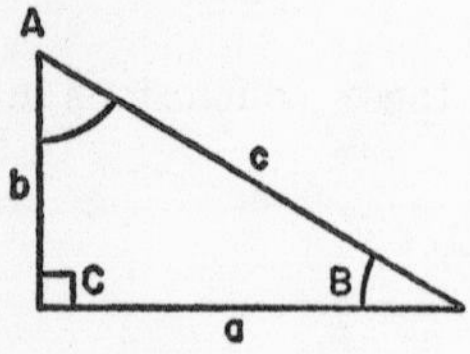

page 309

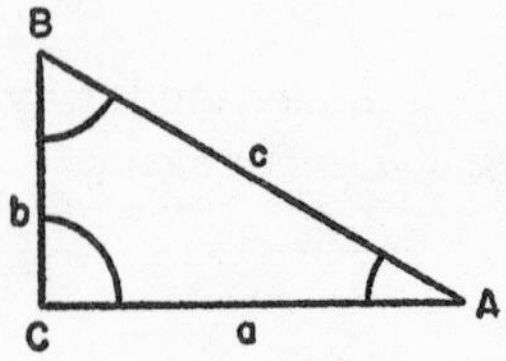

page 315

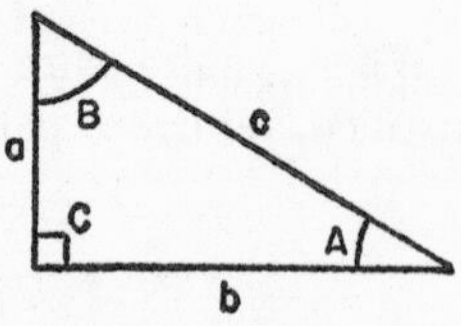

page 319

[*from page 307*]

YOUR ANSWER: $a = 1.803$ in., $b = 1.202$ in.

This answer is incorrect. The longest side of a triangle is the side opposite the largest angle. In a right triangle, then, the longest side is the hypotenuse, the side opposite the right angle. But the answer you chose implies that both side a and side b are longer than the hypotenuse. Here are the triangles again:

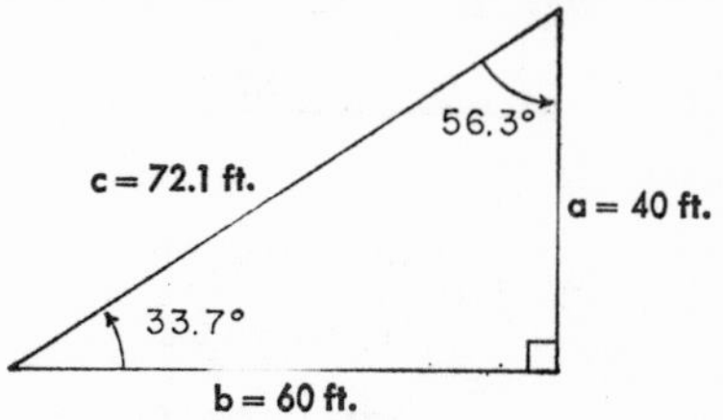

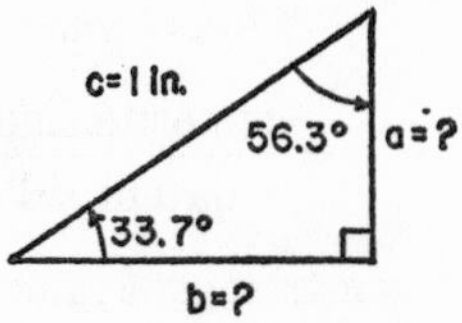

In similar triangles such as these, the ratios of corresponding sides are constant. This makes everything simple, *if* you can tell which sides correspond. In these triangles, the hypotenuse of the smaller triangle corresponds to that of the larger triangle, because each is opposite the 90° angle. Similarly, the sides opposite the 33.7° angles and the 56.3° angles correspond. So a corresponds to A, b corresponds to B, and c corresponds to C. Therefore,

$$\frac{a}{c} = \frac{A}{C} \quad \text{and} \quad \frac{b}{c} = \frac{B}{C}$$

But you can't carelessly turn the right half of each of these proportions upside down without confusing matters. That is,

$$\frac{a}{c} \neq \frac{C}{A} \quad \text{and} \quad \frac{b}{c} \neq \frac{C}{B}$$

Use the *correct* proportions to calculate the values of a and b. Then return to page 307 to choose the right answer.

[*from page 319*]

YOUR ANSWER: Sin $A = 0.800$, cos $A = 0.600$, and tan $A = 0.750$.

Well, you have the tangent right, but you're a little confused about the sine and cosine. Here is the standard triangle again, along with the definitions of the three basic ratios:

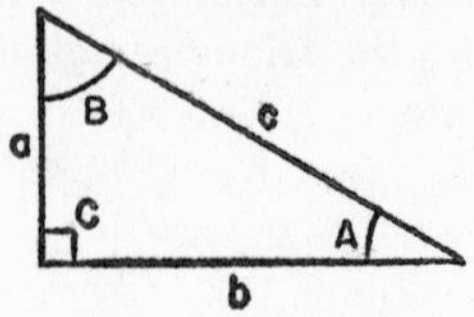

$$\text{sine } A = \frac{\text{opposite side}}{\text{hypotenuse}} = \frac{a}{c}$$

$$\text{cosine } A = \frac{\text{adjacent side}}{\text{hypotenuse}} = \frac{b}{c}$$

$$\text{tangent } A = \frac{\text{opposite side}}{\text{adjacent side}} = \frac{a}{b}$$

Now let's look at the given triangle again:

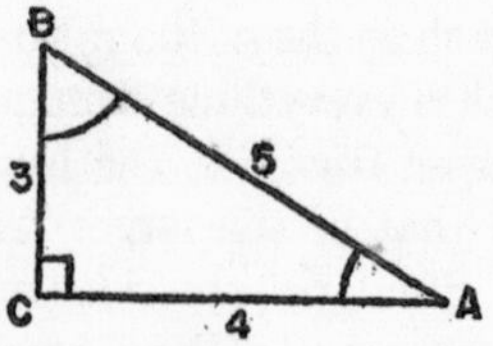

Remember, in the standard notation we are using, side a is opposite angle A, side b is opposite angle B, and side c (the hypotenuse) is opposite angle C (the right angle). In this case, then, side a is 3, side b is 4, and side c is 5. So

$$\sin A = \frac{a}{c} = \frac{3}{5} \qquad \cos A = \frac{b}{c} = \frac{4}{5} \qquad \tan A = \frac{a}{b} = \frac{3}{4}$$

Complete the division, and return to page 319 to select the correct answer.

[*from page 312*]

YOUR ANSWER: This is a correct representation of a 30° right triangle:

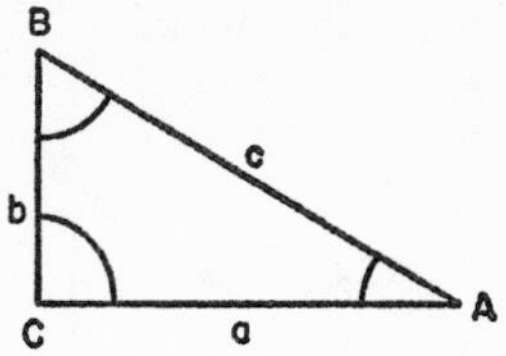

No, it isn't. There are two things wrong with it.

First, the right angle should be marked with the boxlike symbol, rather than with the arc symbol.

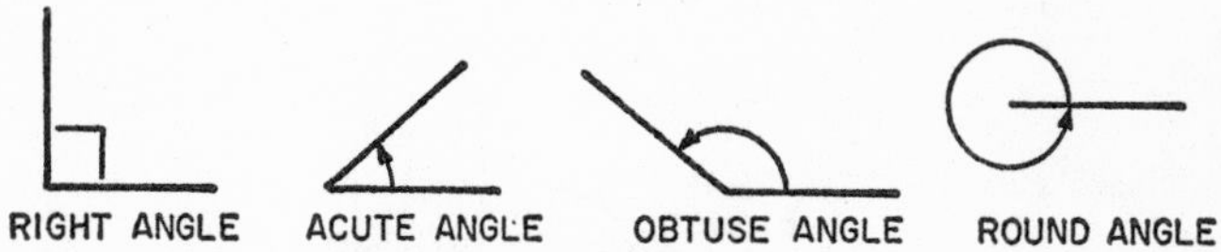

Second, and more important, each side of the triangle should be labeled with the small letter corresponding to the capital letter of the *opposite* angle. So side c is labeled correctly in this figure, but sides a and b are not. The side *opposite* angle A should be labeled a, and the side *opposite* angle B should be labeled b.

With these two things in mind, return to page 312 to make another choice.

[*from page 322*]

YOUR ANSWER: $a = 24.0$ ft.

Wait a minute! You're off the track.
Look at the triangle again:

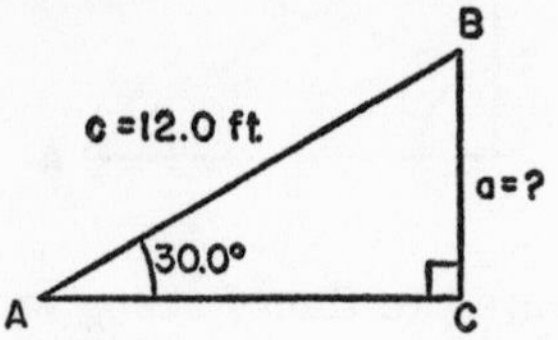

We are given the information that sin 30.0° = 0.500. In other words, we are told that side *a* of the *standard* 30.0° right triangle is 0.500:

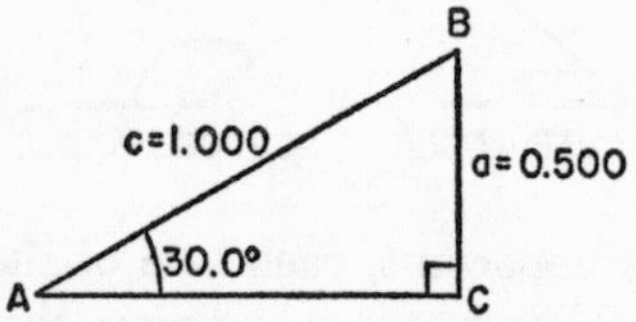

So the correct proportion is

$$\frac{a}{12 \text{ ft.}} = \frac{0.500}{1.000}, \quad \text{or just} \quad \frac{a}{12 \text{ ft.}} = 0.500 \quad \left(\textit{not}\ \frac{12 \text{ ft.}}{a} = 0.500\right)$$

Therefore,

$$a = 0.500 \times 12 \text{ ft.}$$

Study the explanation and complete the multiplication. When you have the correct answer, return to page 322 to try again.

[from page 325]

YOUR ANSWER: $(\sin A)^2 + (\cos A)^2 = 1$.

Good. According to the Pythagorean theorem,

$$a^2 + b^2 = c^2$$

Dividing both sides of this expression by c^2, we get

$$\frac{a^2}{c^2} + \frac{b^2}{c^2} = 1$$

But $\frac{a}{c} = \sin A$, so $\frac{a^2}{c^2} = (\sin A)^2$, or as it's usually written, $\sin^2 A$.

And $\frac{b}{c} = \cos A$, so $\frac{b^2}{c^2} = (\cos A)^2$, or $\cos^2 A$. Therefore,

$$\sin^2 A + \cos^2 A = 1$$

This is true for all right triangles because the Pythagorean theorem is true for all right triangles.

There are many other trigonometric identities which can be proved by algebraic manipulation, combined with the definitions of the basic ratios. Here are these definitions and the general triangle again, for your reference:

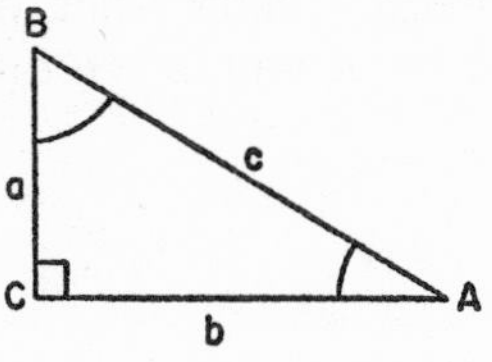

$$\sin A = \frac{\text{opposite side}}{\text{hypotenuse}} = \frac{a}{c}$$

$$\cos A = \frac{\text{adjacent side}}{\text{hypotenuse}} = \frac{b}{c}$$

$$\tan A = \frac{\text{opposite side}}{\text{adjacent side}} = \frac{a}{b}$$

All the identities below are true. Try your hand at proving them.

1. $\frac{\sin A}{\cos A} = \tan A$.
2. $(\tan A) \times (\cos A) = \sin A$.
3. $(1 + \sin A) \times (1 - \sin A) = \cos^2 A$.

Turn to page 320 for the correct solutions.

[*from page 321*]

YOUR ANSWER: If $\cos A = 0.830$, then $\sin A = 0.558$ and $\tan A = 1.49$.

Well, you found the sine correctly, but you missed the tangent. Just for practice, let's go through the whole problem.

Since $\sin^2 A + \cos^2 A = 1$

$$\begin{aligned}\sin^2 A &= 1 - \cos^2 A \\ \sin^2 A &= 1 - 0.830^2 \\ \sin A &= \sqrt{1 - 0.830^2} \\ &= \sqrt{1 - 0.689} \\ &= \sqrt{0.311} \\ &= 0.558\end{aligned}$$

Now for the tangent. We have seen that

$$\tan A = \frac{\sin A}{\cos A}$$

In this case, then,

$$\tan A = \frac{0.558}{0.830} \quad \left(\textit{not}\ \frac{0.830}{0.558}\right)$$

Study this explanation until you're sure you know what you're doing. Then complete the division to find tan A and return to page 321 to choose the correct answer.

[*from page 312*]

YOUR ANSWER: This diagram is a correct representation of a 30° right triangle.

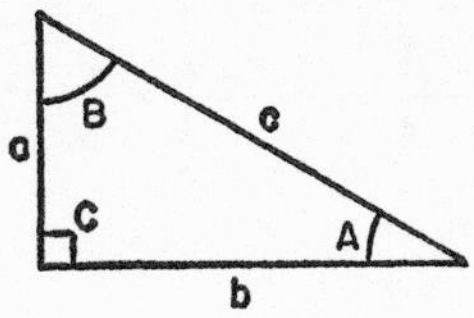

Right. The identifying angle, 30°, is labeled A; the complementary angle, 60°, is labeled B; and the right angle is labeled C. Then side a is opposite angle A; side b is opposite angle B; and the hypotenuse, side c, is opposite angle C.

With the aid of this standard notation, we can define the three basic constant ratios more formally:

1. The ratio of the side opposite the acute angle to the hypotenuse is called the *sine* of the angle: sine $A = \frac{a}{c}$.
2. The ratio of the side adjacent to the acute angle to the hypotenuse is called the *cosine* of the angle: cosine $A = \frac{b}{c}$.
3. The ratio of the side opposite the acute angle to the adjacent side is called the *tangent* of the angle: tangent $A = \frac{a}{b}$.

Find the sine, cosine, and tangent (usually abbreviated to *sin, cos,* and *tan*) of angle A of this triangle:

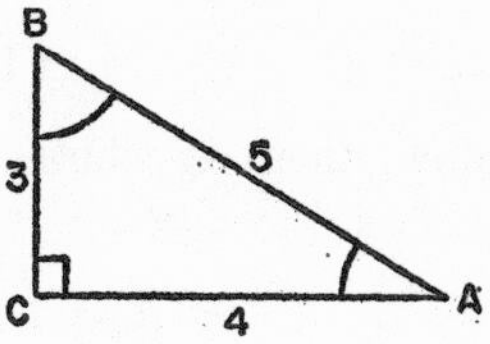

$\sin A = 0.800$, $\cos A = 0.600$, $\tan A = 0.750$. **page 314**

$\sin A = 0.600$, $\cos A = 0.800$, $\tan A = 0.750$. **page 322**

$\sin A = 0.800$, $\cos A = 0.600$, $\tan A = 1.333$. **page 327**

[*from page 317*]

Here are correct proofs for the identities on page 317.

1.
$$\frac{\sin A}{\cos A} = \frac{\frac{a}{c}}{\frac{b}{c}} = \frac{a}{\not{c}} \times \frac{\not{c}}{b} = \frac{a}{b}$$

But $\frac{a}{b} = \tan A$, so

$$\frac{\sin A}{\cos A} = \tan A$$

2.
$$\tan A = \frac{a}{b}, \quad \text{and} \quad \cos A = \frac{b}{c},$$

so

$$(\tan A) \times (\cos A) = \frac{a}{\not{b}} \times \frac{\not{b}}{c} = \frac{a}{c}$$

And $\frac{a}{c} = \sin A$, so

$$(\tan A) \times (\cos A) = \sin A$$

(Incidentally, you might have proved this relationship from the identity $\frac{\sin A}{\cos A} = \tan A$ merely by multiplying both sides by $\cos A$.)

3. The proof of the third identity, $(1 + \sin A) \times (1 - \sin A)$, is just slightly different. First, multiplying the two factors of the left side, we find that

$$(1 + \sin A) \times (1 - \sin A) = 1 - \sin^2 A$$

What we want to know, then, is whether $1 - \sin^2 A = \cos^2 A$. Going back to the very first identity we proved,

$$\sin^2 A + \cos^2 A = 1,$$

and subtracting $\sin^2 A$ from both sides, we see that it is true that

$$\cos^2 A = 1 - \sin^2 A, \quad \text{or} \quad (1 + \sin A) \times (1 - \sin A)$$

To learn about the usefulness of these identities go on to page 321.

[*from page 320*]

We have used the Pythagorean theorem, $a^2 + b^2 = c^2$, to show that for any right triangle, $\sin^2 A + \cos^2 A = 1$. From this relationship, in turn, we've seen that $\cos^2 A = 1 - \sin^2 A$. By the same reasoning, we can show that $\sin^2 A = 1 - \cos^2 A$.

Using the definitions of sine, cosine, and tangent of an angle, we showed that $\dfrac{\sin A}{\cos A} = \tan A$, and that $(\cos A) \times (\tan A) = \sin A$.

The usefulness of these identities should immediately be obvious. Given either the sine or cosine of the acute angle of any right triangle, we can find the other two basic ratios very quickly. For example, suppose we know that $\sin A = 0.832$. Then we know that

$$\cos^2 A = 1 - (0.832)^2$$

Taking the square root of both sides of this expression, we find that

$$\cos A = \sqrt{1 - 0.832^2} = \sqrt{1 - 0.692} = \sqrt{0.308} = 0.555$$

And knowing $\sin A$ and $\cos A$, we can easily find $\tan A$:

$$\tan A = \frac{\sin A}{\cos A} = \frac{0.832}{0.555} = 1.50$$

(You should have no trouble performing these calculations on your slide rule, so we won't bother going through the mechanics here.)

Suppose you try it: If $\cos A = 0.830$, find $\sin A$ and $\tan A$.

$\sin A = 0.558$, $\tan A = 1.49$. **page 318**

$\sin A = 0.558$, $\tan A = 0.672$. **page 324**

$\sin A = 0.311$, $\tan A = 0.375$. **page 330**

[*from page 319*]

YOUR ANSWER: Sin $A = 0.600$, cos $A = 0.800$, and tan $A = 0.750$.

Right. Here is the triangle again:

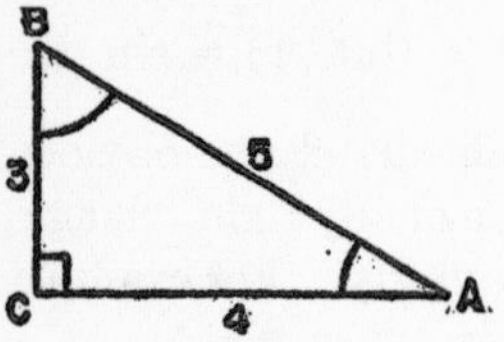

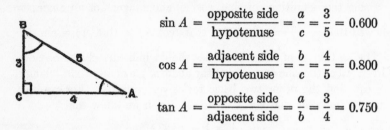

$$\sin A = \frac{\text{opposite side}}{\text{hypotenuse}} = \frac{a}{c} = \frac{3}{5} = 0.600$$

$$\cos A = \frac{\text{adjacent side}}{\text{hypotenuse}} = \frac{b}{c} = \frac{4}{5} = 0.800$$

$$\tan A = \frac{\text{opposite side}}{\text{adjacent side}} = \frac{a}{b} = \frac{3}{4} = 0.750$$

In a right triangle with sides 3, 4, and 5 units long, angle A turns out to be 37.9°. The relationships of the sides remain the same, of course, when the hypotenuse is of unit length.

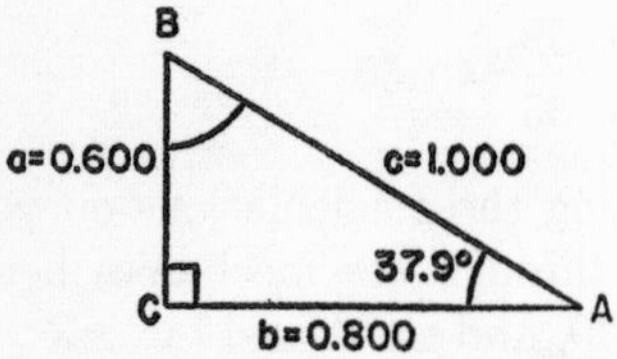

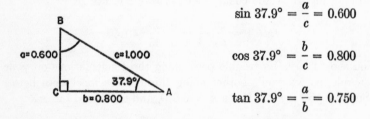

$$\sin 37.9° = \frac{a}{c} = 0.600$$

$$\cos 37.9° = \frac{b}{c} = 0.800$$

$$\tan 37.9° = \frac{a}{b} = 0.750$$

Here is the heart of the matter, then: Knowing the sides of any right triangle, we can construct the standard triangle for the collection of similar right triangles. In this standard triangle, side $a = \sin A$, side $b = \cos A$, and side $c = 1$.

And from this standard triangle, in turn, we can find the unknown sides of any similar triangle, knowing only one side. This is what trigonometry is all about.

Given that the sine of $30.0° = 0.500$, find side a of the triangle below:

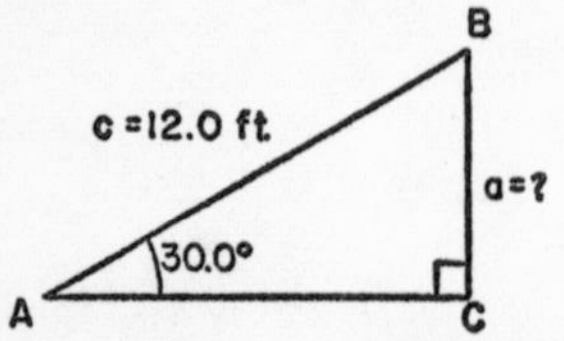

$a = 24.0$ ft. **page 316**

$a = 6.0$ ft. **page 325**

I need some help. **page 328**

[*from page 332*]

YOUR ANSWER: Yes, it is true that the sine of one acute angle of a right triangle is equal to the cosine of the other acute angle.

That's right. The three basic ratios are defined for both acute angles of a right triangle, not just the identifying angle.

$$\text{sine} = \frac{\text{opposite side}}{\text{hypotenuse}} \qquad \sin A = \frac{a}{c} \qquad \sin B = \frac{b}{c}$$

$$\text{cosine} = \frac{\text{adjacent side}}{\text{hypotenuse}} \qquad \cos A = \frac{b}{c} \qquad \cos B = \frac{a}{c}$$

$$\text{tangent} = \frac{\text{opposite side}}{\text{adjacent side}} \qquad \tan A = \frac{a}{b} \qquad \tan B = \frac{b}{a}$$

Clearly, then, for any right triangle,

$$\sin A = \cos B \quad \text{and} \quad \cos A = \sin B$$

In other words, the sine of one acute angle is equal to the cosine of its complementary angle.

Until now, we've found the size of angles by measuring them with a protractor. Now, picture a rod one unit long, pivoted at the center of a large protractor, and having a weighted string hanging from its tip. Such a mechanism could form any right triangle desired. The sketch below shows it in several positions.

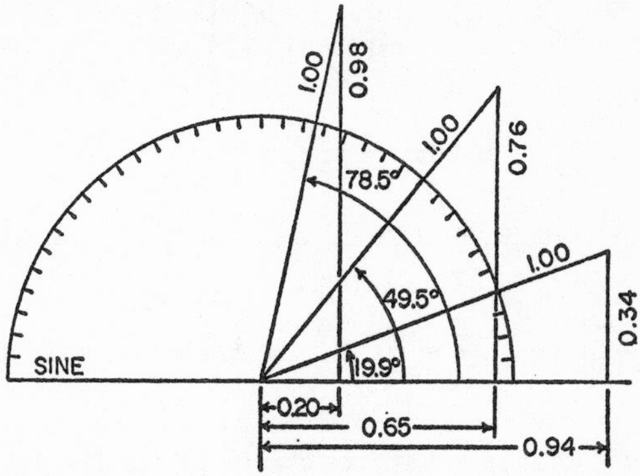

Complete the following sentence. From the sketch, it appears that the ______ has a value of nearly 1 for angles close to 90°.

sine. **page 333** cosine. **page 335** tangent. **page 342**

[*from page 321*]

YOUR ANSWER: If $\cos A = 0.830$, then $\sin A = 0.558$ and $\tan A = 0.672$.

That's right. Here's the way it goes:

We know that $\sin^2 A + \cos^2 A = 1$, so $\sin^2 A = 1 - \cos^2 A$. Since we are told that $\cos A = 0.830$,

$$\begin{aligned} \sin^2 A &= 1 - 0.830^2 \\ \sin A &= \sqrt{1 - 0.830^2} \\ &= \sqrt{1 - 0.689} \\ &= \sqrt{0.311} \\ &= 0.558 \end{aligned}$$

The tangent is found by using the identity $\tan A = \dfrac{\sin A}{\cos A}$:

$$\begin{aligned} \tan A &= \frac{0.558}{0.830} \\ &= 0.672 \end{aligned}$$

Now try this one:

Given that $\sin A = 0.800$, find B, a, b, $\cos A$, and $\tan A$ of the triangle below:

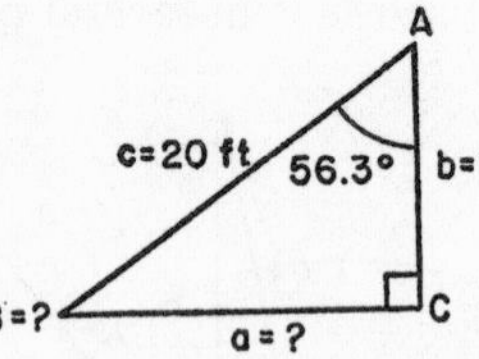

$B = 33.7°$, $a = 16$ ft., $b = 12$ ft., $\cos A = 0.600$, and $\tan A = 1.33$.
page 332

$B = 31.7°$, $a = 13$ ft., $b = 10$ ft., $\cos A = 0.600$, and $\tan A = 1.25$.
page 336

$B = 35.7°$, $a = 14$ ft., $b = 9$ ft., $\cos A = 0.650$, $\tan A = 1.25$. **page 339**

YOUR ANSWER: $a = 6$ ft.

Of course. Here is the triangle again:

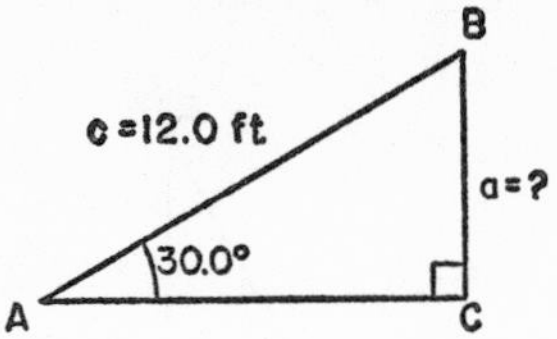

Since we are told that sin 30.0° = 0.500, we know that

$$\frac{a}{12 \text{ ft.}} = 0.500$$

$$a = 0.500 \times 12 \text{ ft.}$$

$$a = 6 \text{ ft.}$$

Similarly, given that cos 30.0° = 0.866, we can find b:

$$\frac{b}{12 \text{ ft.}} = 0.866, \text{ so}$$

$$b = 0.866 \times 12 \text{ ft.}$$

$$b = 10.4 \text{ ft.}$$

So far we have not learned any method by which we can calculate b knowing only c and sin 30.0°. But it can be done.

There are many different expressions relating the sine, cosine, and tangent to each other in various ways. When these relationships are independent of the size of the angles involved, they are usually called *trigonometric identities.* Many of them can be proved by use of the Pythagorean theorem of geometry:

The square of the hypotenuse of a right triangle is equal to the sum of the squares of the other two sides. That is

$$a^2 + b^2 = c^2$$

By dividing both sides of this expression by c^2, we can show that

$(\sin A)^2 + (\cos A)^2 = 1.$ **page 317**

I need some help. **page 331**

$(\tan A)^2 = (\cos A)^2.$ **page 329**

[*from page 333*]

YOUR ANSWER: $a = 43.5$ in., $c = 39.0$ in., and $B = 26.2°$.

Well, you have the complementary angle right, but you seem to have confused the sine and the cosine. Here is the triangle again:

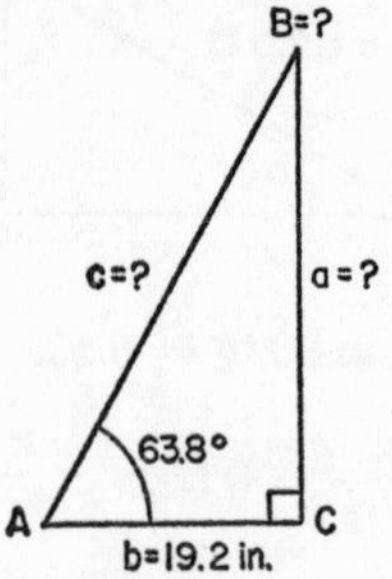

You were told that sin 63.8° = 0.897 and tan 63.8° = 2.03. Since $\frac{a}{b}$ must also be equal to tan 63.8°, and we know the value of b, it's a simple matter to find a:

$$\frac{a}{19.2 \text{ in.}} = 2.03$$

$$a = 19.2 \text{ in.} \times 2.03 = 39.0 \text{ in.}$$

(If you prefer, of course, you can use the proportion directly, setting 203 on the C scale over the left index of the D scale, and sliding the hairline to 192 on the D scale.)

Now—and this may have been where you got off the track—the sine of angle A is $\frac{a}{c}$, *not* $\frac{b}{c}$. Accordingly, since we know that sin 63.8° = 0.897 and $a = 39.0$ inches, we can write the proportion

$$\frac{39.0 \text{ in.}}{c} = 0.897$$

So
$$c = \frac{39.0 \text{ in.}}{0.897} = 43.5 \text{ in.}$$

Study this solution carefully. Then return to page 333 to choose the right answer.

[*from page 319*]

YOUR ANSWER: Sin A = 0.800, cos A = 0.600, and tan A = 1.333.

No. Evidently you are confusing sides a and b. Here is the standard triangle again, along with the definitions of the three basic ratios:

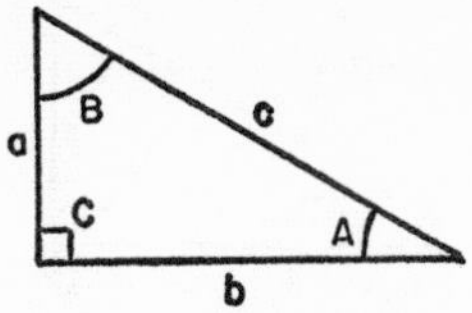

$$\text{sine } A = \frac{\text{opposite side}}{\text{hypotenuse}} = \frac{a}{c}$$

$$\text{cosine } A = \frac{\text{adjacent side}}{\text{hypotenuse}} = \frac{b}{c}$$

$$\text{tangent } A = \frac{\text{opposite side}}{\text{adjacent side}} = \frac{a}{b}$$

Notice again that side a is opposite angle A, side b is opposite angle B, and side c (the hypotenuse) is opposite angle C (the right angle).

Now look at the given triangle again:

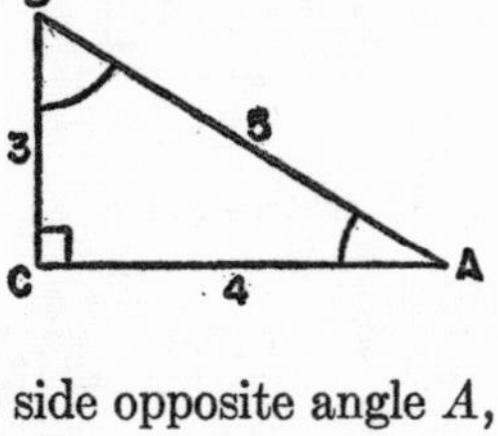

In this case, side a, the side opposite angle A, is 3;
side b, the side opposite angle B, is 4, and
side c, the hypotenuse, is 5.

Therefore:

$$\sin A = \frac{a}{c} = \frac{3}{5} \qquad \cos A = \frac{b}{c} = \frac{4}{5} \quad \text{and} \quad \tan A = \frac{a}{b} = \frac{3}{4}$$

Complete the division, and then return to page 319 to choose the right answer.

[*from page 322*]

YOUR ANSWER: I need some help.

Let's see what we can do. Here is the triangle again:

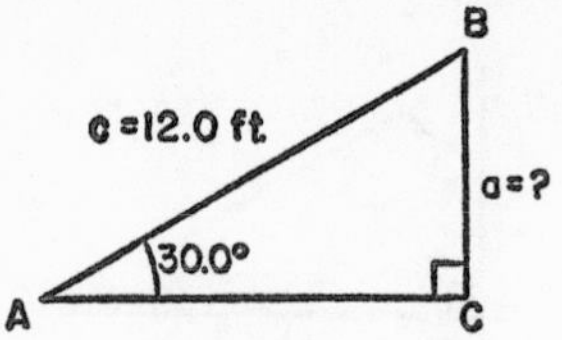

We were given the information that sin 30.0° = 0.500. In other words, we were told that the ratio of side a to the hypotenuse is 0.500:

$$\frac{a}{12 \text{ ft.}} = 0.500$$

$$a = 0.500 \times 12 \text{ ft.}$$

Or you can think of it this way: sin 30.0° = 0.500 means that side a of the *standard* 30.0° right triangle (the 30.0° right triangle with hypotenuse 1) is 0.500:

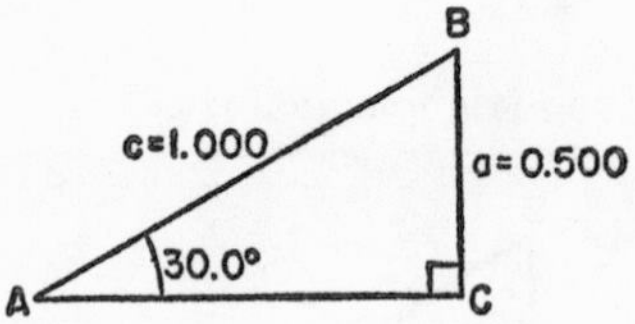

In this case, the appropriate relation is

$$\frac{a}{12 \text{ ft.}} = \frac{0.500}{1.000}, \quad \text{or just} \quad \frac{a}{12 \text{ ft.}} = 0.500$$

From this we see that $a = 0.500 \times 12$ ft. And this is the same relationship we got the other way.

If you still feel hazy about this, return to page 284 for some review. Otherwise complete the multiplication and return to page 322 to select the correct answer.

YOUR ANSWER: $(\tan A)^2 = (\cos A)^2$.

This is a poor guess. Let's start at the beginning.

According to the Pythagorean theorem, the square of the hypotenuse of a right triangle is equal to the sum of the squares of the other two sides. Using our standard notation,

$$a^2 + b^2 = c^2$$

Now, if we divide both sides of this expression by c^2, we get

$$\frac{a^2}{c^2} + \frac{b^2}{c^2} = 1, \quad \text{or} \quad \left(\frac{a}{b}\right)^2 + \left(\frac{b}{c}\right)^2 = 1$$

But $\frac{a}{c} = \sin A$, and $\frac{b}{c} = \cos A$, so

$$\left(\frac{a}{c}\right)^2 + \left(\frac{b}{c}\right)^2 = (\sin A)^2 + (\cos A)^2$$

Therefore,

$$(\sin A)^2 + (\cos A)^2 = 1$$

Or, as it is usually written,

$$\sin^2 A + \cos^2 A = 1$$

Study this explanation carefully. Then return to page 325 to choose the correct answer.

[*from page 321*]

YOUR ANSWER: If $\cos A = 0.830$, then $\sin A = 0.311$ and $\tan A = 0.375$.

No. You left out a vital step. Here's the way it goes:
Since $\sin^2 A + \cos^2 A = 1$

$$\sin^2 A = 1 - \cos^2 A$$

Now—and this is the step you missed—to find $\sin A$ we have to take the square root of each side of this expression. Thus

$$\sin A = \sqrt{1 - \cos^2 A}$$

Then, since we have been told that $\cos A = 0.830$, we see that

$$\begin{aligned} \sin A &= \sqrt{1 - 0.830^2} \\ &= \sqrt{1 - 0.689} \\ &= \sqrt{0.311} \quad (\textit{not} \text{ just } 0.311) \end{aligned}$$

When we know both the sine and cosine, we can easily find the tangent:

$$\tan A = \frac{\sin A}{\cos A}$$

Finish the calculations for yourself. Then return to page 321 to choose the correct answer.

[*from page 325*]

YOUR ANSWER: I need some help.

Let's start at the beginning.

According to the Pythagorean theorem, the square of the hypotenuse of a right triangle is equal to the sum of the squares of the other two sides. Using our standard notation,

$$a^2 + b^2 = c^2$$

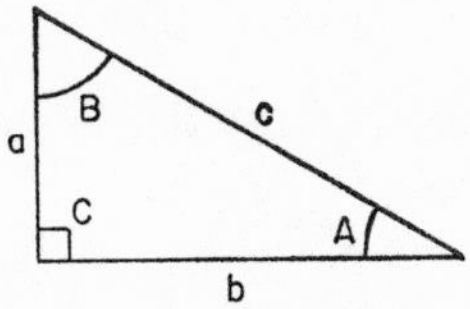

Now, if we divide both sides of this expression by c^2, we get

$$\frac{a^2}{c^2} + \frac{b^2}{c^2} = 1$$

which becomes

$$\left(\frac{a}{c}\right)^2 + \left(\frac{b}{c}\right)^2 = 1$$

But $\frac{a}{c} = \sin A$, and $\frac{b}{c} = \cos A$, so

$$\left(\frac{a}{c}\right)^2 + \left(\frac{b}{c}\right)^2 = (\sin A)^2 + (\cos A)^2$$

Therefore,

$$(\sin A)^2 + (\cos A)^2 = 1$$

Or, as it is usually written,

$$\sin^2 A + \cos^2 A = 1$$

Study this explanation carefully. When you think you understand the procedure, and could duplicate it yourself, return to page 325 to choose the right answer.

[*from page 324*]

YOUR ANSWER: $B = 33.7°$, $a = 16$ ft., $b = 12$ ft., $\cos A = 0.600$, and $\tan A = 1.33$.

Very good. Here's the way it goes:

Sin A was given as 0.800, so $\cos^2 A = 1 - 0.800^2$, and $\cos A = \sqrt{1 - 0.800^2} = \sqrt{1 - 0.640} = \sqrt{0.360} = 0.600$

Next,

$$\tan A = \frac{\sin A}{\cos A} = \frac{0.800}{0.600} = 1.33$$

To find the unknown sides, we use the definitions of sine and cosine:

$$\frac{a}{c} = \sin A, \quad \text{so} \quad a = c \times \sin A = 20 \text{ ft.} \times 0.800 = 16 \text{ ft.}$$

$$\frac{b}{c} = \cos A, \quad \text{so} \quad b = c \times \cos A = 20 \text{ ft.} \times 0.600 = 12 \text{ ft.}$$

Finally, since the sum of the acute angles of a right triangle is 180°,

$$B + 56.3° = 90°, \quad \text{and} \quad B = 90° - 56.3° = 33.7°$$

From our study so far, it's obvious that trigonometry is a powerful tool. All that is necessary now is to find some way of increasing our collection of standard triangles to include all possible right triangles. It turns out that this method is too complicated to go into right now, but we can learn to use the information with which it provides us.

To begin, consider the complementary angles of the triangles we've already studied.

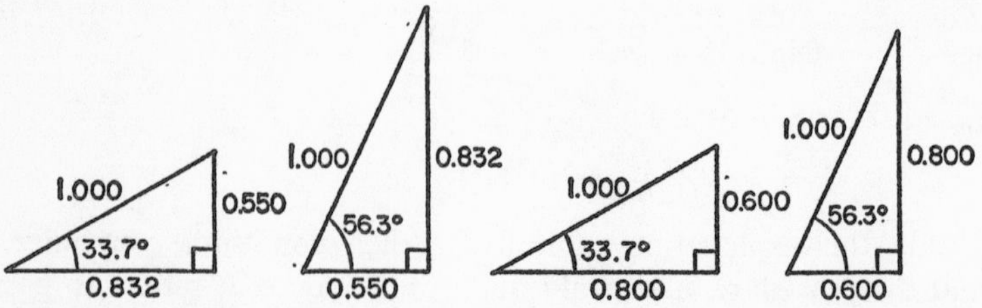

Is it true that the sine of one acute angle of a right triangle is equal to the cosine of the other acute angle?

Yes. **page 323**

No. **page 337**

[*from page 323*]

YOUR ANSWER: From the sketch, it appears that the sine ratio has a value of nearly 1 for angles close to 90°.

Right. For an angle close to 0°, the value of the sine is close to zero, because the opposite side is very small as compared with the hypotenuse. As the angle is increased, the sine gets larger.

For angles very close to 90° the sine ratio is very close to 1, because the opposite side is almost as long as the hypotenuse.

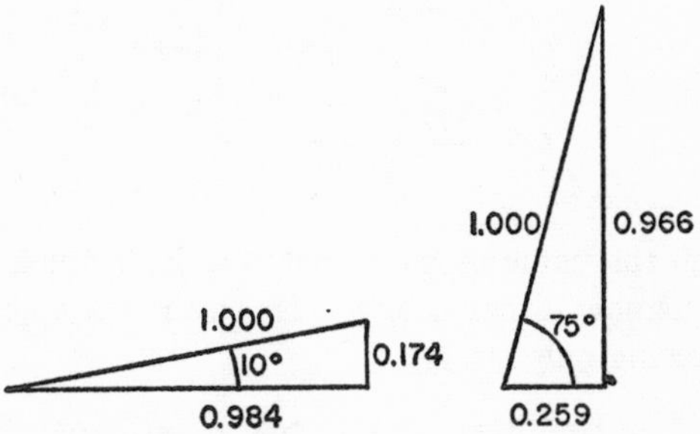

The cosine, on the other hand, is close to 1 when the angle is very small, because for small angles the adjacent side is almost as long as the hypotenuse. For larger angles, close to 90°, the cosine is almost zero, because the adjacent side is then very small in relation to the hypotenuse. So for angles between 0° and 90°, neither the sine nor cosine can be less than zero nor more than 1.

The tangent ratio, however, is not limited in this way. The tangent is close to zero for very small angles, but increases rapidly as the angle becomes larger, nearing 90°.

Now solve this triangle, given the information that sin 63.8° = 0.897 and tan 63.8° = 2.03.

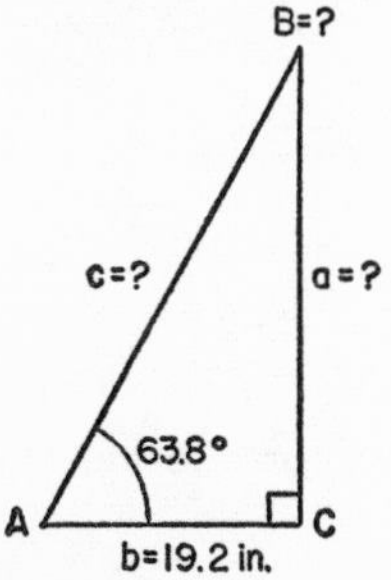

a = 43.5 in., c = 39.0 in., B = 26.2°. **page 326**

a = 39.0 in., c = 43.5 in., B = 26.2°. **page 338**

a = 33.0 in., c = 41.5 in., B = 63.8°. **page 341**

[*from page 338*]

YOUR ANSWER: This solution is incorrect: If $A = 32.0°$, $\sin 32.0° = 0.530$, and $b = 6.21$, then $a = 3.88$ and $c = 7.32$.

No, it's right.

With the given information, we can construct the triangle shown below.

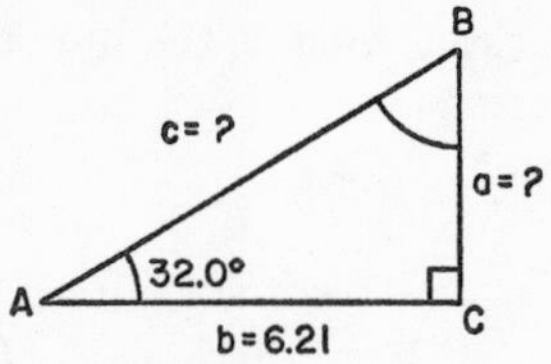

We are given the value of sin A, but that isn't much help at first, since we don't know either a or c. However, we do know how to find cos A knowing only sin A:

$$\sin^2 A + \cos^2 A = 1, \quad \text{so} \quad \cos^2 A = 1 - \sin^2 A,$$

and

$$\cos A = \sqrt{1 - \sin^2 A}.$$

Therefore,

$$\begin{aligned} \cos 32.0° &= \sqrt{1 - 0.530^2} \\ &= \sqrt{1 - 0.281} \\ &= \sqrt{0.719} \\ &= 0.848 \end{aligned}$$

Now, since $\frac{b}{c} = \cos A$, and we know both b and cos A, it's simple to determine c:

$$\frac{6.21}{c} = 0.848, \quad \text{so} \quad c = \frac{6.21}{0.848} = 7.32$$

Next, since $\frac{a}{c} = \sin A$,

$$\frac{a}{7.32} = 0.530, \quad \text{and} \quad a = 0.530 \times 7.32 = 3.88$$

Study this solution, and then return to page 338 for another try.

[*from page 323*]

YOUR ANSWER: From the sketch, it appears that the cosine has a value of nearly 1 for angles close to 90°.

No, you didn't analyze the sketch correctly. Here it is again, with the sides *opposite* the angles to be considered indicated by boldface type.

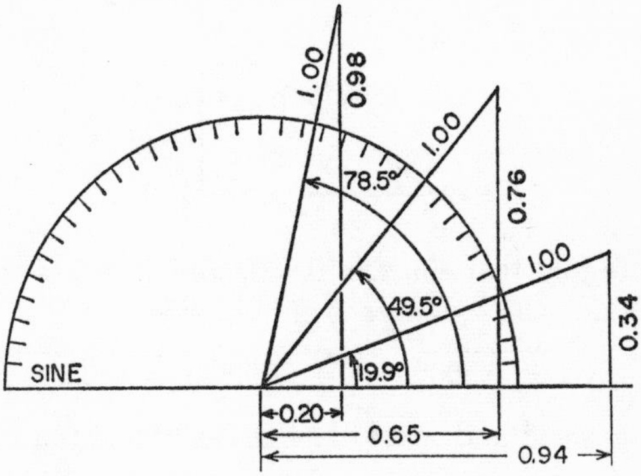

For all three of the triangles shown in the sketch, the hypotenuse is 1. But for the 19.9° angle, the opposite side is 0.34, for the 49.5° angle it is 0.76, and for the 78.5° angle it is 0.98. Now, since the sine of an angle is defined as the ratio of the side opposite the angle to the hypotenuse,

$$\sin 19.9° = \frac{0.34}{1.00} \qquad \sin 49.5° = \frac{0.76}{1.00} \qquad \sin 78.5° = \frac{0.98}{1.00}$$

But 78.5° is fairly close to 90°, and $\frac{0.98}{1.00}$ is just 0.98, which is almost 1. Well, then, which of the three basic ratios has a value of nearly 1 for angles close to 90°?

Return to page 323 and answer the question correctly.

[*from page 324*]

YOUR ANSWER: $B = 31.7°$, $a = 13$ ft., $b = 10$ ft., $\cos A = 0.600$, and $\tan A = 1.25$.

If you had really worked this problem out for yourself, you would have found that only $\cos A = 0.600$ is correct.

Let's make a fresh start.

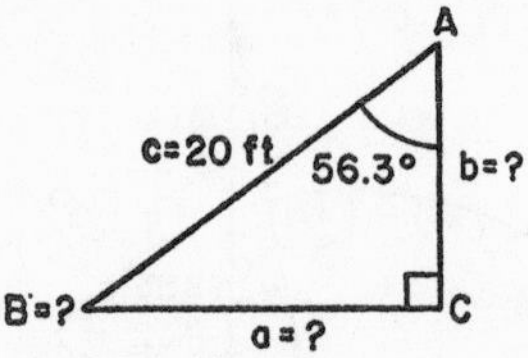

Since we are told that $\sin A = 0.800$, we know that $\cos^2 A = 1 - (0.800)^2$. Taking the square root of both sides,

$$\cos A = \sqrt{1 - 0.800^2} = \sqrt{1 - 0.640} = \sqrt{0.360} = 0.600$$

Now, knowing $\sin A$ and $\cos A$, we can easily find $\tan A$:

$$\tan A = \frac{\sin A}{\cos A} = \frac{0.800}{0.600} = 1.33$$

Next, let's determine the unknown sides:

We know that $\frac{a}{c} = \sin A$. Here, c is 20 ft. and $\sin A$ is 0.800, so

$$\frac{a}{20 \text{ ft.}} = 0.800, \quad \text{and} \quad a = 20 \text{ ft.} \times 0.800 = 16 \text{ ft.}$$

Similarly, $\frac{b}{c} = \cos A$, so

$$\frac{b}{20 \text{ ft.}} = 0.600, \quad \text{and} \quad b = 20 \text{ ft.} \times 0.600 = 12 \text{ ft.}$$

We're now left with only one unknown to determine—the angle B—and it's easiest of all:

The sum of the acute angles of a right triangle is 90°, so

$$B + 56.3° = 90°, \quad \text{and} \quad B = 90° - 56.3° = 33.7°$$

Study this analysis until you're sure you could do this problem. Then return to page 324 to choose the right answer.

YOUR ANSWER: No, it is not true that the sine of one acute angle of a right triangle is equal to the cosine of the other acute angle.

It's true, all right. Look at the general triangle and the definitions of the three basic ratios for angle A again:

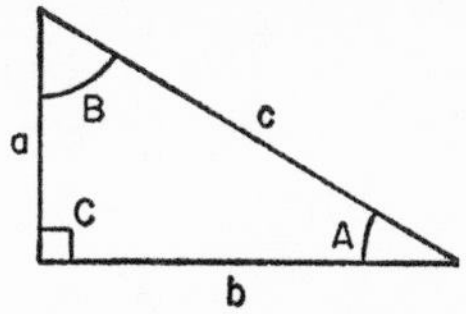

$$\sin A = \frac{\text{opposite side}}{\text{hypotenuse}} = \frac{a}{c}$$

$$\cos A = \frac{\text{adjacent side}}{\text{hypotenuse}} = \frac{b}{c}$$

$$\tan A = \frac{\text{opposite side}}{\text{adjacent side}} = \frac{a}{b}$$

The three basic ratios for angle B would be defined in exactly the same way:

$$\sin B = \frac{\text{opposite side}}{\text{hypotenuse}}$$

$$\cos B = \frac{\text{adjacent side}}{\text{hypotenuse}}$$

$$\tan B = \frac{\text{opposite side}}{\text{adjacent side}}$$

But when we're talking about angle B, the opposite side is side b, and the *adjacent* side is side a. So

$$\sin B = \frac{b}{c} \qquad \cos B = \frac{a}{c} \qquad \tan B = \frac{b}{a}$$

But this means that

$$\sin A = \cos B \quad \text{and} \quad \cos A = \sin B$$

When you are sure you understand this relationship, return to page 332 to select the correct answer.

[*from page 333*]

YOUR ANSWER: $a = 39.0$ in., $c = 43.5$ in., and $B = 26.2°$.

Good. You were told that $A = 63.8°$, $b = 19.2$ inches, $\sin 63.8° = 0.897$, and $\tan 63.8° = 2.03$. Therefore, $\frac{a}{19.2 \text{ in.}} = 2.03$, or $\frac{2.03}{1.000}$, so $a = 39.0$ in. Then $\frac{39.0}{c} = 0.897$, or $\frac{0.897}{1.000}$, so $c = 43.5$ in. And B, of course, is equal to $90° - 63.8°$, or $26.2°$.

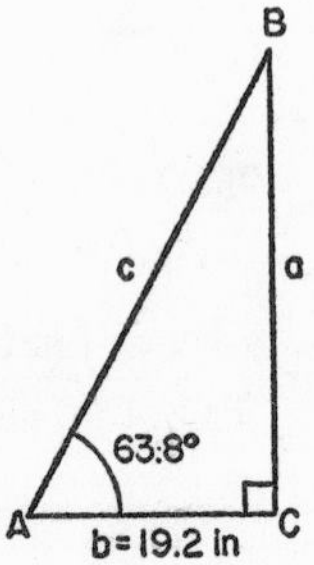

Remember, several proportions can be used to find the unknown values. For example, since $\frac{\sin A}{\cos A} = \tan A$, we know that $\cos A = \frac{\sin A}{\tan A}$. So we might have used the proportion

$$\frac{19.2 \text{ in.}}{c} = \frac{0.897}{2.03}$$

to find the value of c. Don't be afraid to experiment with a problem such as this—you may find an easier way to do it.

Which of the solutions below is incorrect? (For now, don't worry about the units in which the sides are measured.)

If $A = 32.0°$, $\sin 32.0° = 0.530$, and $b = 6.21$, then $a = 3.88$ and $c = 7.32$. **page 334**

If $B = 18.0°$, $\sin 72.0° = 0.951$, $\cos 72.0° = 0.309$, and $c = 84.6$, then $a = 80.5$ and $b = 26.1$. **page 340**

If $A = 46.0°$, $\sin 46.0° = 0.719$, $\tan 46.0° = 1.035$, and $a = 19.9$, then $b = 19.2$ and $c = 28.6$. **page 343**

[*from page 324*]

YOUR ANSWER: $B = 35.7°$, $a = 14$ ft., $b = 9$ ft., $\cos A = 0.650$, and $\tan A = 1.25$.

This looks like a guess, since not one of these figures is correct. Let's make a fresh start. Here is the triangle again:

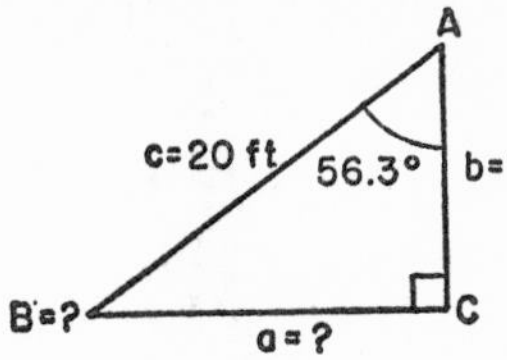

We know that $\cos^2 A = 1 - \sin^2 A$. Since we are told that $\sin A = 0.800$, we know that $\cos^2 A = 1 - (0.800)^2$. Taking the square root of both sides,

$$\cos A = \sqrt{1 - 0.800^2} = \sqrt{1 - 0.640} = \sqrt{0.360} = 0.600$$

Now, knowing $\sin A$ and $\cos A$, we can easily find $\tan A$:

$$\tan A = \frac{\sin A}{\cos A} = \frac{0.800}{0.600} = 1.33$$

Next, let's determine the unknown sides:

We know that $\frac{a}{c} = \sin A$. In this case, c is 20 ft. and $\sin A$ is 0.800, so

$$\frac{a}{20 \text{ ft.}} = 0.800, \quad \text{and} \quad a = 20 \text{ ft.} \times 0.800 = 16 \text{ ft.}$$

Similarly, $\frac{b}{c} = 0.600$, and $b = 20 \text{ ft.} \times 0.600 = 12$ ft.

We're now left with only one unknown to determine—the angle B—and it's the easiest of all:

The sum of the acute angles of a right triangle is 90°, so

$$B + 56.3° = 90°, \quad \text{and} \quad B = 90° - 56.3° = 33.7°$$

Study this analysis uutil you're sure you could do this problem, or a similar one, without any help. Then return to page 324 to choose the right answer.

[*from page 338*]

YOUR ANSWER: This solution is incorrect: If $B = 18.0°$, $\sin 72.0° = 0.951$, $\cos 72.0° = 0.309$, and $c = 84.6$, then $a = 80.5$ and $b = 26.1$.

No, it's right.

With the given information, we can immediately construct the triangle shown below.

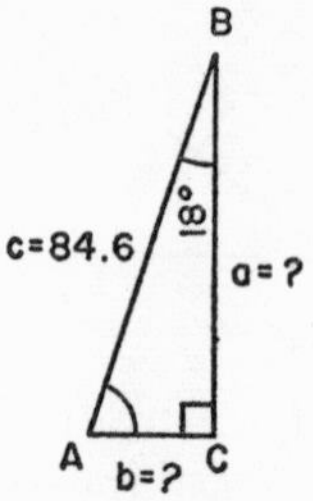

But what about angle A? Well, since $B = 18.0°$, we know that A must be equal to $90.0° - 18.0°$, or $72.0°$. And we are given the information that $\sin 72.0° = 0.951$ and $\cos 72.0° = 0.309$. So it's a simple matter to find a and b:

$$\frac{a}{84.6} = 0.951, \quad \text{so} \quad a = 0.951 \times 84.6 = 80.5$$

$$\frac{b}{84.6} = 0.309, \quad \text{so} \quad b = 0.309 \times 84.6 = 26.1$$

Incidentally, it is possible to do this problem by using the fact that

$$\sin A = \cos B \quad \text{and} \quad \cos A = \sin B$$

In other words, since in this case $B = 18.0°$ and $A = 72.0°$,

$$\sin B = \cos A = 0.309,$$

and

$$\cos B = \sin A = 0.951$$

Study this solution, and then return to page 338 for another try.

[*from page 333*]

YOUR ANSWER: $a = 33.0$ in., $c = 41.5$ in., and $B = 63.8°$.

You'd better look again:

How can angle B be 63.8° if angle A is 63.8°? If both acute angles of the triangle are 63.8°, then the sum of the angles, $A + B + C$, has to be $63.8° + 63.8° + 90°$, or 217.6°.

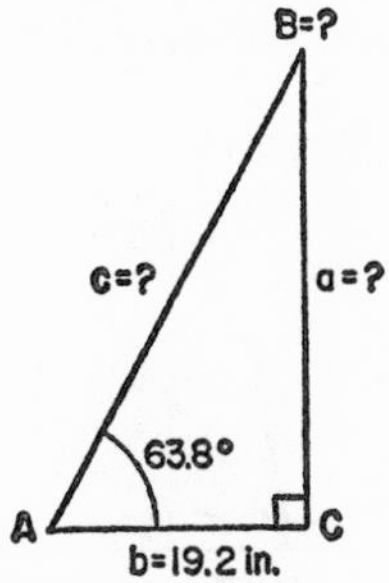

Let's start at the beginning.

You were told that sin 63.8° = 0.897 and tan 63.8° = 2.03. Since $\frac{a}{b}$ must also be equal to tan 63.8°, and we know the value of b, it's a simple matter to find a:

$$\frac{a}{19.2 \text{ in.}} = 2.03, \quad \text{so} \quad a = 19.2 \text{ in.} \times 2.03 = 39.0 \text{ in.}$$

Similarly, knowing a and sin 63.8°, we can easily find side c:

$$\frac{39.0 \text{ in.}}{c} = 0.897, \quad \text{so} \quad c = \frac{39.0 \text{ in.}}{0.897} = 43.5 \text{ in.}$$

Now for angle B. We know angles A and C; they are 63.8° and 90°, respectively. Since $A + B + C = 180°$,

$$B = 180° - A - C = 180° - 63.8° - 90° = 26.2°$$

Study this solution carefully. Then return to page 333 to choose the right answer.

[*from page 323*]

YOUR ANSWER: From the sketch, it appears that the tangent has a value of nearly 1 for angles close to 90°.

No, you didn't analyze the sketch correctly. Here it is again, with the sides opposite the angles to be considered indicated by boldface type.

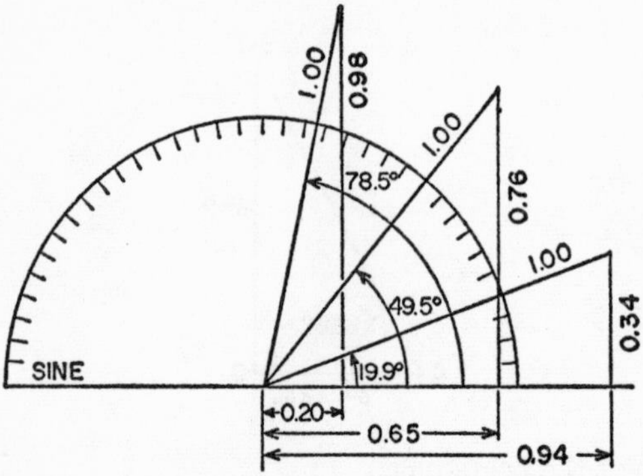

For all three of the triangles shown in the sketch, the hypotenuse is 1. But for the 19.9° angle, the opposite side is 0.34, for the 49.5° angle it is 0.76, and for the 78.5° angle it is 0.98. Now, since the sine of an angle is defined as the ratio of the side opposite the angle to the hypotenuse,

$$\sin 19.9^\circ = \frac{0.34}{1.00} \qquad \sin 49.5^\circ = \frac{0.76}{1.00} \qquad \sin 78.5^\circ = \frac{0.98}{1.00}$$

But 78.5° is fairly close to 90°, and $\frac{0.98}{1.00}$ is just 0.98, which is almost 1. Well, then, which of the three basic ratios has a value of nearly 1 for angles close to 90°?

Return to page 323 and answer the question correctly.

[*from page 338*]

YOUR ANSWER: This solution is incorrect: If $A = 46.0°$, $\sin 46.0° = 0.719$, $\tan 46.0° = 1.035$, and $a = 19.9$, then $b = 19.2$ and $c = 28.6$.

You're right: it is incorrect.

With the given information we can draw the diagram below. We don't even need to find cos 46.0° in order to solve the triangle. We already have all the information we need:

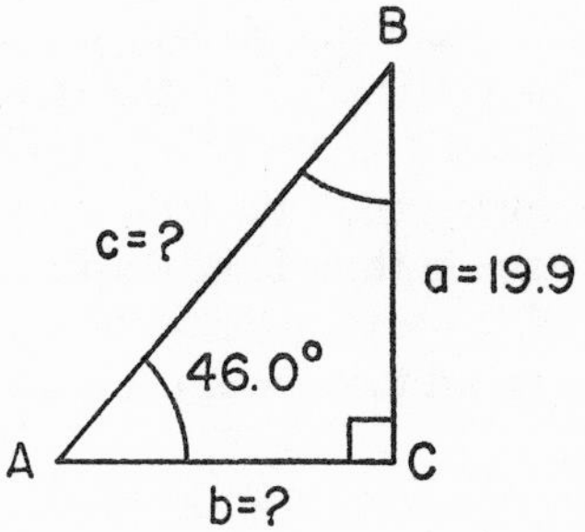

$$\tan 46.0° = 1.035, \quad \text{and also} \quad \tan 46.0° = \frac{a}{b} = \frac{19.9}{b},$$

so
$$\frac{19.9}{b} = 1.035, \quad \text{and} \quad b = 19.2$$

$$\sin 46.0° = 0.719, \quad \text{and also} \quad \sin 46.0° = \frac{a}{c} = \frac{19.9}{c},$$

so
$$\frac{19.9}{c} = 0.719, \quad \text{and} \quad c = 27.7, \quad \textit{not } 28.6$$

Or you might have done the problem this way: First, calculating the value of cos 46.0°, we know that $\frac{\sin 46.0°}{\cos 46.0°} = \tan 46.0°$, so

$$\cos 46.0° = \frac{\sin 46.0°}{\tan 46.0°} = \frac{0.719}{1.035} = 0.691$$

And, knowing both the sine and cosine, it's a simple matter to construct the standard triangle for all 46.0° right triangles:

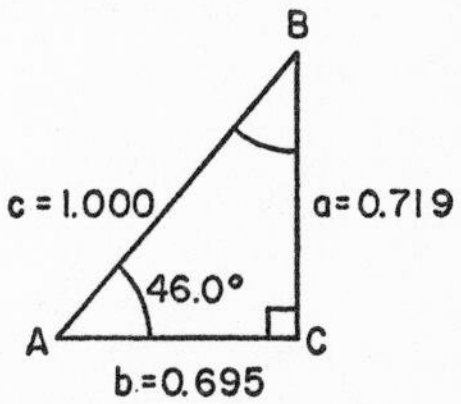

[*from page 343*]

Before we go on to the next chapter, let's review a bit:

1. The basic use of trigonometry is the solution of right triangles, i.e., determining the values of unknown sides and angles of right triangles.
2. The group of all right triangles is divided into collections of similar triangles having the same angles and proportional sides.
3. Within each collection, the triangle with hypotenuse 1 is considered the standard triangle for the collection. By utilizing the proportionality of the standard, the unknown sides of other triangles in the collection are easily determined.
4. The ratios of corresponding sides are constant for all similar triangles. There are three basic ratios:
   a. The ratio of the side opposite the acute angle to the hypotenuse is called the *sine* of the angle.

   $$\sin A = \frac{a}{c}$$

   b. The ratio of the side adjacent to the acute angle to the hypotenuse is called the *cosine* of the angle.

   $$\cos A = \frac{b}{c}$$

   c. The ratio of the side opposite the acute angle to the adjacent side is called the *tangent* of the angle.

   $$\tan A = \frac{a}{b}$$

5. If the ratios for a given triangle are known it is necessary to know the length of only one side in order to find the remaining sides.

That's really all there is to it. What you need now is plenty of practice.

CHAPTER 8

The S and T Scales

Below is one of the triangles we solved in Chapter 7. The solution wasn't particularly involved; we were told that $\frac{a}{84.6} = \sin 72°$, and $\sin 72° = 0.951$. All we had to do was solve for a.

$$a = 84.6 \times \sin 72° = 84.6 \times 0.951 = 80.5$$

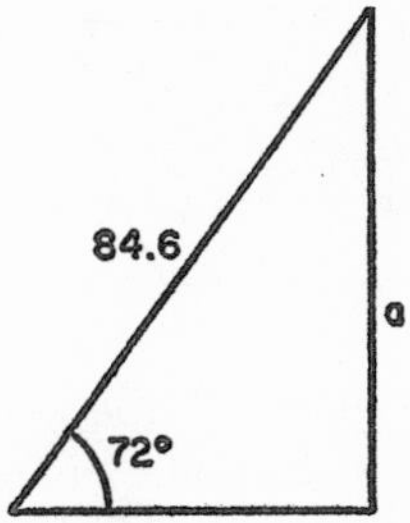

If we hadn't been given the sine of 72°, however, we would have had to look it up in a table of sines. But there's an easier and faster way.

Let's say you knew that 72° right triangles would be cropping up from time to time. Rather than look up the sine of 72° again and again, you could turn the sliding scale over, make a mark opposite the 951 of the right-hand A scale, and label this mark 72°. Then the next time a 72° triangle came up all you'd have to do would be to flip the scale over and use the ready-made mark.

And this is exactly what has been done, not only for 72° angles, but for all the angles between 0° and 90°. The resulting scale is called the S (for *sine*) scale. On most slide rules, the S scale is simply an A scale ruled in degrees. By aligning the S and A scales, the sines of angles from 34′ to 90° can be read directly. (Later we'll talk about the sines of angles less than 34 minutes.) Numbers on the S scale are angles, and should be read as though followed by a degree mark (°).

Please go on to page 346.

[*from page 345*]

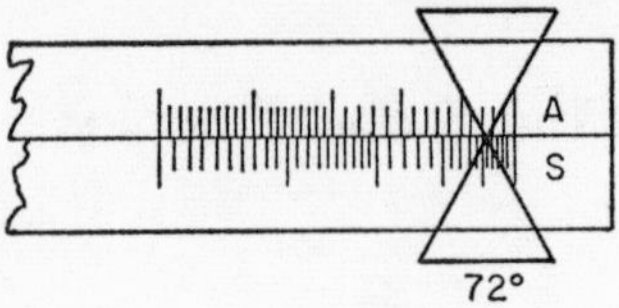

From about 0° 34.4′ at the beginning of the S scale to 5° 44.3′ at the mid-point, the sine ratio varies from 0.0100 to 0.100. Therefore, when reading the sines of angles within this range, it is necessary to place the decimal point so that the sine is between 0.0100 and 0.100. For example, sin 5° = 0.0872, *not* 0.872:

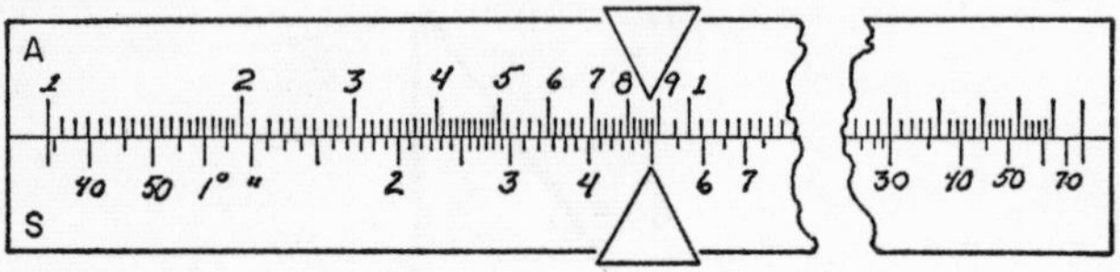

From 0.100 at the mid-point of the scale, the sine increases to 1.00 at 90°, the right end of the scale. (You will almost never have use for the sines of angles greater than 70°; it's much more convenient to work with the smaller angle of a triangle.)

Use your S scale to find out which of the values given below is incorrect:

Sin 2° = 0.0349. **page 349**

Sin 40° = 0.698. **page 358**

The description given doesn't seem to fit my slide rule at all. **page 360**

YOUR ANSWER: $a = 111$, $b = 97$.

Not quite. Since we know that $\frac{a}{c} = \sin A$,

$$\frac{a}{136} = \sin 54.5°$$

$$a = 136 \times \sin 54.5°$$

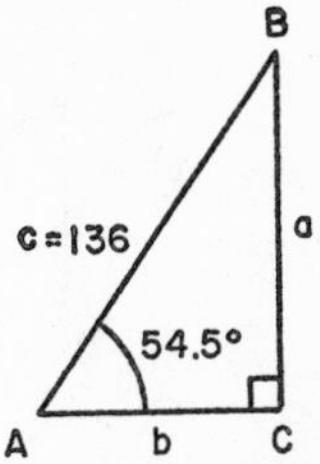

In approximation form, $a = 1 \times 10^2 = 100$ (because 1.36 is just a little more than 1 and sin 54.5° will be just a little less than 1).

On the slide rule:

1. Set the right-hand index of the S scale at 13.6 on the left-hand A scale.
2. Slide the hairline indicator to 54.5° on the S scale.
3. Read 1.11 on the A scale in line with the hairline.

Then $a = 1.11 \times 10^2 = 111$. So that part of your answer is right.

Now for b. We know that $\frac{b}{c} = \cos A$, but we don't know $\cos A$. However, we have seen that for any right triangle, $\cos A = \sin B$. Therefore, $\frac{b}{c} = \sin B$. And B is just $90° - A = 90° - 54.5° = 35.5°$.

So $$\frac{b}{136} = \sin 35.5°$$

and $$b = 136 \times \sin 35.5°$$

On the slide rule:

1. Set the left-hand index of the S scale at 1.36 on the left-hand A scale.
2. Slide the hairline indicator to 35.5° on the S scale.
3. Read the answer on the right-hand A scale, in line with the hairline.

When you have it, return to page 358 to make the correct selection.

[*from page 362*]

YOUR ANSWER: $A = 63°$, $b = 37.2$.

Right. Here's the way it goes: $\sin A = \frac{a}{c} = \frac{73}{82}$. On the slide rule (with the procedure varying slightly according to the kind of rule you have):

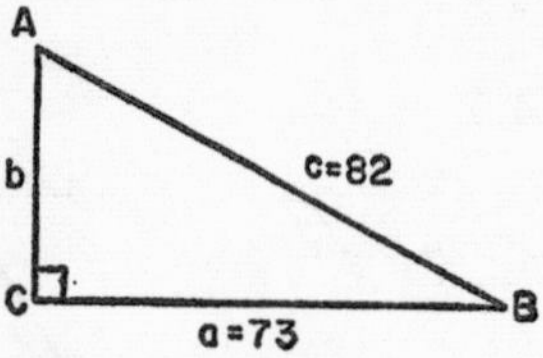

1. Set 73 on the right-hand B scale in line with 82 on the right-hand A scale.
2. Read the angle, 63°, on the S scale in line with the index on the underside of the rule.

To find b, we recall that $\cos A = \sin B$. Therefore, $\frac{b}{c} = \cos A = \sin B$. Since $B = 90° - 63° = 27°$, we see that $b = c \times \sin B = 82 \times \sin 27°$. On the slide rule:

1. Set the right-hand index of the S scale at 82 on the right-hand A scale.
2. Slide the hairline indicator to 27° on the S scale.
3. Read the answer, 37.2, on the right-hand A scale in line with the hairline.

From a study of a trigonometric table we observe that $\frac{\sin A}{\sin B} \approx \frac{A}{B}$ ($\approx$ means approximately equal), where A and B are between 0°0′ and 0°35′. For example,

$$\frac{\sin 14'}{\sin 34.4'} = \frac{14'}{34.4'}$$

Remembering that $\sin 34.4' = 0.0100$, use the A and B scales to find sin 14′.

Sin 14′ = 0.0407. **page 351**

Sin 14′ = 0.0246. **page 359**

Sin 14′ = 0.00407. **page 354**

Sin 14′ = 0.00246. **page 363**

[*from page 346*]

YOUR ANSWER: This value is incorrect: sin 2° = 0.0349.

No, it's right. Here's the way it goes:

Align the S and A scales. Slide the hairline indicator to 2° on the S scale (be careful—don't go to 20°). Then the significant figures, 349, of the sine of 2° appear on the left-hand A scale in line with the hairline. The setting will look like this:

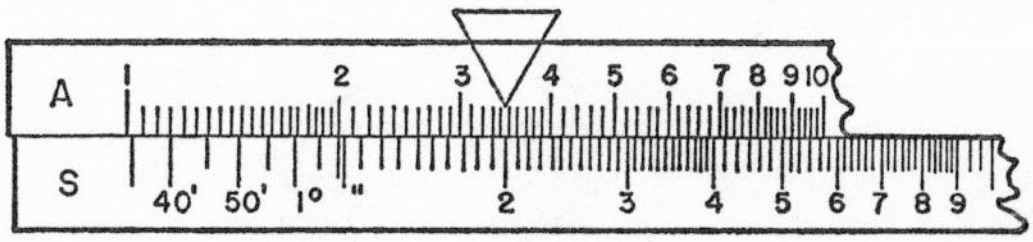

The problem now is to place the decimal point correctly. We have been told that the sines of angles between 0° 34.4′ and 5° 44.3′ are between 0.0100 and 0.100. Accordingly, sin 2° must be more than 0.0100 but less than 0.100. Placing the decimal point immediately before the three significant figures gives us 0.349, which is *greater* than 0.100, so that won't do. And placing two zeros to the right of the decimal point, before the 349, gives 0.00349, which is *less* than 0.0100. Clearly, then, the figures we want are 0.0349—greater than 0.0100 but less than 0.100. Thus

$$\sin 2^\circ = 0.0349$$

When you're sure you understand why this value is correct, return to page 346 for another try.

[*from page 362*]

YOUR ANSWER: $A = 38.6'$, $b = 90$.

You had to make a pretty serious mistake, or a very poor guess, to get here. Let's start all over.

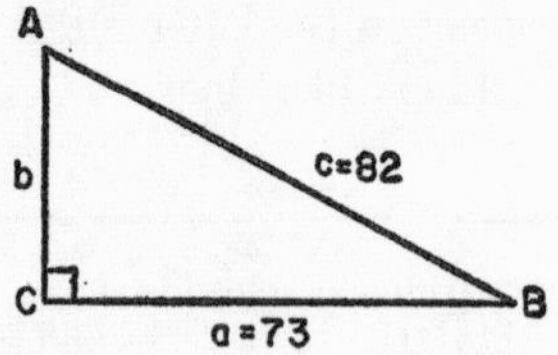

To begin, we know that the sine of angle A is $\frac{a}{c}$, or $\frac{73}{82}$, *not* $\frac{82}{73}$. Now, where you go from here depends on the kind of rule you have. If you have a Mannheim Polyphase with an index on the underside of the rule, the problem is best worked as a proportion:

1. Set 73 on the right-hand B scale in line with 82 on the right-hand A scale.
2. Read the angle on the S scale, in line with the index on the underside of the rule.

If yours is a Mannheim Polyphase *without* the index on the reverse side, you'll have to reverse the sliding scale in the middle of the problem. First, divide 73 on the A scale by 82 on the B scale, using the hairline indicator to mark the result on the A scale. Then reverse the sliding scale so that the S and A scales are on the same side of the rule. Align the two scales, and read the desired angle on the S scale in line with the hairline.

Either way, you'll find that $A = 63°$.

To solve for b, remember that $\cos A = \sin B$. And B is just $90° - A$, or $90° - 63° = 27°$. Therefore,

$$\frac{b}{82} = \cos A = \sin B, \quad \text{so that} \quad b = 82 \times \sin B = 82 \times \sin 27°$$

If you can complete this problem without any more help (as you should be able to), do so, and then return to page 362 to choose the correct answer. If you still don't know how to finish up, however, return to the beginning of this chapter (page 345) for some review.

[*from page 348*]

YOUR ANSWER: Sin 14′ = 0.0407.

Not quite. Apparently you set the problem up correctly on your slide rule, but you misplaced the decimal point. Just to make sure you didn't guess at the answer, however, check your setting with the correct setting shown below:

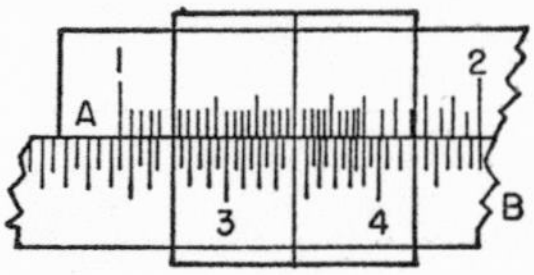

Now for the decimal point. To begin, we know that the sine of 0° is just zero, and the sine of 34.4′ is 0.0100. Therefore, since 14′ is between 0° and 34.4′, sin 14′ must be between 0 and 0.0100. In other words, it must be larger than 0 but smaller than 0.0100. So your answer has to be wrong—0.0470 is larger than 0.0100.

And there's another clue: Since 14′ is roughly four-tenths of 34.4′, we know that sin 14′ will be roughly four-tenths of sin 34.4′. More specifically, sin 14′ is roughly four-tenths of 0.0100, i.e., roughly 0.00400.

When you're sure you understand why your answer is wrong, return to page 348 to pick the right one.

[*from page 355*]

YOUR ANSWER: $d = 81$ miles.

No. Look at the diagram again:

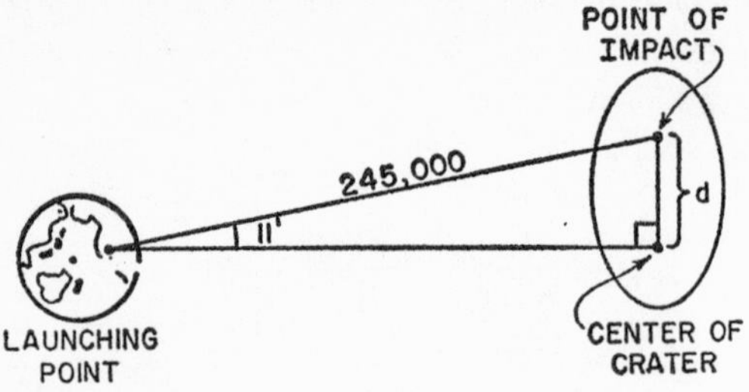

Considering the triangle with angles at the launching point, the crater's center, and the impact point, we find that

$$\frac{d}{245{,}000 \text{ mi.}} = \sin 11'$$

So $$d = 245{,}000 \text{ mi.} \times \sin 11' \quad \left(\textit{not}\ \frac{245{,}000 \text{ mi.}}{\sin 11'}\right)$$

Since $11'$ is about one-third of $34.4'$, $\sin 11'$ is about one-third of $\sin 34.4'$, or 0.003. Therefore, in estimating form,

$$d = 2 \times 10^5 \times 3 \times 10^{-3} = 6 \times 10^2 = 600$$

On the slide rule:

1. Shift the S-scale gauge mark under 1.1 on the A scale.
2. Slide the hairline indicator to the index of the S scale.
3. Reverse the sliding scale and set the left B index at the hairline.
4. Slide the hairline to 2.45 on the B scale.
5. Read the answer on the A scale in line with the hairline.

Or, if you prefer, do it this way:

1. Shift 3.44 on the B scale under 1.1 on the A scale.
2. Slide the hairline indicator to 24.5 on the B scale.
3. Read the answer on the A scale in line with the hairline.

Either way, the answer is the same. When you have it, return to page 355 to make the correct selection.

[*from page 358*]

YOUR ANSWER: $a = 60, b = 97$.

No, you're way off the track on this one.

Here's the way it goes: Since $\frac{a}{c} = \sin A$, we know that

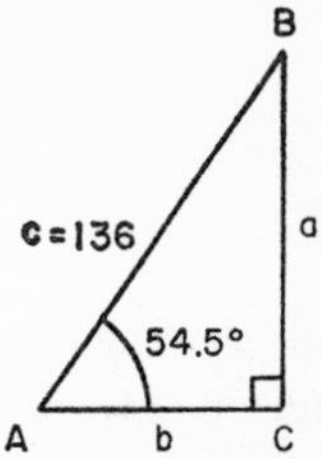

$$\frac{a}{136} = \sin 54.5°. \text{ So}$$

$$a = 136 \times \sin 54.5° \quad \left(\textit{not}\ \frac{136}{\sin 54.5°}\right)$$

In approximation form, $a = 1 \times 10^2 = 100$ (because 1.36 is just a little more than 1 and sin 54.5° will be just a little less than 1).

On the slide rule:

1. Set the right-hand index of the S scale at 1.36 on the left-hand A scale.
2. Slide the hairline indicator to 54.5° on the S scale.
3. Read 1.11 on the A scale in line with the hairline.

So $a = 1.11 \times 10^2 = 111$, *not* 60.

Now for b. We know that $\frac{b}{c} = \cos A$, but we don't know $\cos A$. However, we have seen that for any right triangle, $\cos A = \sin B$. Therefore, $\frac{b}{c} = \sin B$. And B is just $90° - A = 90° - 54.5° = 35.5°$.

So $$\frac{b}{136} = \sin 35.5°$$

and $$b = 136 \times \sin 35.5°$$

Since sin 35.5° is roughly 0.500, b will be about 0.5×136, or 68.

On the slide rule:

1. Set the left-hand index of the S scale at 1.36 on the left-hand A scale.
2. Slide the hairline indicator to 35.5° on the S scale.
3. Read the answer on the right-hand A scale, in line with the hairline.

When you have it, return to page 358 to make the correct selection.

[*from page 348*]

YOUR ANSWER: Sin 14′ = 0.00407.

Good. Here's the correct setting:

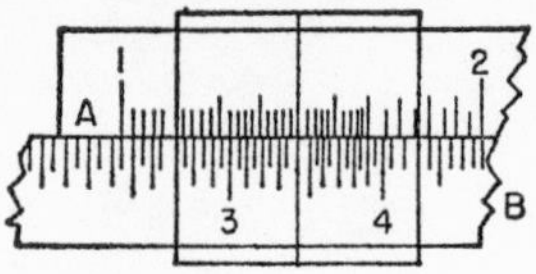

So the significant figures of the sine of 14′ are 407. To place the decimal point, we notice that 14′ is about four-tenths of 34.4′. Therefore, the sine of 14′ must be about four-tenths of the sine of 34.4′: $0.4 \times 0.0100 = 0.00400$. So we see that sin 14′ = 0.00407.

This is a useful method for finding the sine of an angle of less than 34.4′, but it has one drawback—it requires the use of both the A and B scales. This is inconvenient when we are working a problem in which we need the A and S scales on the same side of the rule. However, if you will look closely at the S scale of your slide rule, you'll see that there is a gauge mark just to the left of the 2° mark. The distance from the left index of the S scale to this mark is the same as the distance from the left index of the A or B scale to 34.4 on that scale. This makes it possible to solve for the sines of very small angles without having to reverse the sliding scale; we simply set the gauge mark opposite the desired angle (in minutes) on the A scale, and read the significant figures on the A scale at the index of the S scale.

Please go on to page 355.

[*from page 354*]

To illustrate this, here's how to find the sine of 25′:

First, make an estimate. Since 25′ is approximately seven-tenths of 34.4′, sin 25′ must be approximately seven-tenths of sin 34.4′: $0.7 \times 0.0100 = 0.00700$. Then, on the slide rule:

1. Shift the sliding scale so that the gauge mark on the S scale is in line with 25 on the left-hand A scale.
2. Read 727 on the A scale at the index of the S scale.

Then sin 25′ = 0.00727.

Now try the problem below:

A rocket is fired toward the center of the moon crater Tycho. The test will be considered a "gigantic breakthrough" if the rocket lands within 1,000 miles of the center of the crater. With a large telescope, the scientists are able to measure the angle between the line from the launching point to the center of the crater and the line from the launching point to the actual point of impact. This angular distance is 11′. We assume that the moon is a disc 245,000 miles from the earth.

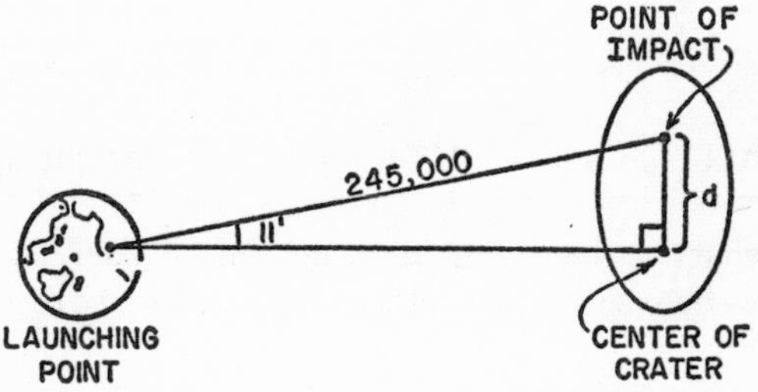

Now, what we want to know is whether or not the rocket landed within 1,000 miles of the center of the crater. In other words, what is the value of *d*?

d = 81 miles. **page 352**

d = 784 miles. **page 364**

d = 1,568 miles. **page 367**

[*from page 364*]

YOUR ANSWER: Sin $4' = 0.0012$.

Right. For any angle A which is smaller than $34.4'$,

$$\sin A = 0.0003 \times A,$$

where 0.0003 (which we remember as *three zeros three*) is the sine of $1'$. Therefore,

$$\sin 4' = 0.0003 \times 4 = 0.0012$$

The problem of locating the decimal point for the sines of very small angles is minimized if the proportionality of these angles and their sines is observed.

For example, the sine of an angle ten times as large as $34.4'$ is roughly ten times as large as the sine of $34.4'$.

$$10 \times \sin 34.4' = 10 \times 0.01 = 0.1$$

And 0.1 is the sine of $5° \, 44.3'$, which is roughly $10 \times 34.4'$, converted to degrees and minutes. The chart below illustrates this relationship:

Angle	344′	34.4′	3.44′	0.344′	0.0344′	0.00344′
Sine	0.1	0.01	0.001	0.0001	0.00001	0.000001

Use this chart to help you find the sine of $2.06''$. (Remember that there are 60 seconds in 1 minute; i.e., $60'' = 1'$.)

Sin $2.06'' = 0.0001$. **page 365**

Sin $2.06'' = 0.00001$. **page 369**

Sin $2.06'' = 0.000001$. **page 372**

I don't know where to start. **page 375**

[*from page 362*]

YOUR ANSWER: $A = 63°$, $b = 18.1$.

Well, you found angle A correctly, but you missed the boat on b. Here's the way it goes:

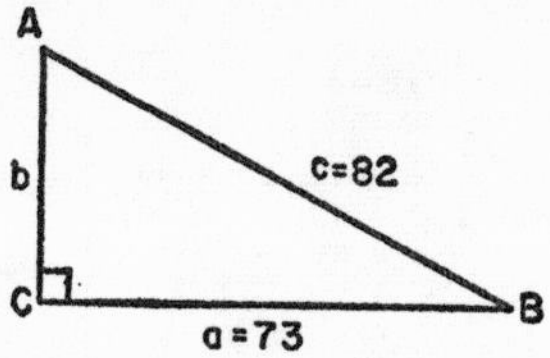

We've seen that for any right triangle, $\cos A = \sin B$. And B, of course, is just $90° - A$, or $27°$. Now, since $\frac{b}{c} = \cos A$,

$$\frac{b}{c} = \sin B$$

$$\frac{b}{82} = \sin 27°$$

$$b = 82 \times \sin 27°$$

You should know how to do this problem on the slide rule by now:

1. Set the right index of the S scale at 82 on the right-hand A scale.
2. Slide the hairline indicator to 27° on the S scale.
3. Read the answer on the A scale in line with the hairline.

When you have the answer, return to page 362 to make the correct choice.

[*from page 346*]

YOUR ANSWER: This value is incorrect: sin 40° = 0.698.

That's right; it's wrong. The incorrect reading is the result of mistaking 4° for 40° on the S scale. Sin 40° = 0.643, but sin 4° = 0.0698. Here's the correct setting:

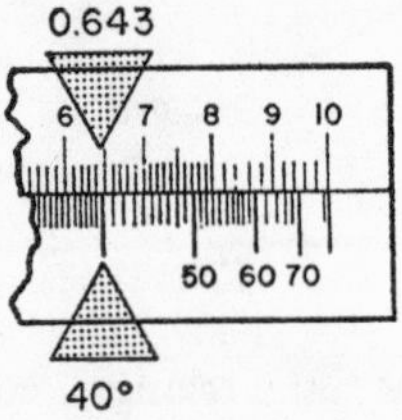

As you have probably realized by now, the position of the decimal point is indicated by where the sine appears, i.e., by whether it appears on the left- or the right-hand A scale. For angles between 0° 34.4′ and 5° 44.3′ the sine appears on the left-hand A scale, and is written with one zero to the right of the decimal point, before the first significant figure: sin 2° = 0.0349. For angles between 5° 44.3′ and 90° the sine appears on the right-hand A scale, and is written with the first significant digit immediately following the decimal point: sin 30° = 0.500. (If yours is a log-log duplex rule, just remember that the angles whose sines appear on the left-hand A scale of a Mannheim Polyphase rule are the angles of your ST scale. The angles whose sines appear on the right-hand A scale are the angles of your S scale.)

Find sides *a* and *b* of the triangle at the right:

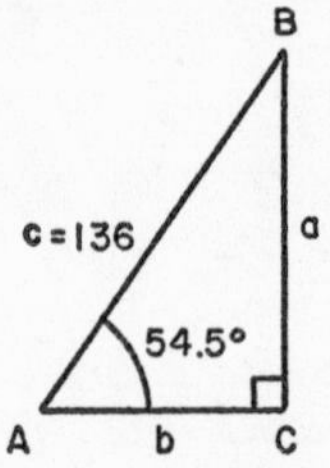

$a = 111, b = 97.$ **page 347**

$a = 111, b = 79.$ **page 362**

$a = 60, b = 97.$ **page 353**

[*from page 348*]

YOUR ANSWER: Sin 14′ = 0.0246.

No. You've misplaced the decimal point, and, more important, seriously distorted the proportion. Here it is again:

$$\frac{\sin 14'}{\sin 34.4'} = \frac{14'}{34.4'}$$

And this is *not* the same as saying that

$$\frac{\sin 14'}{34.4'} = \frac{\sin 34.4'}{14'}$$

To set up the correct proportion on the slide rule, it's necessary to have both sin 14′ and 14′ on one scale and sin 34.4′ and 34.4′ on the other scale. Here is one way to do it:

1. Set 34.4 on the left-hand B scale in line with 14 on the left-hand A scale.
2. Read the significant figures of the sine of 14′ on the A scale in line with the right-hand index of the B scale (because the right-hand index of the B scale represents the sine of 34.4′, 0.0100).

The setting looks like this:

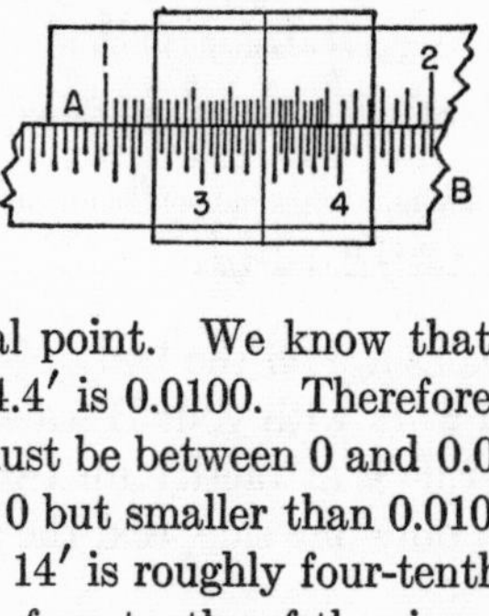

Now for the decimal point. We know that the sine of 0° is just zero, and the sine of 34.4′ is 0.0100. Therefore, since 14′ is between 0° and 34.4′, sin 14′ must be between 0 and 0.0100. In other words, it must be larger than 0 but smaller than 0.0100. And, going a step further, we know that 14′ is roughly four-tenths of 34.4′, so the sine of 14′ must be roughly four-tenths of the sine of 34.4′.

These hints should help you find the right answer. When you have it, return to page 348 to make the correct selection.

[*from page 346*]

YOUR ANSWER: The description given doesn't seem to fit my slide rule at all.

In this case, your rule probably isn't just a Mannheim Polyphase slide rule, but instead one of the several possible variations. However, by this time you've gotten a firm enough grasp of the basic slide rule principles so that you'll have no trouble proceeding.

One common variation looks like this:

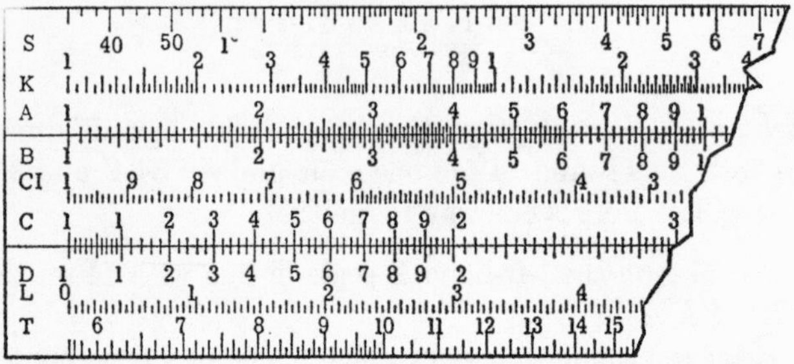

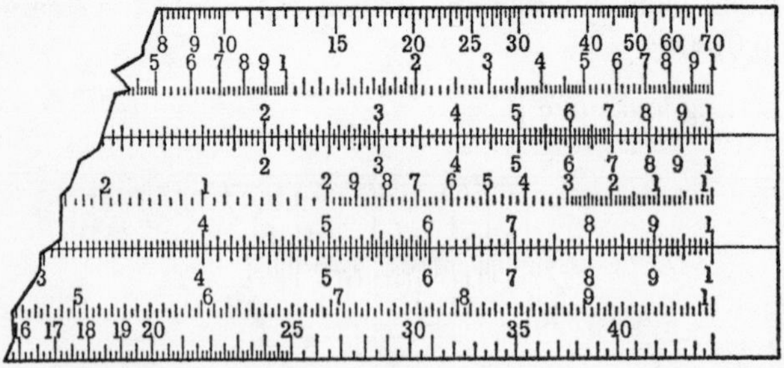

Here the S and T scales are on the body of the rule. If you have this kind of rule, you'll work with your B scale instead of the A scale in this lesson. Such a rule is attractive for two reasons: it's easier to make, having scales on only one side; and the sliding scale never has to be turned over.

You may also have a rule like this:

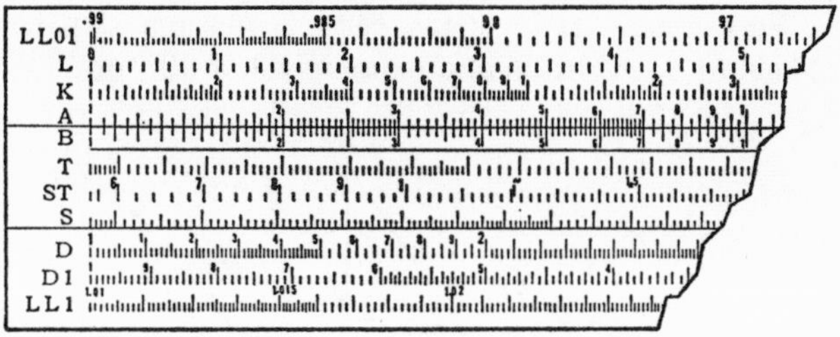

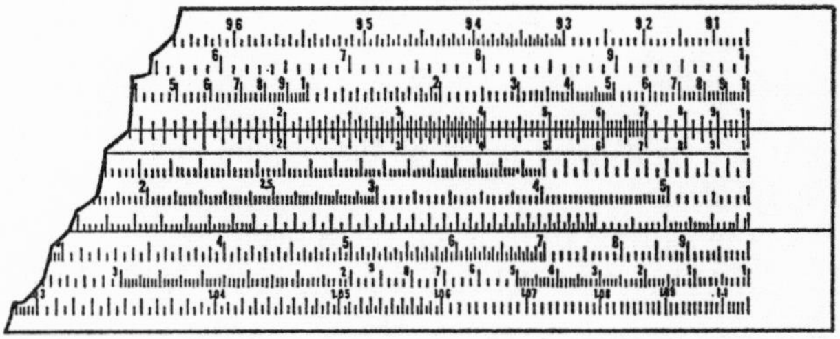

This is a log-log duplex slide rule, and there are two S scales instead of one. Each scale is comparable to a D scale, and the accuracy available is correspondingly greater. Angles from about 5° 45′ to 90° are on the S scale, and for these angles, you need only use your D scale whenever the text refers to the right-hand A scale. Angles smaller than 5° 45′ down to 34.3′ are found on the SRT, or ST, scale, and for these angles the D scale substitutes for the left-hand A scale.

After a page or so, you'll find no difficulty in adapting the text for your particular rule. Return to page 346 and work the one wrong series there.

[*from page 358*]

YOUR ANSWER: $a = 111$, $b = 79$.

Right. Very good. Here is the correct solution, step by step: $a = 136 \times \sin 54.5°$, which is approximately 1×10^2, or 100.

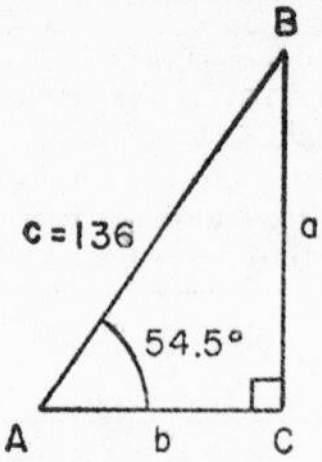

On the slide rule:

1. Shift the right-hand index of the S scale to 1.36 on the left-hand A scale.
2. Slide the hairline to 54.5° on the S scale.
3. Read 1.11 on the left-hand A scale, in line with the hairline.

Then $a = 1.11 \times 10^2$, or 111.

Similarly, $b = 136 \times \cos 54.5°$, or $136 \times \sin 35.5°$ (because $\cos A = \sin B$). So b is roughly equal to $1 \times 0.5 \times 10^2$, or 50.

On the slide rule:

1. Set the left-hand index of the S scale at 1.36 on the left-hand A scale.
2. Slide the hairline indicator to 35.5° on the S scale.
3. Read 79 on the right-hand A scale in line with the hairline.

Then $b = 79$.

Now find angle A and side b of the triangle at the right:

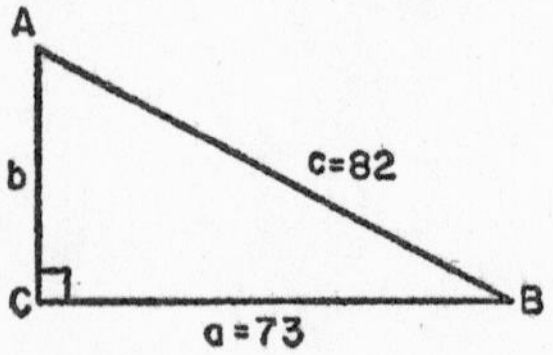

$A = 63°$, $b = 37.2$. **page 348**

$A = 63°$, $b = 18.1$. **page 357**

$A = 38.6'$, $b = 90$. **page 350**

[*from page 348*]

YOUR ANSWER: Sin 14′ = 0.00246.

No, you've seriously distorted the proportion. Here it is again:

$$\frac{\sin 14'}{\sin 34.4'} = \frac{14'}{34.4'}$$

And this is *not* the same as saying that

$$\frac{\sin 14'}{34.4'} = \frac{\sin 34.4'}{14'}$$

To set up the correct proportion on the slide rule, it's necessary to have both sin 14′ and 14′ on the same scale, and both sin 34.4′ and 34.4′ on the other scale. Here is one way to do it:

1. Set 34.4 on the left-hand B scale in line with 14 on the left-hand A scale.
2. Read the significant figures of the sine of 14′ on the A scale in line with the right-hand index of the B scale (because the right-hand index of the B scale represents the sine of 34.4′, 0.0100).

The correct setting looks like this:

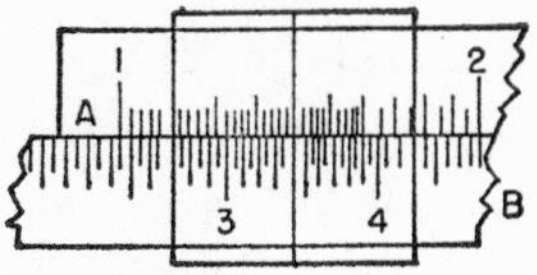

When you're sure you understand your mistake, return to page 348 to choose the correct answer.

[*from page 355*]

YOUR ANSWER: $d = 784$ miles.

Very good. Considering the triangle with angles at the launching point, the crater's center, and the impact point,

$$\frac{d}{245{,}000 \text{ mi.}} = \sin 11'$$

So

$$d = 245{,}000 \text{ mi.} \times \sin 11'$$

Since $11'$ is about one-third of $34.4'$, $\sin 11'$ is about one-third of $\sin 34.4'$, or 0.003. Therefore, in estimating form,

$$d = 2 \times 10^5 \times 3 \times 10^{-3} = 6 \times 10^2 = 600$$

On the slide rule, we can do it this way:

1. Shift the S-scale gauge mark under 1.1 on the A scale.
2. Slide the hairline indicator to the index of the S scale.
3. Reverse the sliding scale, and set the left B index at the hairline.
4. Slide the hairline to 2.45 on the B scale.
5. Read 78.4 on the A scale in line with the hairline.

Or this way:

1. Shift 3.44 on the B scale under 1.1 on the A scale.
2. Slide the hairline indicator to 24.5 on the B scale.
3. Read 7.84 on the A scale in line with the hairline.

Either way, we see that $d = 784$ miles. So the rocket landed well within 1,000 miles of the center of the crater, as desired.

When we're working with angles of less than $34.4'$, the fact that the sine of $1'$ is 0.000292 often provides a handy short cut. It's easy to remember this sine as *three zeros three.* And since for all practical purposes angles smaller than $34.4'$ and their sines are proportional, we know that for any angle of A within this range, $\frac{A}{1'} = \frac{\sin A}{0.0003}$.

So we find: $\sin A = 0.0003 \times A$

Use this relationship to find the sine of $4'$.

$\sin 4' = 0.0012$. **page 356** $\sin 4' = 0.0004$. **page 371**

$\sin 4' = 0.00008$. **page 368**

YOUR ANSWER: Sin 2.06″ = 0.0001.

No.

First, we know that 60″ = 1′. Therefore,

$$\frac{x}{1'} = \frac{2.06''}{60''}$$

where x is the equivalent, in minutes, of 2.06″. Then x is roughly equal to $\frac{1}{3} \times 10^{-1}$, or 0.033.

On the slide rule, it's easiest to do the problem in proportion form:

1. Set 2.06 on the C scale over 6.0 on the D scale.
2. Read the answer, 3.44, on the C scale at the index of the D scale.

(Or you can use the A and B scales, if you'd rather.) Then x = 0.0344′ (*not* 0.344′).

Now, look at the chart again:

Angle	344′	34.4′	3.44′	0.344′	0.0344′	0.00344′
Sine	0.1	0.01	0.001	0.0001	0.00001	0.000001

Obviously, since 2.06″ = 0.0344′, the sine of 2.06″ must be equal to the sine of 0.0344′.

When you have it, return to page 356 to choose the correct answer.

[*from page 369*]

YOUR ANSWER: d = about 0.25 miles.

No. Here is the diagram again:

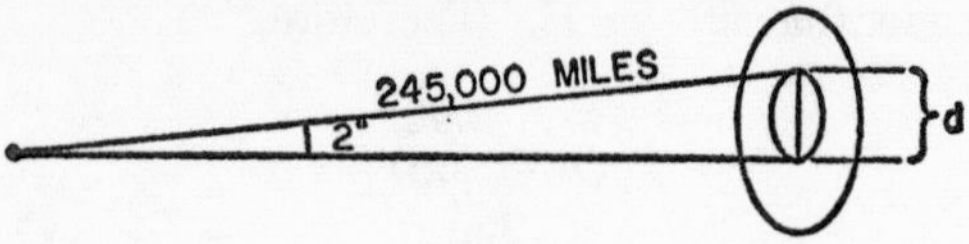

The diameter of the hole, d, can be considered the side opposite the 2″ angle; and 245,000 miles, the distance from the launching point to the moon, can be considered the hypotenuse. Then $\frac{d}{245{,}000 \text{ mi.}} =$ sin 2″, so that $d = 245{,}000 \text{ mi.} \times \sin 2''$.

But we still need to find the sine of 2″. For this we use:

$$\frac{\sin 2''}{\sin 2.06''} = \frac{2''}{2.06''}$$

Since the sine of 2.06″ is just 0.00001 (as we've already demonstrated, and as shown on the chart), this proportion becomes

$$\frac{\sin 2''}{0.00001} = \frac{2''}{2.06''}$$

Clearly, the sine of 2″ will be just a little smaller than 0.00001, because 2″ is just a little less than 2.06″.

The easiest procedure on the slide rule is to

1. Set 2 on the A scale over 2.06 on the B scale.
2. Read the significant figures of the sine of 2″, 97.1, on the A scale at the index of the B scale.

Then sin 2″ = 0.00000971, just slightly less than 0.00001 (*not* 0.000000971, which is more than ten times as small as 0.00001).

Finally,

$$d = 245{,}000 \text{ mi.} \times 0.00000971 = 2.45 \times 9.71 \times 10^{-1}$$

In approximation form,

$$d = 2 \times 10 \times 10^{-1} \text{ mi.} = 2.0 \text{ mi.}$$

Complete the problem, making sure that your answer is in the neighborhood of 2.0 miles. Then return to page 369 to make the correct choice.

[*from page 355*]

YOUR ANSWER: $d = 1{,}568$ miles.

No. And this looks like a guess.
Let's start over. Here's the diagram again:

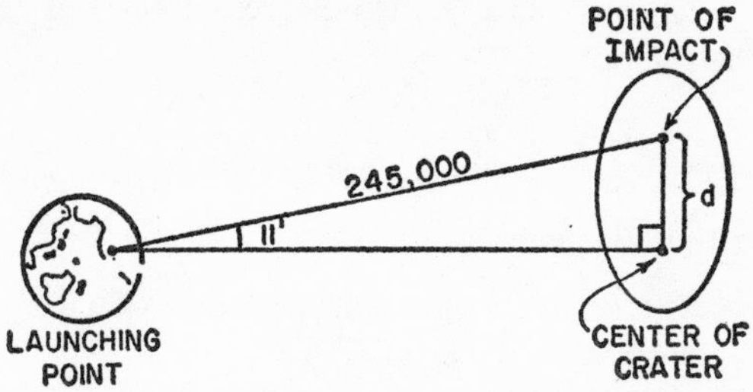

Considering the triangle with angles at the launching point, the crater's center, and the impact point, we find that

$$\frac{d}{245{,}000 \text{ mi.}} = \sin 11'$$

So
$$d = 245{,}000 \text{ mi.} \times \sin 11'$$

Since 11′ is about one-third of 34.4′, sin 11′ is about one-third of sin 34.4′, or 0.003. Therefore, in estimating form,

$$d = 2 \times 10^5 \times 3 \times 10^{-3} = 6 \times 10^2 = 600$$

On your slide rule:

1. Shift the S-scale gauge mark under 1.1 on the A scale.
2. Slide the hairline indicator to the index of the S scale.
3. Reverse the sliding scale and set the left B index at the hairline.
4. Slide the hairline to 2.45 on the B scale.
5. Read the answer on the A scale in line with the hairline.

Or, if you prefer, do it this way:

1. Shift 3.44 on the B scale under 1.1 on the A scale.
2. Slide the hairline indicator to 24.5 on the B scale.
3. Read the answer on the A scale in line with the hairline.

Either way, the answer will be the same. When you have it, return to page 355 to make the correct selection.

[*from page 364*]

YOUR ANSWER: Sin $4' = 0.00008$.

Wrong. Let's go through the reasoning again.

We have seen that angles smaller than $34.4'$ are proportional to their sines. That is, for any two angles—let's call them A and B—within this range,

$$\frac{A}{\sin A} = \frac{B}{\sin B}$$

Or we can write it this way:

$$\frac{A}{B} = \frac{\sin A}{\sin B}$$

If $B = 1'$, then this relationship becomes

$$\frac{A}{1'} = \frac{\sin A}{\sin 1'}$$

Since $\sin 1'$ is *three zeros three*,

$$A = \frac{\sin A}{0.0003}$$

Finally, multiplying both sides of this expression by 0.0003,

$$\sin A = A \times 0.0003$$

So all we need do to find the sine of $4'$ is substitute 4 for A:

$$\sin 4' = 4 \times 0.0003$$

(Evidently you divided 0.0003 by 4 instead of multiplying.)

Complete the multiplication, and return to page 364 to choose the correct answer.

[*from page 356*]

YOUR ANSWER: Sin 2.06″ = 0.00001.

Right. Since 60″ = 1′, we know that $\frac{x}{1'} = \frac{2.06''}{60''}$, where x is the equivalent, in minutes, of 2.06″. Then $x = \frac{2.06 \times 1'}{60}$, or 0.034′. Consulting the chart, we see that the sine of 0.034′ is 0.00001. Therefore, sin 2.06″ = 0.00001.

We can use this same procedure to find the sines of 20.6″, 0.206″, 0.0206″, and so forth. Or we can use the method we used to find the sine of 344′ from that of 34′. Either way, we can come up with the more complete chart below:

Angle	344′ 5° 44.3′	34.4′	3.44′ 206″	0.344′ 20.6″	0.0344′ 2.06″	0.00344′ 0.206″
Sine	0.1	0.01	0.001	0.0001	0.00001	0.000001

Here is another problem dealing with the rocket aimed at the moon crater Tycho:

The scientists are able to determine that the hole created when the rocket smashed into the moon *subtends* an angle of 2″. That is, the angle between an imaginary line from the launching point to one side of the hole and a similar line from the launching point to the other side of the hole is 2″.

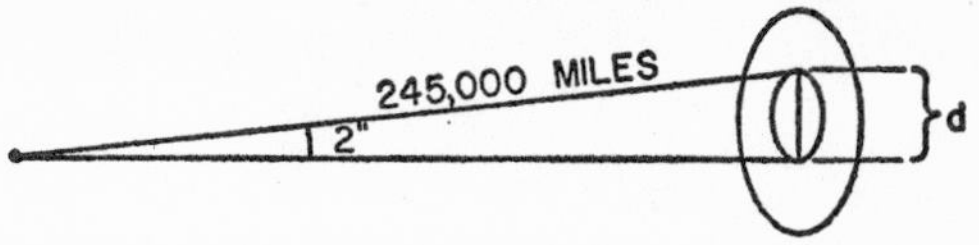

Then the diameter (d) of the hole can be considered one side of a triangle, so that d = sin 2″ × 245,000. Since sin 2.06″ = 0.0001, we can write the proportion

$$\frac{\sin 2''}{\sin 2.06''} = \frac{2''}{2.06''}$$

Use this proportion to find the sine of 2″. Then find d.

d = about 0.25 miles. **page 366** d = about 25 miles. **page 376**

d = about 2.5 miles. **page 373**

[*from page 373*]

YOUR ANSWER: Sin 23″ = 0.000112 is incorrect.

Let's check it out.

To find the sine of an angle in seconds, simply set the seconds gauge mark on the S scale (or 2.06 on the B scale) under the angle in seconds on the A scale. Then read the significant figures of the sine on the A scale at the index of the S (or B) scale.

So to find the sine of 23″:

1. Set the seconds mark on the S scale (or 2.06 on the B scale) under 23 on the A scale.
2. Read the significant figures, 11.15, of the sine of 23″ on the A scale at the index of the S (or B) scale.

Since we know the gauge mark corresponds to 2.06 on the B scale, and sin 2.06″ = 0.00001, what we've really done here is solve this proportion for sin 23″:

$$\frac{\sin 23''}{\sin 2.06''} = \frac{23''}{2.06''}$$

And because 23″ is approximately eleven times 2.06″, we know that the sine of 23″ must be approximately 11 × 0.00001, or 0.00011. Therefore, using the significant figures from the slide rule,

$$\sin 23'' = 0.0001115$$

Or, to three figures of accuracy,

$$\sin 23'' = 0.000112$$

So the given figure was correct.

Study this analysis. Then return to page 373 and try again.

[*from page 364*]

YOUR ANSWER: Sin $4' = 0.0004$.

No. Apparently you don't understand how the proportionality of small angles and their sines really works. Or else this is a guess.

Let's go through the reasoning again.

We have seen that angles smaller than 34.4′ are proportional to their sines. That is, for any two angles—let's call them A and B—within this range,

$$\frac{A}{\sin A} = \frac{B}{\sin B}$$

Or we can write it this way:

$$\frac{A}{B} = \frac{\sin A}{\sin B}$$

If $B = 1'$, then this relationship becomes

$$\frac{A}{1'} = \frac{\sin A}{\sin 1'}$$

Since sin 1′ is *three zeros three,*

$$A = \frac{\sin A}{0.0003}$$

Finally, multiplying both sides of this expression by 0.0003,

$$\sin A = A \times 0.0003$$

So all we need do to find the sine of 4′ is substitute 4 for A:

$$\sin 4' = 4 \times 0.0003$$

Complete the multiplication, and return to page 364 to choose the correct answer.

[*from page 356*]

YOUR ANSWER: Sin 2.06″ = 0.000001.

No.

First, we know that 60″ = 1′. Therefore,

$$\frac{x}{1'} = \frac{2.06''}{60''}$$

where x is the equivalent, in minutes, of 2.06″. Then x is roughly equal to $\frac{1}{3} \times 10^{-1}$, or 0.033.

On the slide rule, it's easiest to do the problem in proportion form:

1. Set 2.06 on the C scale over 6.0 on the D scale.
2. Read the answer, 3.44, on the C scale at the index of the D scale.

(Or you can use the A and B scales, if you'd rather.) Then x = 0.0344′ (*not* 0.00344′).

Now, look at the chart again:

Angle	344′	34.4′	3.44′	0.344′	0.0344′	0.00344′
Sine	0.1	0.01	0.001	0.0001	0.00001	0.000001

Obviously, since 2.06″ = 0.0344′, the sine of 2.06″ must be equal to the sine of 0.0344′.

When you have it, return to page 356 to choose the correct answer.

[*from page 369*]

YOUR ANSWER: The diameter of the hole is 2.5 miles.

Right.

Here's the way it went: $d = 245{,}000$ mi. $\times \sin 2''$, and $\dfrac{\sin 2''}{\sin 2.06''} = \dfrac{2''}{2.06''}$.

Since we've seen that the sine of 2.06″ is just 0.00001,

$$\frac{\sin 2''}{0.00001} = \frac{2''}{2.06''}$$

Then $\sin 2'' = 0.00000971$, and $d = 245{,}000$ mi. $\times$ 0.00000971, or 2.38 miles. Considering the accuracy of the data, then, we can say that the hole is roughly $2\frac{1}{2}$ miles across.

On the S scale, in line with 2.06 on the B scale, you'll find a gauge mark for finding the sines of angles in seconds. It's used in the same way as the minutes mark:

To find the sine of an angle in seconds, set the seconds gauge mark under the angle in seconds on the A scale. Read the significant figures of the sine on the A scale at the index of the S scale.

For example, to find the sine of 8″:

1. Shift the seconds mark under 8 on the A scale.
2. Read 3.88 on the A scale at the index of the S scale.

Then $\sin 8'' = 0.0000388$, about 4 times the sine of 2.06″, because 8″ is about four times 2.06″.

Which of the values given below is incorrect?

Sin 23″ = 0.000112. **page 370**

Sin 10.3″ = 0.0000500. **page 377**

Sin 14″ = 0.00000680. **page 380**

[*from page 380*]

YOUR ANSWER: Sin 5.2″ = 0.0000521.

No. We'd better start over.
First, we know that for very small angles measured in seconds,

$$\frac{\sin A}{\sin 1''} = \frac{A}{1''}$$

Next, remembering sin 1″ as *five zeros five*, we get

$$\frac{\sin A}{0.000005} = \frac{A}{1''}$$

Now, we want to find the sine of 5.2″. Substituting 5.2″ for A in the proportion above, we get

$$\frac{\sin 5.2''}{0.000005} = \frac{5.2''}{1''}$$

The seconds appearing in the right side of this equation cancel out, so we get

$$\sin 5.2'' = 5.2 \times 0.000005$$

In approximation form,

$$5 \times 5 \times 10^{-6} = 25 \times 10^{-6}$$
$$= 0.000025$$

Finish the problem for yourself, and then return to page 380 to choose the correct answer.

[from page 356]

YOUR ANSWER: I don't know where to start.

You were asked to find the sine of 2.06″ with the aid of this chart:

Angle	344′	34.4′	3.44′	0.344′	0.0344′	0.00344′
Sine	0.1	0.01	0.001	0.0001	0.00001	0.000001

The first thing to do, then, is convert 2.06″ to its equivalent in minutes, and see if this value corresponds to one of the angles given in the chart.

Since 60″ = 1′, we know that

$$\frac{x}{1'} = \frac{2.06''}{60''}$$

where x is the equivalent, in minutes, of 2.06″. Then x is roughly equal to $\frac{1}{3} \times 10^{-1}$, or 0.033.

On the slide rule, it's quickest to use the proportion form:

1. Set 2.06 on the C scale over 6.0 on the D scale.
2. Read the answer on the C scale at the index of the D scale.

(Or, if you'd rather, you can use the A and B scales.)

You will find, as you would suspect, that x does correspond to one of the angles on the chart. Consequently, the sine of that angle is the sine of 2.06″.

When you have it, return to page 356 to choose the correct answer.

[*from page 369*]

YOUR ANSWER: d = about 25 miles.

No. Here is the diagram again:

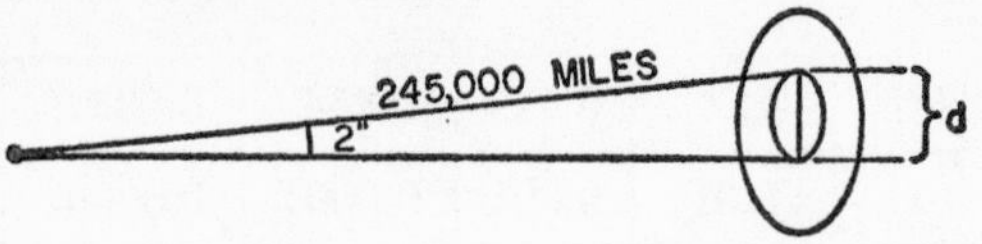

The diameter of the hole, d, can be considered the side opposite the $2''$ angle; and 245,000 miles, the distance from the launching point to the moon, can be considered the hypotenuse. Then $\frac{d}{245{,}000 \text{ mi.}} = \sin 2''$, so that $d = 245{,}000 \text{ mi.} \times \sin 2''$.

But we still need to find the sine of $2''$. For this we use:

$$\frac{\sin 2''}{\sin 2.06''} = \frac{2''}{2.06''}$$

Since the sine of $2.06''$ is just 0.00001 (as we've already demonstrated, and as shown on the chart), this proportion becomes

$$\frac{\sin 2''}{0.00001} = \frac{2''}{2.06''}$$

Clearly, the sine of $2''$ will be just a little smaller than 0.00001, because $2''$ is just a little less than $2.06''$.

The easiest procedure on the slide rule is to

1. Set 2 on the A scale over 2.06 on the B scale.
2. Read the significant figures of the sine of $2''$, 97.1, on the A scale at the index of the B scale.

Then $\sin 2'' = 0.00000971$, just slightly less than 0.00001 (*not* 0.0000971, which is almost ten times as large as 0.00001).

Finally,

$$d = 245{,}000 \text{ mi.} \times 0.00000971 = 2.45 \times 9.71 \times 10^{-1}$$

In approximation form,

$$d = 2 \times 10 \times 10^{-1} \text{ mi.} = 2.0 \text{ mi.}$$

Complete the problem, making sure that your answer is in the neighborhood of 2.0 miles. Then return to page 369 to make the correct choice.

[*from page 373*]

YOUR ANSWER: Sin 10.3″ = 0.0000500 is incorrect.

Well, let's see.

To find the sine of an angle in seconds, simply set the seconds gauge mark on the S scale (or 2.06 on the B scale) under the angle in seconds on the A scale. Then read the significant figures of the sine on the A scale at the index of the S (or B) scale.

To find the sine of 10.3″:

1. Set the seconds mark on the S scale (or 2.06 on the B scale) under 10.3 on the A scale. (Be careful not to mistake 1.30 for 10.3.)
2. Then read the significant figures, 5.00, of the sine of 10.3″ on the A scale at the index of the S (or B) scale.

Because the gauge mark corresponds to 2.06 on the B scale, and the sine of 2.06″ is 0.00001, this operation amounts to solving this proportion for sin 10.3″:

$$\frac{\sin 10.3''}{\sin 2.06''} = \frac{10.3''}{2.06''}$$

Finally, since 10.3″ is approximately five times 2.06″, we know that the sine of 10.3″ must be approximately 5 × 0.00001, or 0.00005. Therefore, using the significant figures from the slide rule,

$$\sin 10.3'' = 0.0000500$$

So the given value was correct.

When you're sure you understand how we arrived at this answer, return to page 373 for another try.

[*from page 387*]

YOUR ANSWER: This group contains an error:

$\sin 51' = 0.0148 \qquad \sin 90' = 0.0262 \qquad \sin 23^\circ 24' = 0.397$

No, all these values are correct. Follow the explanations below:

The sine of $0^\circ 34.4'$ is 0.0100 and that of $5^\circ 44.3'$ is 0.100. Since $51'$ is just slightly more than $34.4'$, we know that the sine of $51'$ must be just slightly more than 0.0100, and less than 0.100. On the slide rule:

1. Slide the minutes gauge mark on the S scale under 51 on the A scale.
2. Read 14.8 on the A scale at the index of the S scale.

Then $\sin 51' = 0.0148$.

Recalling that there are 60 minutes in a degree, we know that $90' = 1^\circ 30' = 1.5^\circ$. Therefore, $\sin 90' = \sin 1.5^\circ$. Furthermore, since $90'$, or 1.5°, is greater than $0^\circ 34.4'$ but less than $5^\circ 44.3'$, we know that $\sin 90'$ must be greater than 0.0100 but less than 0.100. On the slide rule:

1. Align the S and A scales.
2. Slide the hairline indicator to 1.5° on the S scale.
3. Read 2.62 on the A scale under the hairline.

Then $\sin 90' = 0.0262$.

Finally, since there are 60 minutes in a degree, and $\frac{24}{60} = \frac{4}{10}$, or 0.4, $23^\circ 24' = 23.4^\circ$. On the slide rule:

1. Align the S and A scales.
2. Slide the hairline indicator to 23.4° on the S scale.
3. Read 39.7 on the A scale under the hairline.

Then $\sin 23^\circ 24' = 0.397$ (more than 0.100, the sine of $5^\circ 44.3'$, but less than 1.000, the sine of 90°).

If you're sure you understand these procedures, return to page 387 for another try. If, however, you still feel unsure of yourself on this material, return to page 345 for some review.

[*from page 391*]

YOUR ANSWER: Side $a = 109.67$.

Well, you may have used the right relationship to calculate your answer, but evidently you used a table of sines rather than a slide rule. The slide rule can give, at the very most, four significant figures. The answer you selected has five.

Let's start from scratch.

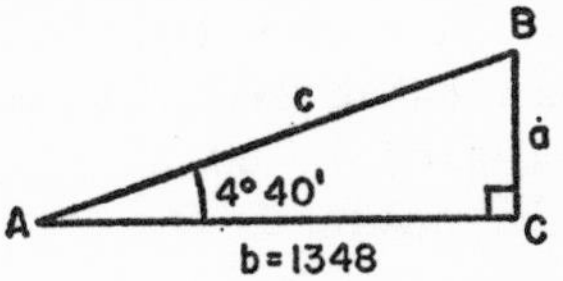

We've seen that in a triangle such as this one, where the angle between the adjacent side and the hypotenuse is very small and the adjacent side is relatively long, the hypotenuse and the adjacent side are almost equal. Therefore, the sine and tangent of the angle are almost equal. That is,

$$\frac{a}{c} \text{ is almost equal to } \frac{a}{b} \text{ because } c \text{ is almost equal to } b.$$

Therefore, we can use the sine ratio in place of the tangent to calculate side a knowing only side b. We write

$$\frac{a}{1{,}348} = \sin 4^\circ 40' \quad (\text{instead of } \mathit{tan}\ 4^\circ 40')$$

Then $$a = 1{,}348 \times \sin 4^\circ 40'$$

In approximation form, since the sine of $4^\circ 40'$ is only slightly less than that of $5^\circ 44.3'$, which is 0.100,

$$a = 1 \times 10^3 \times 1 \times 10^{-1} = 1 \times 10^2 = 100$$

On the slide rule:

1. Index the S scale at 1.348 on the A scale.
2. Slide the hairline indicator to $4^\circ 40'$ on the S scale.
3. Read the answer on the A scale under the hairline.

When you have the complete answer, return to page 391 to make the correct choice.

[*from page 373*]

YOUR ANSWER: Sin 14″ = 0.00000680 is incorrect.

You're right; it's wrong. Here's the way it goes:

1. Set the seconds mark on the S scale (or 2.06 on the B scale) under 14 on the A scale.
2. Read the significant figures, 6.80, on the A scale at the index of the S (or B) scale.

Now, 14″ is roughly seven times 2.06″, so the sine of 14″ should be roughly seven times that of 2.06″. Since sin 2.06″ is 0.00001, $7 \times \sin 2.06'' = 7 \times 0.00001 = 0.00007$. Therefore, using the significant figures from the slide rule,

$$\sin 14'' = 0.0000680, \quad \textit{not} \quad 0.00000680$$

Just as we can remember the sine of 1′ as *three zeros three,* we can easily remember the sine of 1″, 0.00000485, as *five zeros five.* And for angles measured in seconds,

$$\frac{\sin A}{\sin 1''} = \frac{A}{1''}$$

Use this method to find the sine of 5.2″.

Sin 5.2″ = 0.0000521. **page 374**

Sin 5.2″ = 0.00000521. **page 383**

Sin 5.2″ = 0.0000260. **page 387**

Sin 5.2″ = 0.00000260. **page 389**

[*from page 387*]

YOUR ANSWER: This group contains an error:

sin 19′ = 0.00553 sin 0.300° = 0.00524 sin 4.3′ = 0.0013

Sorry, but all are correct. Follow the explanations below:
To find the sine of 19′ on the slide rule:

1. Slide the minutes gauge mark on the S scale under 19 on the A scale.
2. Read 5.53 on the A scale at the index of the S scale.

Since 19′ is roughly half of 34.4′, the sine of 19′ should be about half of 0.0100, the sine of 34.4′. Therefore, using the figures we got on the rule, we find that sin 19′ = 0.00553.

The second problem is only slightly more complicated. We begin by converting 0.300° to minutes. Since there are 60 minutes in a degree, we know that

$$\frac{x}{60'} = \frac{0.300^\circ}{1^\circ}$$

where x is the equivalent, in minutes, of 0.300°. Then

$$x = 60' \times 0.300 = 18'$$

Therefore, sin 0.300° = sin 18′. And we can find the sine of 18′ just as we found that of 19′ in the problem above.

This same method can be used to find the sine of 4.3′. Setting the gauge mark on the S scale under 43 on the A scale, we read 12.5 on the A scale at the index of the S scale. Then, since 4.3′ is roughly one-eighth of 0° 34.4′, whose sine is 0.0100, we can place the decimal point correctly: sin 4.3′ = 0.00125. Using the *three zeros three* method,

$$\frac{\sin 4.3'}{\sin 1'} = \frac{4.3'}{1'}$$

so that

$$\sin 4.3' = 4.3 \times \sin 1' = 4.3 \times 0.0003 = 0.00129$$

The difference between the two answers is primarily the result of the fact that the sine of 1′ is not really 0.0003, but 0.000292. However, both the answers round off to 0.0013, which would be accurate enough for most purposes.

If you understand this material, return to page 387 for another try. If you still feel shaky, go back to page 345 for review.

[*from page 391*]

YOUR ANSWER: Side a = 109.9.

Right. In the given triangle, angle A is small, and side b is relatively long. This means that the hypotenuse and side b are nearly equal. And this, in turn, means that the sine and tangent of angle A are nearly equal:

$$\frac{a}{c} \text{ is almost equal to } \frac{a}{b} \text{ because } c \text{ is almost equal to } b.$$

So we can write

$$\frac{a}{1{,}348} = \sin 4°\,40' \quad (\text{instead of } \mathit{tan}\ 4°\,40')$$

or

$$a = 1{,}348 \times \sin 4°\,40'$$

In approximation form, since the sine of 4° 40′ is only slightly less than that of 5° 44.3′, which is 0.100,

$$a = 1 \times 10^3 \times 1 \times 10^{-1} = 1 \times 10^2 = 100$$

On the slide rule:

1. Index the S scale at 1.348 on the A scale.
2. Slide the hairline indicator to 4° 40′ on the S scale.
3. Read 10.99 on the A scale under the hairline.

Then the complete answer is 109.9.

As you will soon see, a knowledge of the T (for *tangent*) scale will simplify the problem of finding such solutions.

Now, before we go on to solving triangles that do not contain right angles, let's try one more right triangle.

Find side (a) of the triangle below (please use trigonometric methods, rather than the Pythagorean theorem).

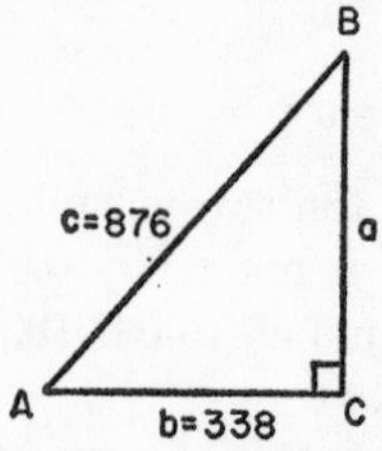

a = 338. **page 385** a = 796. **page 388** a = 808. **page 392**

[*from page 380*]

YOUR ANSWER: Sin $5.2'' = 0.00000521$.

No, you're pretty far off on this one.

Let's start over.

First, we know that for very small angles measured in seconds,

$$\frac{\sin A}{\sin 1''} = \frac{A}{1''}$$

Next, remembering sin $1''$ as *five zeros five*, we get

$$\frac{\sin A}{0.000005} = \frac{A}{1''}$$

Now, we want to find the sine of $5.2''$. Substituting $5.2''$ for A in the proportion above, we get

$$\frac{\sin 5.2''}{0.000005} = \frac{5.2''}{1''}$$

The seconds appearing in the right side of this equation cancel out, so we get

$$\sin 5.2'' = 5.2 \times 0.000005$$

In approximation form,

$$5 \times 5 \times 10^{-6} = 25 \times 10^{-6}$$
$$= 0.000025$$

Finish the problem for yourself, and then return to page 380 to choose the correct answer.

[*from page 393*]

YOUR ANSWER: Drawing a line from angle C perpendicular to side c, we get $\frac{b}{\sin B} = \frac{a}{\sin A}$.

You're correct. The figure that results when the described line is drawn is shown at the right.

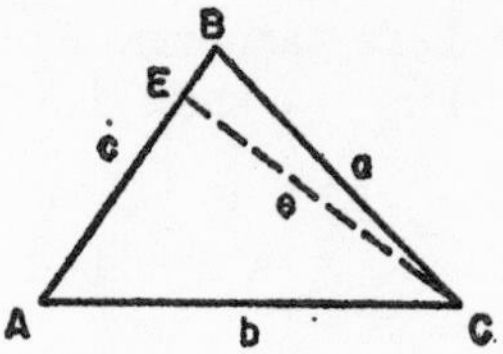

From this figure, we see that $\frac{e}{a} = \sin B$, so that $e = a \times \sin B$, and also $\frac{e}{b} = \sin A$, so that $e = b \times \sin A$. Therefore, $a \times \sin B = b \times \sin A$, or, dividing first by $\sin B$ and then by $\sin A$, $\frac{a}{\sin A} = \frac{b}{\sin B}$.

Since we've already seen that $\frac{a}{\sin A} = \frac{c}{\sin C}$, we now have the complete relationship

$$\frac{a}{\sin A} = \frac{b}{\sin B} = \frac{c}{\sin C}$$

This is called the *law of sines*, and holds for any triangle.

It may surprise you to learn that you've been using the law of sines for some time. Whenever you write $\frac{a}{c} = \sin A$, you're really writing $\frac{a}{c} = \frac{\sin A}{\sin C}$. But in the right triangles we've been working with, C is always 90°, so $\sin C = 1$. Thus, in right triangles, $\frac{\sin A}{\sin C} = \frac{\sin A}{1}$.

Use the law of sines to find the unknown sides of this triangle:

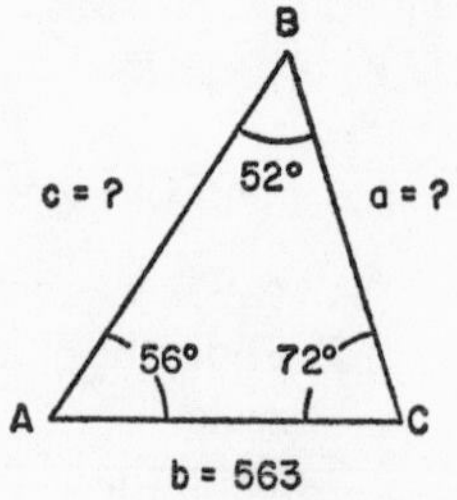

$a = 647$, $c = 535$. **page 394**

$a = 593$, $c = 680$. **page 400**

$a = 585$, $c = 687$. **page 397**

[*from page 382*]

YOUR ANSWER: $a = 338$.

No, it's not quite that simple.
Let's go through it step by step.

We want to find side a of the triangle at the right, knowing only that $b = 338$ and $c = 876$. Basically, the procedure we'll use is as follows:

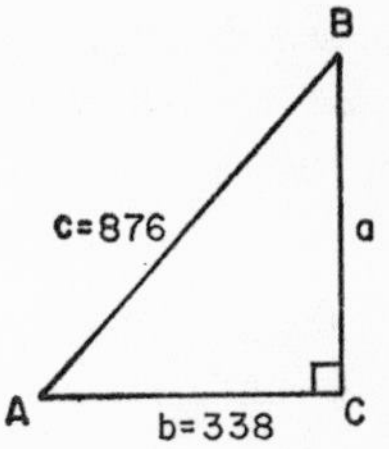

First, since $\frac{b}{c} = \sin B$, we can use this relationship to find angle B.

Here's the way it's done with the slide rule:

1. Shift 8.76 on the B scale under 3.38 on the A scale.
2. Slide the hairline indicator to the index of the A scale.
3. Reverse the sliding scale and align the S scale with the A scale.
4. Read angle B on the S scale under the hairline.

We find that $B = 22° 45'$ (or 22.75°). Therefore, since $A = 90° - B$,

$$A = 90° - 22° 45' = 67° 15' \text{ (or } 67.25°)$$

And $$\frac{a}{876} = \sin 67° 15', \quad \text{so that} \quad a = 876 \times \sin 67° 15'$$

We know that the sine of 67° 15′ is fairly close to 1.000, the sine of 90°, so for estimating purposes let's say that $\sin 67° 15' = 0.900$. Then in approximation form,

$$a = 9 \times 10^2 \times 9 \times 10^{-1} = 81 \times 10 = 810$$

Again, on the slide rule:

1. Index the S scale at 87.6 on the A scale.
2. Slide the hairline indicator to 67° 15′ (or 67.25°) on the S scale.
3. Read the significant figures of the answer on the A scale under the hairline.

Study this procedure carefully and finish the problem. Then return to page 382 to choose the correct answer.

[*from page 391*]

YOUR ANSWER: Side a = 110.04.

Unless you guessed, you couldn't have arrived at this answer without using a table of tangents. And that means that you've missed the whole point.

Let's start over.

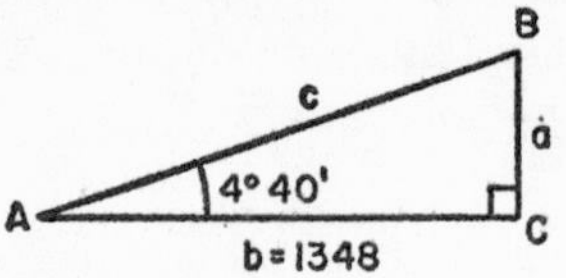

We've seen that in a triangle such as this one, where the angle between the adjacent side and the hypotenuse is very small and the adjacent side is relatively long, the hypotenuse and the adjacent side are almost equal. Therefore, the sine and tangent of the angle are almost equal. That is,

$$\frac{a}{c} \text{ is almost equal to } \frac{a}{b} \text{ because } c \text{ is almost equal to } b.$$

Therefore, we can use the sine ratio in place of the tangent to calculate side a knowing only side b. We write

$$\frac{a}{1{,}348} = \sin 4° \, 40' \quad \text{(instead of } \mathit{tan} \; 4° \, 40'\text{)}$$

Then
$$a = 1348 \times \sin 4° \, 40'$$

In approximation form, since the sine of 4° 40′ is only slightly less than that of 5° 44.3′, which is 0.100,

$$a = 1 \times 10^3 \times 1 \times 10^{-1} = 1 \times 10^2 = 100$$

On the slide rule:

1. Index the S scale at 1.348 on the A scale.
2. Slide the hairline indicator to 4° 40′ on the S scale.
3. Read the answer on the A scale under the hairline.

When you have the complete answer, return to page 391 to make the correct choice.

YOUR ANSWER: Sin 5.2″ = 0.0000260.

That's correct. Using *five zeros five* for the sine of 1″, and the proportion

$$\frac{\sin A}{\sin 1''} = \frac{A}{1''}$$

we get
$$\frac{\sin 5.2''}{0.000005} = \frac{5.2''}{1''}$$

So
$$\sin 5.2'' = 5.2 \times 0.000005 = 0.0000260$$

Now, use any of the methods you've learned to check the values below. Then select the group that contains an error. As an aid in placing the decimal points correctly, remember that

$$\sin 2.06'' = 0.00001$$
$$\sin 0^\circ\, 34.4' = 0.0100$$
$$\sin 5^\circ\, 44.3' = 0.100$$
$$\sin 90^\circ = 1.000$$

and also

$\sin 1' = 0.0003$ (*three zeros three*)

$\sin 1'' = 0.000005$ (*five zeros five*)

$\sin 51' = 0.0148$

$\sin 90' = 0.0262$

$\sin 23^\circ\, 24' = 0.397$

This group contains an error.

page 378

$\sin 19' = 0.00553$

$\sin 0.300^\circ = 0.00524$

$\sin 4.3' = 0.0013$

This group contains an error.

page 381

$\sin 52'' = 0.000260$ (using the seconds gauge mark)

$\sin 37'' = 0.000185$ (using *five zeros five*)

$\sin 3.3'' = 0.0000160$ (using the seconds gauge mark)

This group contains an error.

page 390

[*from page 382*]

YOUR ANSWER: $a = 796$.

No. And this looks like a guess. Let's go through it step by step.

We want to find side a of the triangle at the right, knowing only that $b = 338$ and $c = 876$. Basically, the procedure we'll use is as follows:

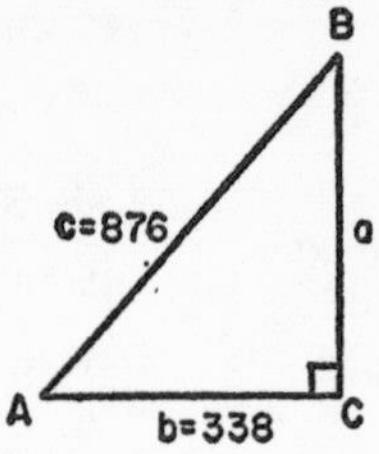

First, since $\frac{b}{c} = \sin B$, we can use this relationship to find angle B. Here's the way it's done with the slide rule:

1. Shift 8.76 on the B scale under 3.38 on the A scale.
2. Slide the hairline indicator to the index of the A scale.
3. Reverse the sliding scale and align the S scale with the A scale.
4. Read angle B on the S scale under the hairline.

We find that $B = 22° 45'$ (or 22.75°). Therefore, since $A = 90° - B$,

$$A = 90° - 22° 45' = 67° 15' \text{ (or } 67.25°)$$

And $\quad \frac{a}{876} = \sin 67° 15', \quad$ so that $\quad a = 876 \times \sin 67° 15'$

We know that the sine of 67° 15′ is fairly close to 1.000, the sine of 90°, so for estimating purposes let's say that $\sin 67° 15' = 0.900$. Then in approximation form,

$$a = 9 \times 10^2 \times 9 \times 10^{-1} = 81 \times 10 = 810$$

Again, on the slide rule:

1. Index the S scale at 87.6 on the A scale.
2. Slide the hairline indicator to 67° 15′ (or 67.25°) on the S scale.
3. Read the significant figures of the answer on the A scale under the hairline.

Study this procedure carefully and finish the problem. Then return to page 382 to choose the correct answer.

[*from page 380*]

YOUR ANSWER: Sin $5.2'' = 0.00000260$.

Well, you have the significant figures right, but you've misplaced the decimal point.

Just for practice, let's start from scratch.

First, we know that for very small angles, in seconds,

$$\frac{\sin A}{\sin 1''} = \frac{A}{1''}$$

Next, remembering sin $1''$ as *five zeros five*,

$$\frac{\sin A}{0.000005} = \frac{A}{1''}$$

In this case, $A = 5.2''$, so

$$\frac{\sin 5.2''}{0.000005} = \frac{5.2''}{1''}$$

The seconds appearing in the right side of this equation cancel out, so we get

$$\sin 5.2'' = 5.2 \times 0.000005$$

And 5.2×0.000005 is roughly 0.0000250, about five times the sine of $1''$. The answer you chose, on the other hand, is actually *smaller* than the sine of $1''$.

When you're sure you understand where you went wrong, return to page 380 to choose the correct answer.

[*from page 387*]

YOUR ANSWER: This group contains an error:

sin 52″ = 0.000260 sin 37″ = 0.000185 sin 3.3″ = 0.0000160

You are right.

To find sin 52″ with the aid of the seconds gauge mark:

1. Slide the seconds gauge mark on the S scale under 52 on the A scale.
2. Read 25.0 on the A scale at the index of the S scale.

Since 52″ is approximately 26 times as great as 2.06″, whose sine is 0.00001, sin 52″ is approximately 26×0.00001, or 0.00026. Therefore, using the figures we got on the rule, we find that sin 52″ = 0.000252, not 0.000260.

However, if we use the *five zeros five* method, we find that

$$\sin 52'' = 52 \times 0.000005 = 0.000260$$

The difference between the two answers is primarily the result of the fact that sin 1″ is really 0.00000485, not 0.000005.

Similarly, using the gauge mark method, we get sin 37″ = 0.000179, while with *five zeros five* we get sin 37″ = 0.000185. And sin 3.3″ = 0.0000160 with the seconds gauge mark, but 0.0000165 by *five zeros five*.

Despite such discrepancies, however, the *five zeros five* method is sufficiently accurate for most purposes.

Please go on to page 391.

[*from page 390*]

Now let's look again at the triangle we used to determine the diameter of the blast hole made by the rocket:

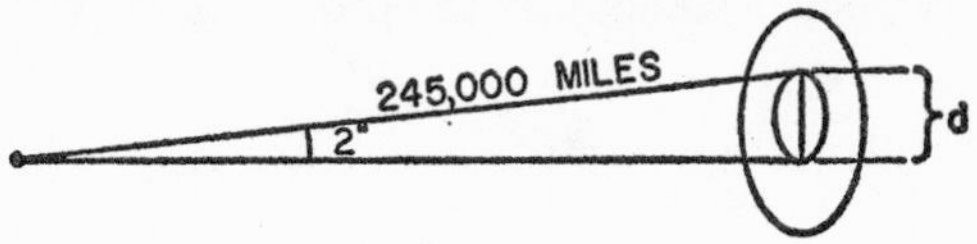

We called the uppermost side of this triangle the hypotenuse. Actually, this was just an arbitrary selection. Since the distance from the launching point to the bottom of the crater is also approximately 245,000 miles, we could just as well have chosen this side the hypotenuse of the triangle. Either way, we find that the hypotenuse (c) and the long side (b) of the triangle have to be almost the same. Accordingly, the tangent $\frac{a}{b}$ and sine $\frac{a}{c}$ of the angle between them are almost the same. For most practical purposes, then, we can say that

$$\sin 2'' = \tan 2'' = \frac{d}{245{,}000 \text{ mi.}}$$

This relationship gives us a short-cut method for calculating the short side of such a triangle if we know the long side but not the hypotenuse. That is, we simply substitute the sine ratio of the small angle opposite the short side for the tangent ratio.

Use this method to find side a of the triangle below without finding the hypotenuse first:

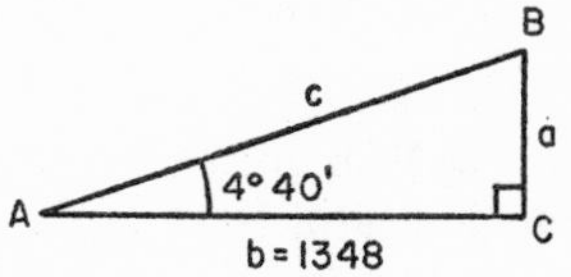

Side a = 109.67. **page 379**

Side a = 109.9. **page 382**

Side a = 110.04. **page 386**

[*from page 382*]

YOUR ANSWER: $a = 808$.

Right. Very good. Essentially the procedure is as follows:

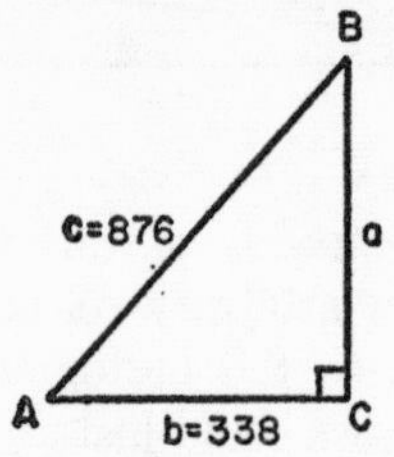

First, we used the relationship $\frac{b}{c} = \sin B$ to find angle B.

Next, we used $A = 90° - B$ to find angle A.

Finally, we used the fact that $\frac{a}{c} = \sin A$ to find the value of side a.

On the slide rule, it goes like this:

1. Shift 8.76 on the B scale under 3.38 on the A scale.
2. Slide the hairline indicator to the index of the A scale.
3. Reverse the sliding scale and align the S scale with the A scale.
4. Read angle B, 22° 45′ (or 22.75°), on the S scale under the hairline.

Then $A = 90° - 22° 45' = 67° 15'$ (or 67.25°), and $a = 876 \times \sin 67° 15'$. (By the usual approximation method, we find that a is roughly 810.)

5. Index the S scale at 87.6 on the A scale.
6. Slide the hairline indicator to 67° 15′ on the S scale.
7. Read 80.8 on the A scale under the hairline.

Then $a = 808$.

Of course, the necessity for several readings of the rule, as well as several re-indexings, reduces the accuracy of our answer somewhat. Nevertheless, the method is theoretically correct, so you should be able to get fairly accurate results with it.

Now, to learn how to solve triangles that do not contain right angles, please go on to page 393.

[*from page 392*]

In discussing the methods used to solve triangles that are not right triangles, we will consider the general or *oblique* triangle, as shown at right.

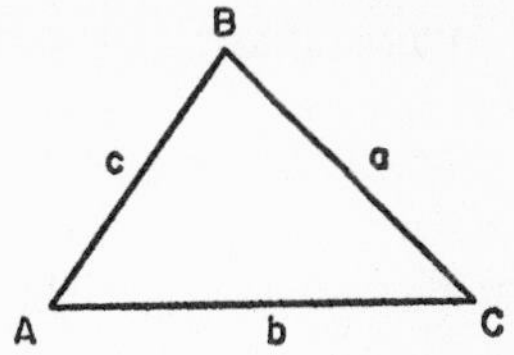

All triangles may be reduced to a pair of right triangles, simply by dropping a line from one of the angles perpendicular to (i.e., making a right angle with) the opposite side. If this perpendicular line is drawn from angle B to side b in the triangle above, and the foot of the perpendicular is labeled D, then the triangles formed are ABD and CBD:

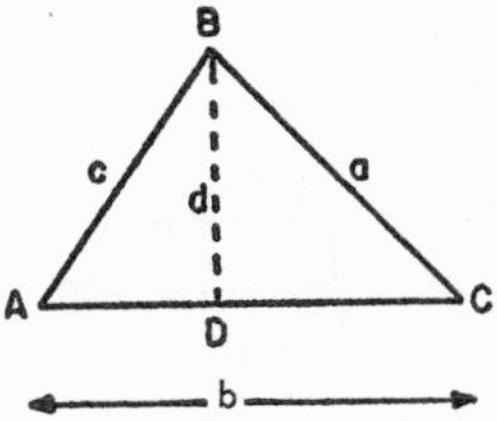

With the aid of these two triangles, we can obtain several useful expressions. First, since the side labeled d is common to both triangles, we know that $\frac{d}{a} = \sin C$, so $d = a \times \sin C$, and also $\frac{d}{c} = \sin A$, so $d = c \times \sin A$. Therefore, since $d = a \times \sin C$ and also $c \times \sin A$,

$$a \times \sin C = c \times \sin A.$$

Dividing through, first by $\sin C$ and then by $\sin A$, we get

$$\frac{a}{\sin A} = \frac{c}{\sin C}$$

If we were to draw a perpendicular line from angle C to side c, and proceed as we did above, what expression would result?

$\frac{b}{\sin B} = \frac{a}{\sin A}$. **page 384**

$\frac{b}{\sin A} = \frac{a}{\sin B}$. **page 399**

$\frac{b}{\sin B} = \frac{c}{\sin C}$. **page 396**

I don't understand. **page 401**

[*from page 384*]

YOUR ANSWER: $a = 647$, $c = 535$.

You'd better take another look at the law of sines. It says that in any triangle, the ratio of each side to the sine of the opposite angle is constant. That is,

$$\frac{a}{\sin A} = \frac{b}{\sin B} = \frac{c}{\sin C}$$

Now, look at the given triangle again:

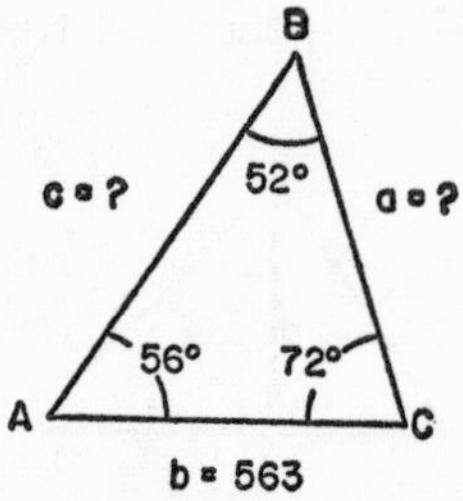

From the law of sines, we see that

$$\frac{a}{\sin 56^\circ} = \frac{563}{\sin 52^\circ} = \frac{c}{\sin 72^\circ} \quad \left(\textit{not}\ \frac{a}{\sin 72^\circ} = \frac{563}{\sin 56^\circ} = \frac{c}{\sin 52^\circ}\right)$$

So
$$a = \sin 56^\circ \times \frac{563}{\sin 52^\circ}$$

$$c = \sin 72^\circ \times \frac{563}{\sin 52^\circ}$$

Using our regular approximation method, we can quickly see that a is roughly 600 and c is roughly 675. On the slide rule:

1. Shift 52° on the S scale under 56.3 on the A scale.
2. Slide the hairline indicator to 56° on the S scale.
3. Read the significant figures of side a on the A scale under the hairline.
4. Slide the hairline indicator to 72° on the S scale.
5. Read the significant figures of c on the A scale under the hairline.

Return to page 384 to choose the right answer.

[*from page 400*]

YOUR ANSWER: Sin 136° = 0.695 is incorrect.

No, the given value is correct. Let's review a bit.

First, you should recall from elementary geometry that *supplementary* angles are two angles whose sum is 180°. Thus, since 75° + 105° = 180°, 75° is the supplementary angle of 105°. Similarly, 31° 38′ is the supplement (or supplementary angle) of 148° 22′, because 31° 38′ + 148° 22′ = 180°.

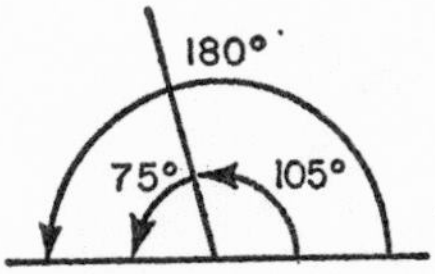

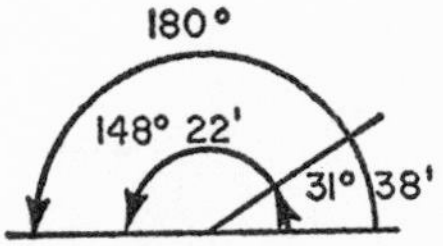

To find the supplement of any angle, then, we simply subtract that angle from 180°. So the supplement of 136° is 44°, because

$$180° - 136° = 44°$$

Now, we were told that the sine of an angle between 90° and 180° is the same as the sine of its supplementary angle. Therefore, the sine of 136° is the same as that of 44°. And it's a simple matter to find the sine of 44° with the slide rule:

1. Align the A and S scales.
2. Slide the hairline indicator to 44° on the S scale.
3. Read 69.5 on the A scale under the hairline.

Since 44° is larger than 5° 44.3′, for which the sine ratio is 0.100, but smaller than 90°, for which the sine is 1.000, we see that sin 44° = 0.695. Therefore, sin 136° = 0.695, and the given figure is correct.

Study this analysis of the problem. Then return to page 400 for another try.

[*from page 393*]

YOUR ANSWER: Drawing a line from angle C perpendicular to side c, we get $\frac{b}{\sin B} = \frac{c}{\sin C}$.

No, we don't. At least, not directly. Let's draw the indicated line and see what's really happening:

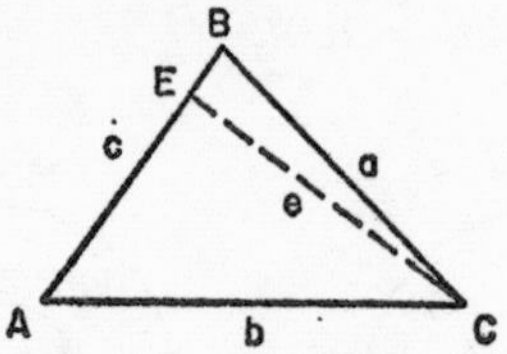

The side labeled e is common to both triangles (ACE and BCE). Clearly, since e is perpendicular to side c (i.e., makes a right angle with side c),

$$\frac{e}{a} = \sin B, \quad \text{so that} \quad e = a \times \sin B,$$

and also

$$\frac{e}{b} = \sin A, \quad \text{so that} \quad e = b \times \sin A.$$

Therefore, since $e = a \times \sin B$ and also $b \times \sin A$, we can equate these two expressions:

$$a \times \sin B = b \times \sin A$$

Dividing through, first by $\sin B$ and then by $\sin A$, we get

$$\frac{a}{\sin A} = \frac{b}{\sin B}$$

(Now, since we've already seen that $\frac{a}{\sin A} = \frac{c}{\sin C}$, it is true that $\frac{b}{\sin B} = \frac{c}{\sin C}$. But this result cannot be obtained directly from the figure obtained by drawing a perpendicular from C to c; you need to get the $\frac{a}{\sin A} = \frac{b}{\sin B}$ relationship first.)

Study this analysis carefully. Then return to page 393 to choose the correct answer.

[from page 384]

YOUR ANSWER: $a = 585$, $c = 687$.

No. And this looks like a guess. Look at the given triangle again:

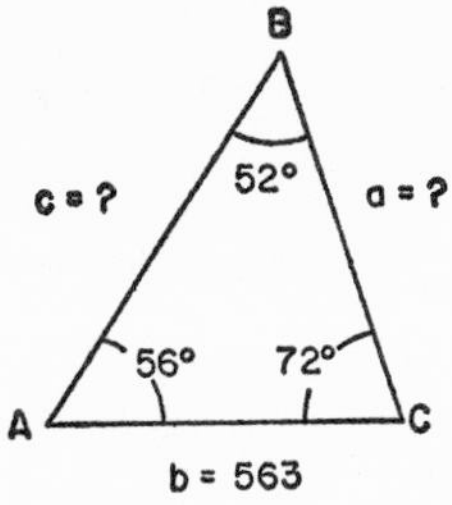

According to the law of sines,

$$\frac{a}{\sin A} = \frac{b}{\sin B} = \frac{c}{\sin C}$$

Substituting known values,

$$\frac{a}{\sin 56°} = \frac{563}{\sin 52°} = \frac{c}{\sin 72°}$$

So

$$a = \sin 56° \times \frac{563}{\sin 52°}$$

$$c = \sin 72° \times \frac{563}{\sin 52°}$$

Using our regular approximation method, we can quickly see that a is roughly 600 and c is roughly 675.

On the slide rule:

1. Shift 52° on the S scale under 56.3 on the A scale.
2. Slide the hairline indicator to 56° on the S scale.
3. Read the significant figures of side a on the A scale under the hairline.
4. Slide the hairline indicator to 72° on the S scale.
5. Read the significant figures of c on the A scale under the hairline.

When you have the correct values, return to page 384 to choose the right answer.

[*from page 403*]

YOUR ANSWER: $b = 293$, $B = 131° 29.2'$, $C = 1° 30.8'$.

No. Evidently you used the incorrect relationship.

$$\sin C = \frac{286}{\sin 47° \times 153}$$

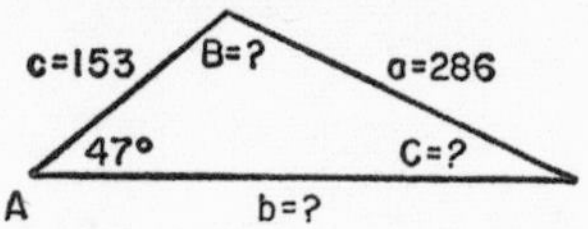

We'd better start at the beginning. From the law of sines,

$$\frac{286}{\sin 47°} = \frac{b}{\sin B} = \frac{153}{\sin C}$$

To find C, then, we can use a simple proportion setting of the rule:

1. Shift 47° on the S scale under 28.6 on the A scale.
2. Slide the hairline indicator to 15.3 on the A scale.
3. Read 23° on the S scale under the hairline.

So $C = 23°$. (Incidentally, be sure to read the 28.6 and 15.3 on the *same* part of the A scale. That is, if you use the 28.6 on the right half of the A scale, you must also use the 15.3 on that half of the scale. Similarly, if you use the 2.86 on the left half of the A scale, you must slide the hairline indicator to 1.53 on that half of the scale.)

At this point we may find angle B. The angles of a triangle must add up to 180°, so $B = 180° - 47° - 23° = 110°$.

To find side b, we need to know the value of sin B. We've seen that the sine of an angle between 90° and 180° is equal to the sine of its supplementary angle. Therefore,

$$\sin B = \sin 110° = \sin (180° - 110°) = \sin 70°$$

The slide rule is already set so that 47° on the S scale is under 28.6 on the A scale. Thus all we need do to solve the proportion $\frac{286}{\sin 47°} = \frac{b}{\sin 70°}$ is:

1. Slide the hairline indicator to 70° on the S scale.
2. Read the significant figures of the value of b on the A scale under the hairline.

Use the usual approximation methods to place the decimal point correctly. Then, when you have the complete answer, return to page 403 to make the right choice.

[*from page 393*]

YOUR ANSWER: Drawing a line from angle C perpendicular to side c, we get $\dfrac{b}{\sin A} = \dfrac{a}{\sin B}$.

No, we don't. And this answer looks like a guess.

Let's start over. Here is the figure that results when a perpendicular line is drawn from angle C to side c:

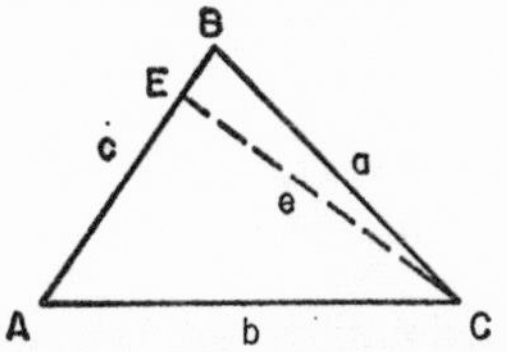

The side labeled e is common to both triangles (ACE and BCE). Clearly, since e is perpendicular to side c (i.e., makes a right angle with side c),

$$\frac{e}{a} = \sin B, \quad \text{so that} \quad e = a \times \sin B,$$

and also

$$\frac{e}{b} = \sin A, \quad \text{so that} \quad e = b \times \sin A.$$

Therefore, since $e = a \times \sin B$ and also $b \times \sin A$, we can equate these two expressions:

$$a \times \sin B = b \times \sin A$$

Dividing first by $\sin B$, we get

$$a = \frac{b \times \sin A}{\sin B}$$

And dividing by $\sin A$, we get the relationship we want:

$$\frac{a}{\sin A} = \frac{b}{\sin B}$$

This is the relationship that corresponds to the $\dfrac{a}{\sin A} = \dfrac{c}{\sin C}$ relationship we obtained when we drew a perpendicular line from angle B to side b.

Study this analysis carefully. Then return to page 393 to choose the correct answer.

[*from page 384*]

YOUR ANSWER: $a = 593$, $c = 680$.

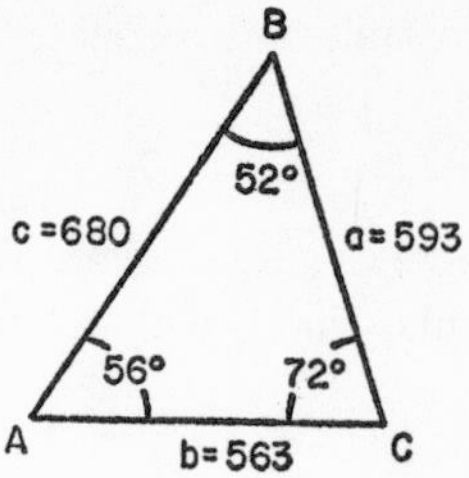

Right. By the law of sines,

$$\frac{563}{\sin 52°} = \frac{a}{\sin 56°} = \frac{c}{\sin 72°}$$

So $\quad a = \sin 56° \times \dfrac{563}{\sin 52°} \qquad c = \sin 72° \times \dfrac{563}{\sin 52°}$

With the usual approximation methods, we find that a is roughly 600 and c is roughly 675. The calculation is especially easy on the slide rule, since we need set the $\dfrac{563}{\sin 52°}$ part of the problem only once.

On the slide rule:

1. Shift 52° on the S scale under 56.3 on the A scale.
2. Slide the hairline indicator to 56° on the S scale.
3. Read 59.3 on the A scale under the hairline.

Then $a = 593$.

4. Slide the hairline indicator to 72° on the S scale.
5. Read 68.0 on the A scale under the hairline.

Then $c = 680$.

Not infrequently we encounter a triangle in which one of the angles is greater than 90°. Though we won't take time to discuss it in detail here, it can be shown that the sine of an angle between 90° and 180° is the same as the sine of its supplementary angle. (Supplementary angles, you recall, are two angles whose sum is 180°. Thus the supplement of any angle x is $180° - x$.)

Which of the sines below is incorrect?

Sin 136° = 0.695. **page 395** Sin 170° 25′ = 0.166. **page 406**

Sin 150° = 0.0523. **page 403** Sin 179° 59′ 53″ = 0.0000339. **page 408**

[*from page 393*]

YOUR ANSWER: I don't understand.

Well, let's start by drawing the line from angle C perpendicular (i.e., making a right angle with) side c. The resulting figure is shown below.

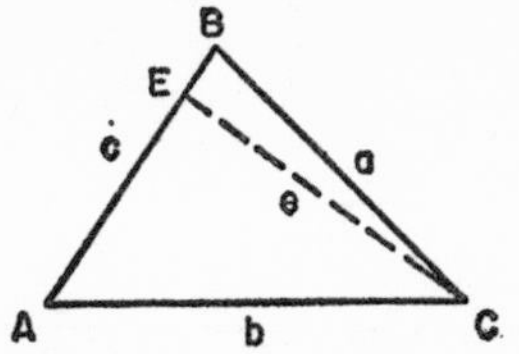

From this figure we want to find the relationship that corresponds to the $\frac{a}{\sin A} = \frac{c}{\sin C}$ relationship we got when we drew a perpendicular line from angle B to side b.

To begin, notice that the side labeled e is common to both triangles. And since e makes a right angle with side c, both the triangles are right triangles. Therefore,

$$\frac{e}{a} = \sin B, \quad \text{so that} \quad e = a \times \sin B,$$

and also

$$\frac{e}{b} = \sin A, \quad \text{so that} \quad e = b \times \sin A.$$

Because $e = a \times \sin B$ and also $b \times \sin A$, we can set these two expressions equal to each other:

$$a \times \sin B = b \times \sin A$$

Then, dividing through first by $\sin B$ and then by $\sin A$ (although the order of division really doesn't make any difference), we get

$$\frac{a}{\sin A} = \frac{b}{\sin B}$$

And this is the relationship we're looking for.

Study this analysis carefully. Then return to page 393 and look again at the explanation there. When you're sure you understand the procedure, choose the right answer.

[*from page 411*]

YOUR ANSWER: This statement is incorrect: Side $b_1 = 1{,}070$.

No, it's right. Here's the way it goes:

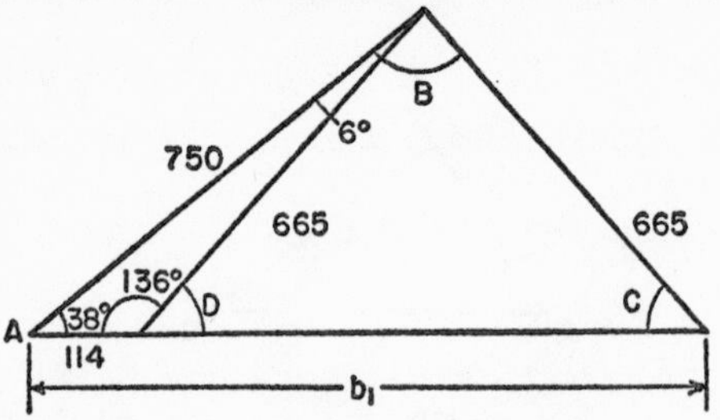

Since b_1 is a straight line, we know that angle $D + 136°$ must be equal to 180°. Therefore,

$$D = 180° - 136° = 44°.$$

Now, how about angle C? Well, we notice that triangle BCD is isosceles. That is, it has two equal sides: the side opposite angle C is 665 and the side opposite angle D is also 665. Therefore, we can conclude that angle C is the same as angle D. So $C = 44°$.

Now we can find angle B. Since $A + B + C = 180°$,

$$B = 180° - A - C = 180° - 38° - 44° = 98°$$

Then, from the law of sines,

$$\frac{b_1}{\sin 98°} = \frac{750}{\sin 44°} \quad \left(\text{or } \frac{665}{\sin 38°}\text{—either proportion will do}\right)$$

The sine of an angle between 90° and 180° is the same as the sine of its supplementary angle. Thus $\sin 98° = \sin (180° - 98°) = \sin 82°$.

To find b on the slide rule:

1. Shift 44° on the S scale under 7.50 on the A scale.
2. Slide the hairline indicator to 82° on the S scale.
3. Read 10.7 on the A scale under the hairline.

Using the usual approximation method to help us place the decimal point correctly, we get $b = 1{,}070$.

Study this analysis carefully. Then return to page 411 to find the error.

[*from page 400*]

YOUR ANSWER: Sin 150° = 0.0523 is incorrect.

You are right. The sine of an angle between 90° and 180° is the same as the sine of its supplementary angle. Therefore,

$$\sin 150° = \sin (180° - 150°) = \sin 30°$$

(This is easy to check; supplementary angles are two angles whose sum is 180°, and 30° + 150° = 180°.) All we need to do with the slide rule, then, is look up the sine of 30°:

1. Align the S and A scales.
2. Slide the hairline indicator to 30° (*not* 3°—be careful) on the S scale.
3. Read 50.0 on the right-hand A scale under the hairline. Since 30° is larger than 5° 44.3′, for which the sine ratio is 0.100, but smaller than 90°, for which the sine is 1.000, we see that sin 30° = 0.500. Therefore, sin 150° = 0.500.

Here's a triangle with one angle greater than 90°. Solve it for the unknown values:

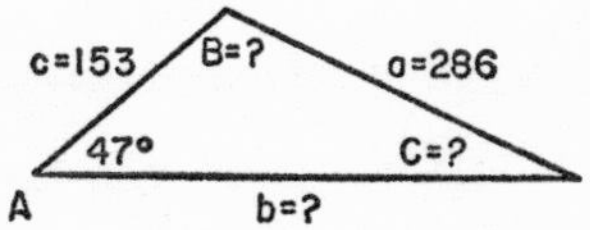

b = 293, B = 131° 29.2′, C = 1° 30.8′. **page 398**

b = 368, B = 110°, C = 23°. **page 410**

b = 375, B = 118°, C = 15°. **page 414**

[*from page 417*]

YOUR ANSWER: $c^2 = a^2 + b^2 - 2ab(\cos C)$.

Right. Very good. Since $\cos C = \frac{e}{a}$, $e = a(\cos C)$. Substituting $a(\cos C)$ for e in the equation $c^2 = a^2 + b^2 - 2be$, we get

$$c^2 = a^2 + b^2 - 2b \times a(\cos C), \quad \text{or} \quad c^2 = a^2 + b^2 - 2ab(\cos C)$$

By drawing a perpendicular line from C to c, and from A to a, we can also prove that

$$a^2 = b^2 + c^2 - 2bc(\cos A),$$

and

$$b^2 = a^2 + c^2 - 2ac(\cos B)$$

Together, these three equations constitute the *law of cosines.* In words, the law of cosines says that

> in any triangle, the square of any side is equal to the sum of the squares of the other two sides minus twice the product of those sides and the cosine of their included angle.

The law of cosines, in combination with the law of sines, will solve any triangle.

Just to make sure that you understand what the law of cosines says, find side a of the triangle below:

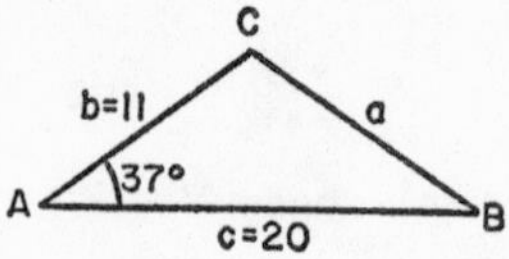

$a = 26.5$. **page 413**

$a = 17.3$. **page 418**

$a = 13.1$. **page 420**

[*from page 411*]

YOUR ANSWER: This statement is incorrect: Side $b_1 = 956$.

Right; it's wrong. Here's a complete analysis of the problem:

Since $D + 136°$ must equal 180°, we know that $D = 180° - 136° = 44°$. And angle C must be the same as angle D, because the triangle BCD is isosceles (i.e., has two equal sides) and therefore has two equal angles. So $C = 44°$; the given value is correct.

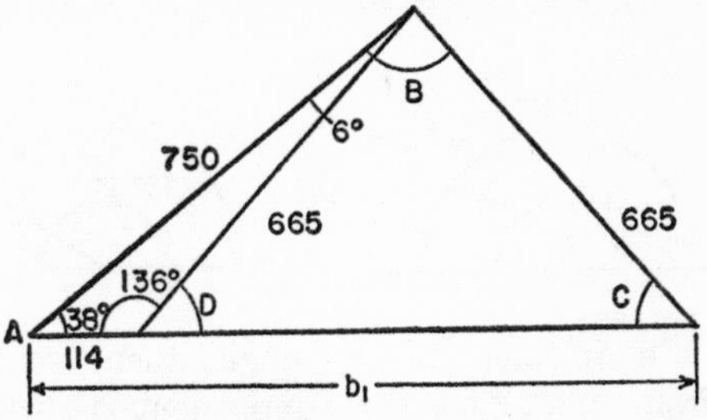

Now, knowing angles A and C of the large triangle ABC, we can find angle B: $B = 180° - 38° - 44° = 98°$

Then, from the law of sines,

$$\frac{b_1}{\sin 98°} = \frac{750}{\sin 44°} \quad \left(\text{or, if you prefer, } \frac{665}{\sin 38°}\right)$$

And of course $\sin 98° = \sin (180° - 98°) = \sin 82°$. Therefore, to find b on the slide rule:

1. Shift 44° on the S scale under 7.50 on the A scale.
2. Slide the hairline indicator to 82° on the S scale.
3. Read 10.7 on the A scale under the hairline.

Then, using the usual approximation method to place the decimal point correctly, we find that $b_1 = 1{,}070$. (The incorrect answer 956 is the result of calculating B to be $180° - 44° - 44°$, or 92°.)

Now, look at this triangle: Can you use the law of sines to solve it?

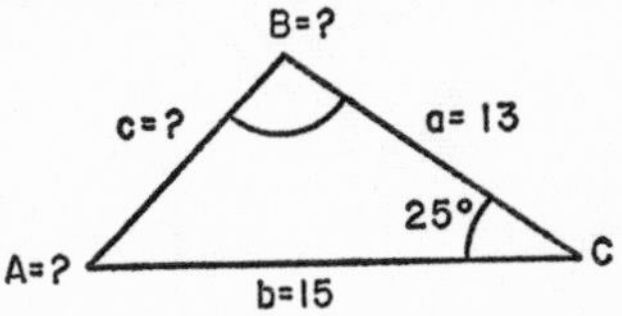

Yes. **page 409**

No. **page 416**

[*from page 400*]

YOUR ANSWER: Sin 170° 25′ = 0.166 is incorrect.

No, the given value is correct. Let's review a bit.

First, you should recall from elementary geometry that *supplementary* angles are two angles whose sum is 180°. Thus, since 75° + 105° = 180°, 75° is the supplementary angle of 105°. Similarly, 31° 38′ is the supplement (or supplementary angle) of 148° 22′, because 31° 38′ + 148° 22′ = 180°.

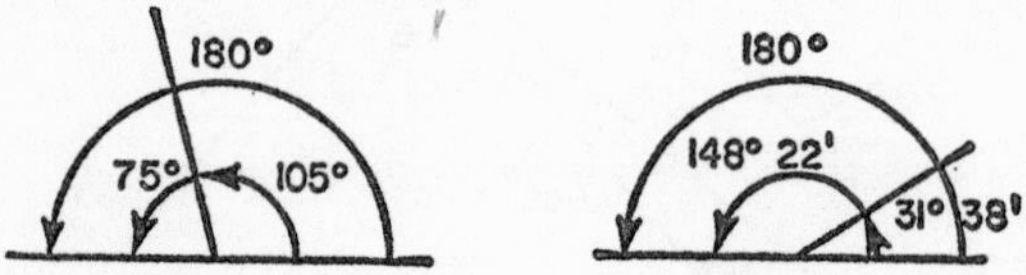

To find the supplement of any angle, then, we simply subtract that angle from 180°. So the supplement of 170° 25′ is 9° 35′, because

$$180° - 170° 25' = 9° 35'$$

Now, we were told that the sine of an angle between 90° and 180° is the same as the sine of its supplementary angle. Therefore, the sine of 170° 25′ is the same as that of 9° 35′. And it's a simple matter to find the sine of 9° 35′ with the slide rule:

1. Align the A and S scales.
2. Slide the hairline indicator to 9° 35′ on the S scale.
3. Read 16.6 on the A scale under the hairline.

Since 9° 35′ is larger than 5° 44.3′, for which the sine ratio is 0.100, but smaller than 90°, for which the sine is 1.000, we see that sin 9° 35′ = 0.166. Therefore, sin 170° 25′ = 0.166, and the given figure is correct.

Study this analysis of the problem. Then return to page 400 for another try.

[*from page 411*]

YOUR ANSWER: This statement is incorrect: Angle $C = 44°$.

No, it's right. Here's the diagram again:

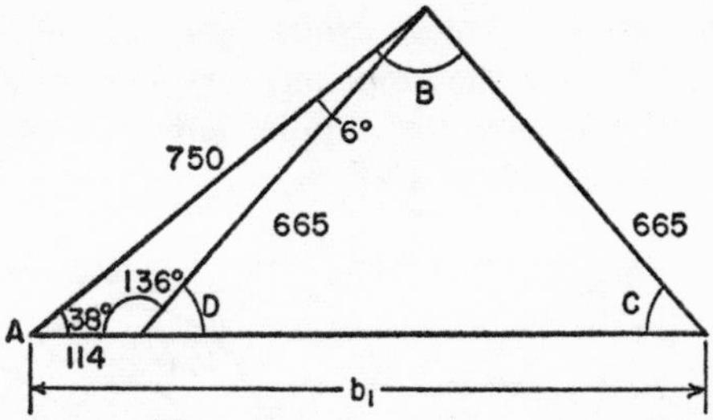

First, notice that b_1 is a straight line. As you should recall, a straight line can be considered a 180° angle. Think of it as the sum of two angles, if you like. Then $136° + x° = 180°$.

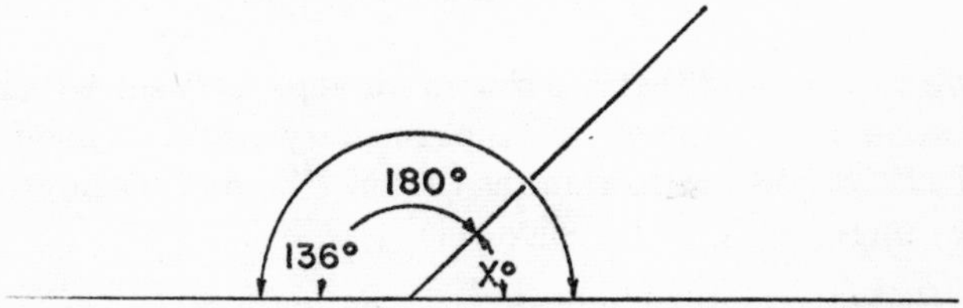

Therefore, $$x = 180° - 136° = 44°$$

Now, what about angle C? Well, notice that triangle BCD is isosceles. That is, it has two equal sides: the side opposite angle C is 665 and the side opposite angle D is also 665. You should remember that there is a theorem from elementary geometry that says that angles opposite equal sides of a triangle are equal. In other words, angle C is the same as angle D. Therefore,

$$C = 44°$$

So the given value is correct.

Study this analysis until you understand where you went wrong. Then return to page 411 for another try.

[*from page 400*]

YOUR ANSWER: Sin 179° 59′ 53″ = 0.0000339 is incorrect.

No, the given value is correct. Let's review a bit.

First, you should recall from elementary geometry that *supplementary* angles are two angles whose sum is 180°. Thus, since 75° + 105° = 180°, 75° is the supplementary angle of 105°. Similarly, 31° 38′ is the supplement (or supplementary angle) of 148° 22′, because 31° 38′ + 148° 22′ = 180°.

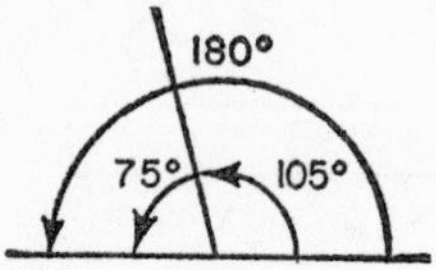

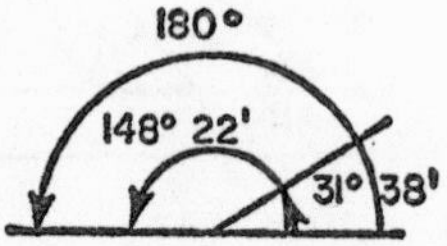

To find the supplement of any angle, then, we simply subtract that angle from 180°. The supplement of 179° 59′ 53″ is 7″, because

$$179° \, 59' \, 53'' + 7'' = 180°$$

Now, we were told that the sine of an angle between 90° and 180° is the same as the sine of its supplementary angle. Therefore, the sine of 179° 59′ 53″ is the same as that of 7″. And it's no trouble to find the sine of 7″ with the slide rule:

1. Slide the hairline indicator to 7 on the A scale.
2. Shift the seconds gauge mark on the S scale under the hairline.
3. Read 3.39 on the A scale at the index of the S scale.

We remember the sine of 1″ as *five zeros five*, or 0.000005. Since 7″ is seven times 1″, the sine of 7″ should be about seven times 0.000005, or 0.000035. Therefore, using the figure from the slide rule, we get

$$\sin 179° \, 59' \, 53'' = \sin 7'' = 0.0000339$$

Study this analysis until you're sure you understand why it's correct. Then return to page 400 for another try.

[*from page 405*]

YOUR ANSWER: Yes, the law of sines can be used to solve this triangle.

Well, let's check. The law of sines says that

$$\frac{a}{\sin A} = \frac{b}{\sin B} = \frac{c}{\sin C}$$

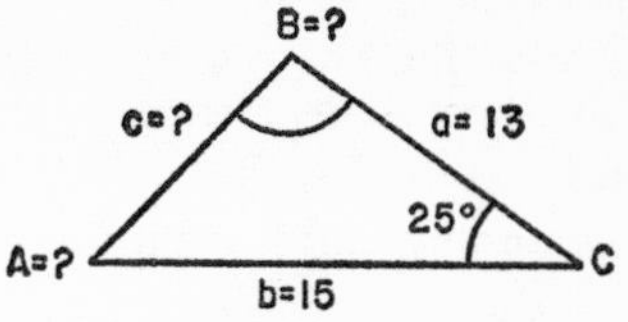

According to the law of sines, $\frac{13}{\sin A} = \frac{15}{\sin B} = \frac{c}{\sin 25°}$.

But when we try to solve for A, B, or c, we run into trouble. Look what happens:

Suppose we try to solve the proportion $\frac{13}{\sin A} = \frac{15}{\sin B}$ for $\sin A$. We get

$$\sin A = \frac{13 \times \sin B}{15}$$

And this isn't any help, because there is still an unknown quantity, $\sin B$, on the right side of the equation. Similarly, if we solve for $\sin B$, we get

$$\sin B = \frac{15 \times \sin A}{13}$$

with the unknown $\sin A$ appearing on the right.

Let's consider some other combination. How about solving $\frac{13}{\sin A} = \frac{c}{\sin 25°}$ for c? Well, we get

$$c = \frac{13 \times \sin 25°}{\sin A}$$

And this is the same problem we ran into before—there's an unknown quantity on the right side of the equation.

In fact, none of the proportions afforded by the law of sines will do the job. We always end up with an equation in two unknowns.

Return to page 405 and choose the right answer.

[*from page 403*]

YOUR ANSWER: $b = 368$, $B = 110°$, $C = 23°$.

Right. Here's the way it went:

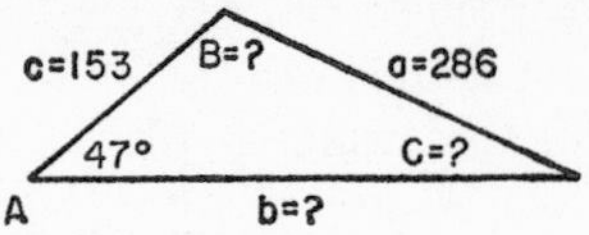

From the law of sines,

$$\frac{286}{\sin 47°} = \frac{b}{\sin B} = \frac{153}{\sin C}$$

We can easily find C from this information:

1. Shift 47° on the S scale under 28.6 on the A scale.
2. Slide the hairline indicator to 15.3 on the A scale.
3. Read 23° on the S scale under the hairline.

We may now find B, since the angles of a triangle must add up to 180°.

$$B = 180° - 47° - 23° = 110°.$$

To find b, we need to know the value of $\sin B$. Since the sine of an angle between 90° and 180° is equal to the sine of its supplementary angle, we know that $\sin 110° = 70°$ (because $110° + 70° = 180°$). Since the slide rule is already set so that 47° on the S scale is under 286 on the A scale, all we need do to find b is:

1. Slide the hairline indicator to 70° on the S scale.
2. Read 36.8 on the A scale under the hairline.

In approximation form,

$$b = \frac{3 \times 10^2 \times 9 \times 10^{-1}}{8 \times 10^{-1}} = 3.4 \times 10^2\text{, or } 340$$

Therefore, $b = 368$.

In case you haven't discovered it, a short cut for finding the angle whose sine is equivalent to that of the obtuse angle of a triangle is simply to add the acute angles. In the problem above, for example, $B = 110°$. So

$$\sin B = \sin 110° = \sin (180° - 110°) = \sin 70°$$

And also, $$A + C = 47° + 23° = 70°$$

Please go on to page 411.

[*from page 410*]

Until now we've generally been given sketches of the triangles we've been working with. But suppose we were simply given values for A, a, and b, without an accompanying sketch. Could we draw a triangle which would be a reasonably accurate representation of the desired one?

The answer is yes, we can. The usual method is to draw side b at A degrees from the horizontal, and then swing an arc with radius equal to side a until it intersects the horizontal line, like this:

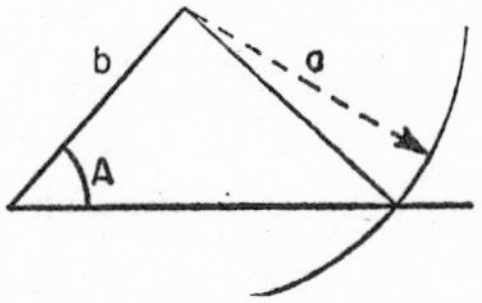

If side a is a bit shorter than side b, however, look what can happen—two triangles!

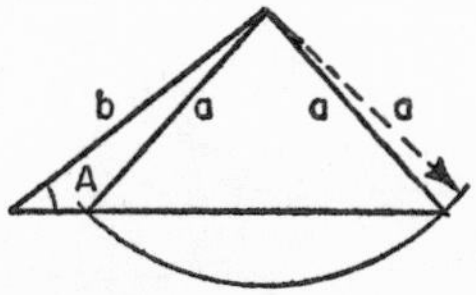

Below is such a situation. One of the possible solutions has been found. You find the other one. That is, find B, C, and b_1. Then choose the incorrect statement below. (Hint: What can you say about angles D and C? Remember that D and 136° must add up to 180°.)

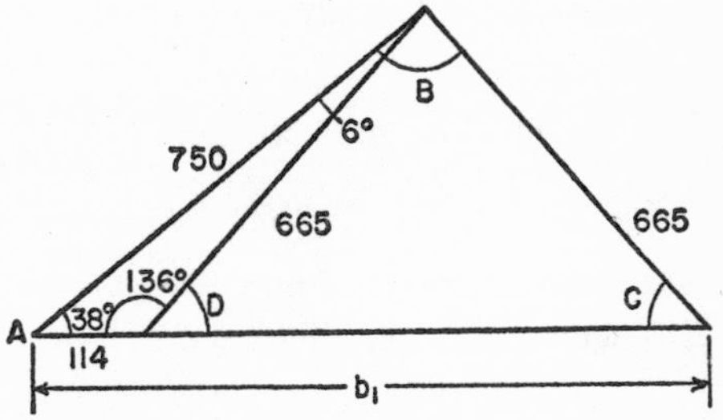

Side b_1 = 1,070. **page 402**

Angle C = 44°. **page 407**

Side b_1 = 956. **page 405**

Angle B = 98°. **page 415**

[*from page 417*]

YOUR ANSWER: $c^2 = a^2 + b^2 - 2ac(\cos B)$.

No. And this looks like a guess. Let's start over.

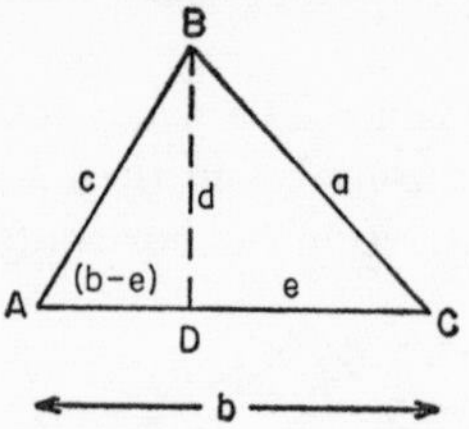

We began by drawing a perpendicular line from angle B to side b, thus dividing triangle ABC into two right triangles, ABD and CBD. Then, since side d is common to both triangles, we found that

$$d^2 = a^2 - e^2 \quad \text{in } CBD \quad \text{and} \quad d^2 = c^2 - (b - e)^2 \quad \text{in } ABD$$

Therefore,

$$c^2 - (b - e)^2 = a^2 - e^2$$

Solving for c^2 and simplifying, we get

$$c^2 = a^2 + b^2 - 2be$$

At this point we want to eliminate e from the equation to arrive at an equation which will give us c in terms of the information we have, i.e., in terms of a, b, and C. To do this, notice that in the triangle DCB, $\cos C = \frac{e}{a}$. Then $e = a \times \cos C$, or $a(\cos C)$. So we can substitute $a(\cos C)$ for e in the equation $c^2 = a^2 + b^2 - 2be$. When we do, we find that

$$c^2 = a^2 + b^2 - 2b \times a(\cos C)$$

$$c^2 = a^2 + b^2 - 2ab(\cos C)$$

When you're sure you understand how we arrived at this result, return to page 417 to choose the correct answer.

[*from page 404*]

YOUR ANSWER: $a = 26.5$.

Wait a minute! Evidently you used the *sine* of 37° to calculate your answer, rather than the cosine. Let's start over.

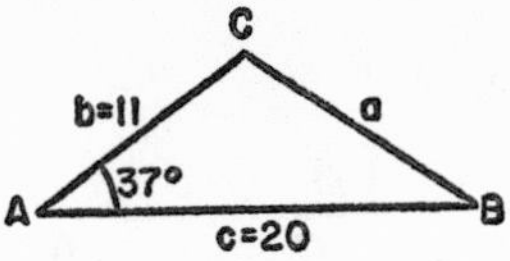

According to the law of cosines,

$$a^2 = b^2 + c^2 - 2bc(\cos A)$$

In the given problem, then,

$$a^2 = 11^2 + 20^2 - 2(11)(20)(\cos 37°)$$

Now—and here's where you missed the boat—

$$\cos 37° = \sin 53°$$

because $53° = 90° - 37°$. And you ought to know by now that $\sin 37°$ does *not* equal $\cos 37°$.

So our problem becomes

$$a^2 = 11^2 + 20^2 - 2(11)(20)(\sin 53°)$$

You shouldn't have any trouble solving this equation for a. When you have the answer, return to page 404 to make the correct choice.

[*from page 403*]

YOUR ANSWER: $b = 375$, $B = 118°$, $C = 15°$.

No. And you couldn't have arrived at this answer through any logical process of thought. You must have guessed. We'd better start at the beginning.

From the law of sines,

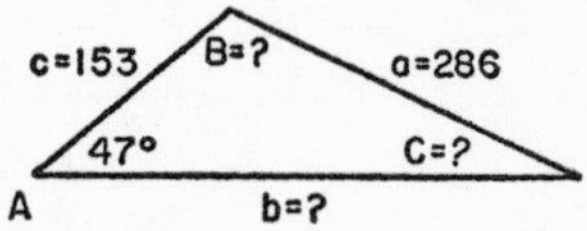

$$\frac{286}{\sin 47°} = \frac{b}{\sin B} = \frac{153}{\sin C}$$

To find C, then, we can use a simple proportion setting of the rule:

1. Shift 47° on the S scale under 28.6 on the A scale.
2. Slide the hairline indicator to 15.3 on the A scale.
3. Read 23° on the S scale under the hairline.

So $C = 23°$. (Incidentally, be sure to read the 28.6 and 15.3 on the *same* part of the A scale. That is, if you use the 28.6 on the right half of the A scale, you must also use the 15.3 on that half of the scale. Similarly, if you use the 2.86 on the left half of the A scale, you must slide the hairline indicator to 1.53 on that half of the scale.)

At this point we may find angle B. The angles of a triangle must add up to 180°, so $B = 180° - 47° - 23° = 110°$.

To find side b, we need to know the value of $\sin B$. We've seen that the sine of an angle between 90° and 180° is equal to the sine of its supplementary angle. Therefore,

$$\sin B = \sin 110° = \sin (180° - 110°) = \sin 70°$$

The slide rule is already set so that 47° on the S scale is under 28.6 on the A scale. Thus all we need do to solve the proportion $\frac{286}{\sin 47°} = \frac{b}{\sin 70°}$ is

1. Slide the hairline indicator to 70° on the S scale.
2. Read the significant figures of the value of b on the A scale under the hairline.

Use the usual approximation methods to place the decimal point correctly. Then, when you have the complete answer, return to page 403 to make the right choice.

[*from page 411*]

YOUR ANSWER: This statement is incorrect: Angle $B = 98°$.

No, it's right. Look at the diagram again:

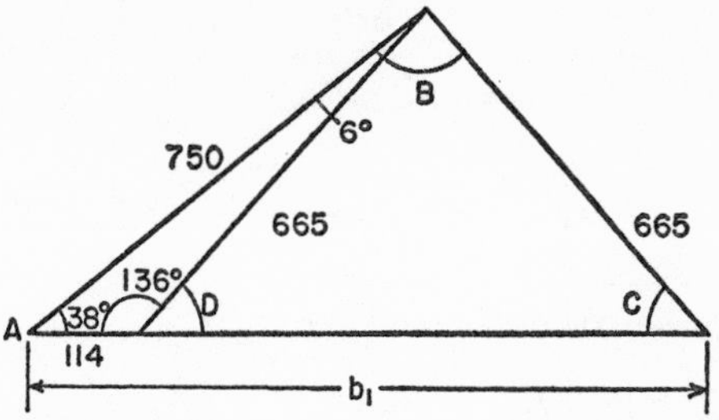

Since b_1 is a straight line, or, what is the same thing, an angle of 180°, we know that angle $D + 136°$ must be 180°. Therefore,

$$D = 180° - 136° = 44°$$

Now, what about angle C? Notice that triangle BCD is isosceles. That is, it has two equal sides: the side opposite angle C is 665 and the side opposite angle D is also 665. You should remember that there is a theorem from elementary geometry that says that angles opposite equal sides of a triangle are equal. In other words, angle C is the same as angle D:

$$C = 44°$$

We can now find angle B very easily, because we know angles A and C of the large triangle ABC:

$$A + B + C = 38° + B + 44° = 180°,$$

so

$$B = 180° - 38° - 44° = 98°$$

We see that the given value is correct.

Study this explanation until you understand where you went wrong. Then return to page 411 to try again.

[*from page 405*]

YOUR ANSWER: No, the law of sines will not solve this triangle.

That's right; it won't. Look at the triangle again:

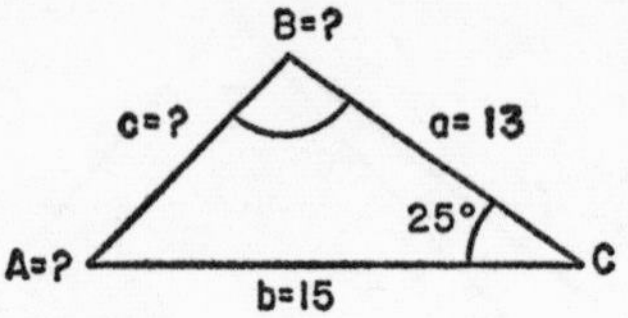

According to the law of sines,

$$\frac{13}{\sin A} = \frac{15}{\sin B} = \frac{c}{\sin 25°}$$

And no matter how we try to solve these proportions for A, B, and c, we find that we just don't have enough information. We always end up with an expression in two unknowns.

So we find that there is a limitation on the usefulness of the law of sines. It is not enough just to know three of the six quantities a, b, c, A, B, and C. We have to have a certain kind of information:

To solve a triangle by means of the law of sines, we must know either

1. two sides and the angle opposite one of them, or
2. two angles and the side opposite one of them.

In the example above, we are given the values of two sides and one angle, but because the angle is opposite neither of the known sides we cannot solve the problem with the law of sines. We need to find some other law or rule that will give us the solution.

Please go on to page 417.

[*from page 416*]

As a start, you should recall that every triangle may be reduced to a pair of right triangles, as shown below:

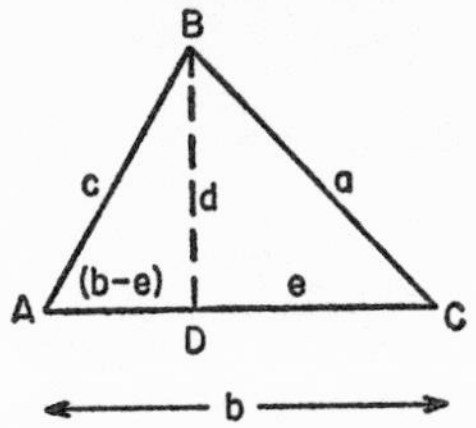

Side d is common to both triangles ABD and CBD. From the Pythagorean theorem (which says that the square of the hypotenuse of a right triangle is equal to the sum of the squares of the sides),

$$d^2 = a^2 - e^2 \quad \text{in triangle } CBD,$$

and

$$d^2 = c^2 - (b - e)^2 \quad \text{in triangle } ABD$$

Therefore,

$$c^2 - (b - e)^2 = a^2 - e^2$$

Solving this equation for c^2 and simplifying, we get

$$\begin{aligned} c^2 &= a^2 - e^2 + (b - e)^2 \\ &= a^2 - e^2 + b^2 - 2be + e^2 \\ &= a^2 + b^2 - 2be \end{aligned}$$

All that's left now is to eliminate e from the expression

$$c^2 = a^2 + b^2 - 2be$$

Which of the expressions below is the result? (Hint: Notice that in the triangle DCB, $\cos C = \frac{e}{a}$.)

$c^2 = a^2 + b^2 - 2ab(\cos C)$. **page 404**

$c^2 = a^2 + b^2 - 2ac(\cos B)$. **page 412**

$c^2 = a^2 + b^2 - 2bc(\cos A)$. **page 419**

I need some help. **page 422**

[*from page 404*]

YOUR ANSWER: $a = 17.3$.

No. And at this stage in the game you should know better than to try to guess!

Let's begin again. Here's the given triangle:

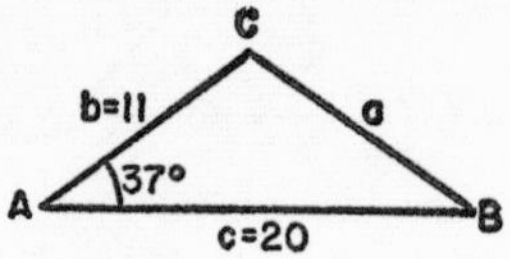

The law of cosines says that for any triangle,

$$a^2 = b^2 + c^2 - 2bc(\cos A)$$

For the triangle above, then,

$$a^2 = 11^2 + 20^2 - 2(11)(20)(\cos 37°)$$

We can't work directly with cosines on some slide rules, but we do know that the cosine of an angle is equal to the sine of the complement of the angle. That is,

$$\cos A = \sin (90° - A)$$

So

$$\cos 37° = \sin (90° - 37°) = \sin 53°$$

Our problem now becomes

$$a^2 = 11^2 + 20^2 - 2(11)(20)(\sin 53°)$$

In approximation form we find that a^2 is roughly 180, so that a is about 13.4.

At this point, you should be able to complete the calculation for yourself. When you have the answer, return to page 404 to make the correct choice.

[*from page 417*]

YOUR ANSWER: $c^2 = a^2 + b^2 - 2bc(\cos A)$.

No. And this looks like a guess. Let's start over.

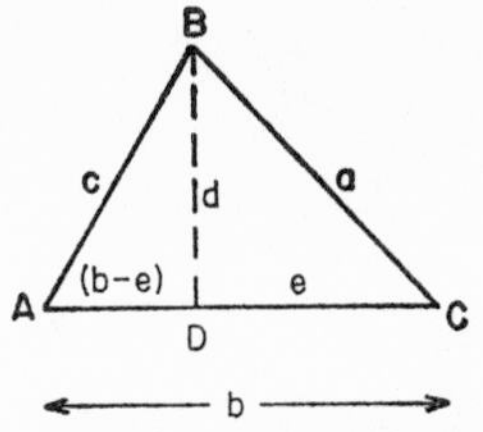

We began by drawing a perpendicular line from angle B to side b, thus dividing triangle ABC into two right triangles, ABD and CBD. Then, since side d is common to both triangles, we found that

$$d^2 = a^2 - e^2 \quad \text{in } CBD \quad \text{and} \quad d^2 = c^2 - (b - e)^2 \quad \text{in } ABD$$

Therefore,

$$c^2 - (b - e)^2 = a^2 - e^2$$

Solving for c^2 and simplifying, we get

$$c^2 = a^2 + b^2 - 2be$$

At this point we want to eliminate e from the equation to arrive at an equation which will give us c in terms of the information we have, i.e., in terms of a, b, and C. To do this, notice that in the triangle DCB, $\cos C = \frac{e}{a}$. Then $e = a \times \cos C$, or $a(\cos C)$. So we can substitute $a(\cos C)$ for e in the equation $c^2 = a^2 + b^2 - 2be$. When we do, we find that

$$c^2 = a^2 + b^2 - 2b \times a(\cos C)$$

$$c^2 = a^2 + b^2 - 2ab(\cos C)$$

When you're sure you understand how we arrived at this result, return to page 417 to choose the correct answer.

[*from page 404*]

YOUR ANSWER: $a = 13.1$.

Right. Here is the triangle again:

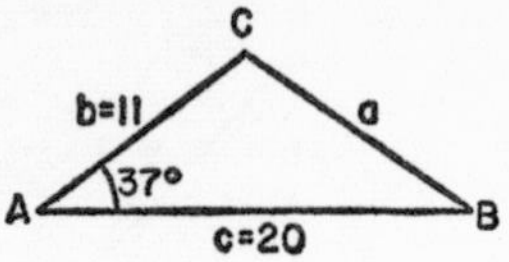

According to the law of cosines,

$$a^2 = b^2 + c^2 - 2bc(\cos A)$$

In this case, then

$$a^2 = 11^2 + 20^2 - 2(11)(20)(\cos 37°)$$

and since the cosine of 37° is equal to the sine of 53° (because 90° − 37° = 53°),

$$a^2 = 11^2 + 20^2 - 2(11)(20)(\sin 53°)$$

With the usual approximation method, we find that a should be about 13.4. In this particular problem we can find the squares of b and c by inspection, without using the D and A scales ($11^2 = 121$ and $20^2 = 400$). Similarly, $2(11)(20) = (\sin 53°)\ 440(\sin 53°)$. Then, on the slide rule:

1. Index the S scale at 440 on the A scale.
2. Slide the hairline indicator to 53° on the S scale.
3. Read 351 on the A scale under the hairline.

Since the sine of 53° is about 0.800, we conclude that $440(\sin 53°) = 351$. Then

$$a^2 = 121 + 400 - 351 = 170$$

Finally, to find a,

1. Slide the hairline indicator to 1.70 on the left-hand A scale.
2. Read 1.305 on the D scale in line with the hairline.

Then $a = 13.05$, or, to three figures, $a = 13.1$.
Go right on to page 421.

[*from page 420*]

We've seen that the S scale is simply another application of the basic slide rule principles. With knowledge of these principles and the basic ideas of trigonometry we can solve many problems that would have been difficult if not impossible by ordinary algebraic methods.

The ease with which such problems can be solved is further increased by knowledge of the T, or tangent, scale. With the T scale we can read the tangent of any angle from about 5° 45′ to 45° directly on the D scale. (More about the tangents of larger and smaller angles later.)

To help you place the decimal point correctly, just remember that at the left end of the scale, tan 5° 44.5′ = 0.100, and at the right end of the scale, tan 45° = 1.000. (The reason for this is the fact that a 45° right triangle is an isosceles triangle. Angles *A* and *B* are equal, and sides *a* and *b* are equal. Therefore, the tangent, which is defined as the ratio of the opposite side to the adjacent side, is equal to 1: $\tan 45° = \frac{a}{b} = 1$, because $a = b$.)

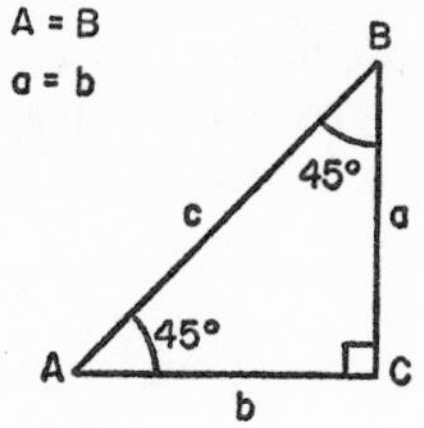

Which of these is incorrect?

Tan 22° = 0.404. **page 424**

Tan 38° = 0.780. **page 427**

Tan 6° = 0.0105. **page 431**

[*from page 417*]

YOUR ANSWER: I need some help.

Let's review what we've already done.

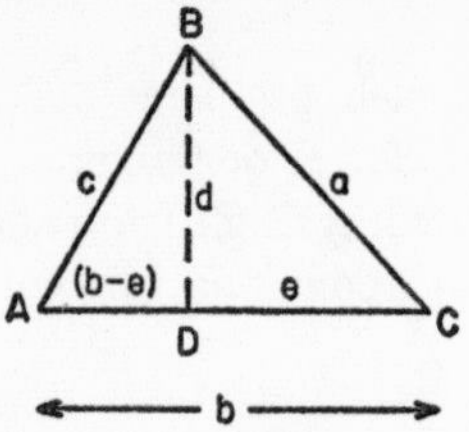

We began by drawing a perpendicular line from angle B to side b, thus dividing triangle ABC into two right triangles, ABD and CBD. Then, since side d is common to both triangles, we found that

$$d^2 = a^2 - e^2 \quad \text{in } CBD \quad \text{and} \quad d^2 = c^2 - (b - e)^2 \quad \text{in } ABD$$

Therefore,

$$c^2 - (b - e)^2 = a^2 - e^2$$

Solving for c^2 and simplifying, we get

$$c^2 = a^2 + b^2 - 2be$$

At this point we want to eliminate e from the equation to arrive at an equation which will give us c in terms of the information we know, i.e., in terms of a, b, and C. To do this, notice that in the triangle DCB, $\cos C = \frac{e}{a}$. Then $e = a \times \cos C$, or $a(\cos C)$. So we can substitute $a(\cos C)$ for e in the equation $c^2 = a^2 + b^2 - 2be$. When we do, we find that

$$c^2 = a^2 + b^2 - 2b \times a(\cos C)$$

$$c^2 = a^2 + b^2 - 2ab(\cos C)$$

When you're sure you understand how we arrived at this result, return to page 417 to choose the correct answer.

YOUR ANSWER: Side $a = 216$.

Right. And we didn't really need to know the value of c in order to arrive at this answer. Since $\frac{a}{b} = \tan A$,

$$a = b \times \tan A = 276 \times \tan 38°$$

In approximation form,

$$a = 3 \times 10^2 \times 8 \times 10^{-1} = 24 \times 10 = 240.$$

On the slide rule:

1. Shift the right-hand T-scale index opposite 276 on the D scale.
2. Slide the hairline indicator to 38° on the T scale.
3. Read 216 on the D scale under the hairline.

Then $a = 216$.

When only sides a and b are known, as in the triangle at the right, we can use a proportion to find angle A:

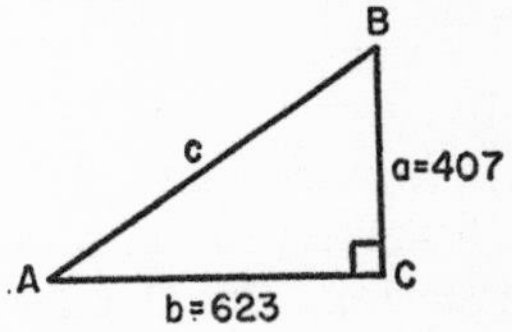

$$\tan A = \frac{\tan A}{1} = \frac{a}{b} = \frac{407}{623}$$

Then, dividing by 407,

$$\frac{\tan A}{407} = \frac{1}{623}$$

On the slide rule:

1. Shift 45° on the T scale (because sin 45° = 1) over 623 on the D scale.
2. Slide the hairline indicator to 407 on the D scale.
3. Read 33° 10′ on the T scale.

So $A = 33° 10'$.

What is the value of angle A in the triangle at the right?

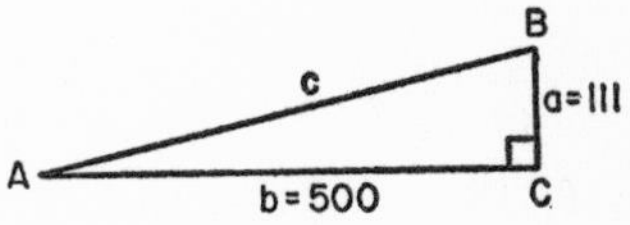

$A = 8° 43'$. **page 430**

$A = 12° 30'$. **page 443**

$A = 12° 50'$. **page 438**

[*from page 421*]

YOUR ANSWER: This is incorrect: Tan 22° = 0.404.

No, it's right. Here's the way it goes:

1. Align the T and D scales.
2. Slide the hairline indicator to 22° on the T scale.
3. Read 404 on the T scale under the hairline.

The setting will look like this:

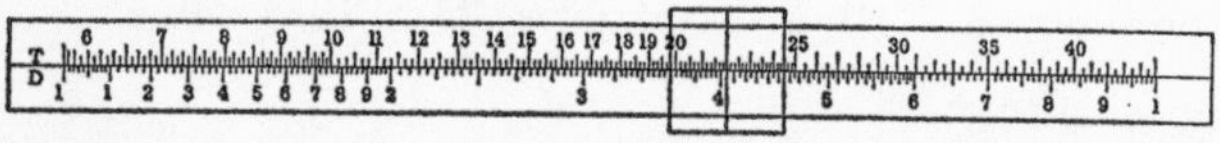

You shouldn't have any trouble placing the decimal point correctly; 22° is between 5° 44.5′, whose tangent is 0.100, and 45°, whose tangent is 1.000. Therefore, the decimal point goes directly in front of the first significant figure:

$$\tan 22° = 0.404$$

which is larger than 0.100 but smaller than 1.000.

Whenever you are reading the tangent of an angle on the T scale directly from the D scale, the decimal point should go immediately before the first significant figure.

Return to page 421 for another try.

[*from page 443*]

YOUR ANSWER: Side a is 555 in triangle I.

Well, let's check. Here's the triangle again:

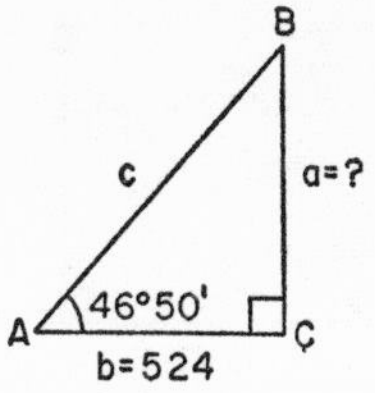

Since angle A is greater than 45°, we'll have to work with the complementary angle, B.

$$B = 90° - A = 90° - 46° \, 50' = 43° \, 10'$$

The tangent of an angle of a right triangle is defined as the ratio of the opposite side to the adjacent side, so

$$\frac{b}{a} = \tan B$$

From this we see that

$$a = \frac{b}{\tan B} = \frac{524}{\tan 43° \, 10'}$$

The tangent of 43° 10′ is roughly 0.900, so in approximation form

$$a = \frac{5 \times 10^2}{9 \times 10^{-1}} = 0.555 \cdots \times 10^3 = 556,$$

to three figures. But you must remember that this is only a rough estimate.

On the slide rule:

1. Slide the hairline indicator to 5.24 on the D scale.
2. Shift 43° 10′ on the T scale under the hairline.
3. Read 5.59 on the D scale at the index of the T scale.

Then $a = 559$, not 555.

Return to page 443 to try again.

[*from page 431*]

YOUR ANSWER: Side $a = 300$.

No, this guess is way off. Look at the triangle again:

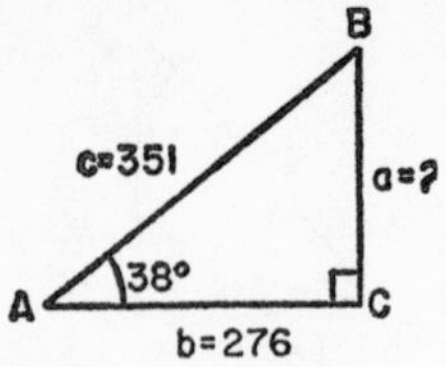

The tangent is defined as the ratio of the opposite side to the adjacent side:

$$\tan A = \frac{a}{b}$$

Therefore, $a = b \times \tan A = 276 \times \tan 38°$

In approximation form

$$a = 3 \times 10^2 \times 8 \times 10^{-1}$$
$$= 24 \times 10$$
$$= 240$$

The operation is very simple on the slide rule:

1. Shift the right-hand T-scale index opposite 276 on the D scale.
2. Slide the hairline indicator to 38° on the T scale.
3. Read the significant figures of the answer on the D scale under the hairline.

When you have the final answer, return to page 431 to make the correct choice.

[*from page 421*]

YOUR ANSWER: This is incorrect: Tan 38° = 0.780.

No, it's right. Here's the way it goes:

1. Align the T and D scales.
2. Slide the hairline indicator to 38° on the T scale.
3. Read 780 on the D scale under the hairline.

The setting will look like this:

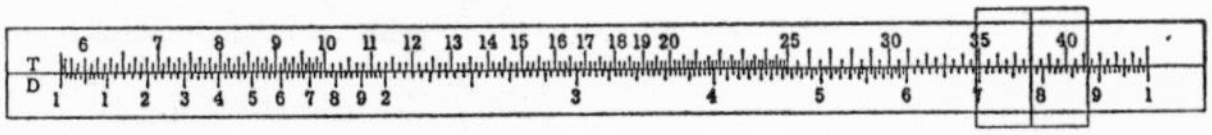

You shouldn't have any trouble placing the decimal point correctly; 38° is between 5° 44.5′, whose tangent is 0.100, and 45°, whose tangent is 1.000. Therefore, the decimal point goes directly in front of the first significant figure:

$$\tan 38° = 0.780$$

which is larger than 0.100, but smaller than 1.000.

Whenever you are reading the tangent of an angle on the T scale directly from the D scale, the decimal point should go immediately before the first significant figure.

Return to page 421 to try again.

[*from page 435*]

YOUR ANSWER: Tan $A = \dfrac{1}{\tan B}$.

Right. It's easy to check:

In any right triangle,

$$\tan A = \frac{a}{b}$$

and

$$\tan B = \frac{b}{a}.$$

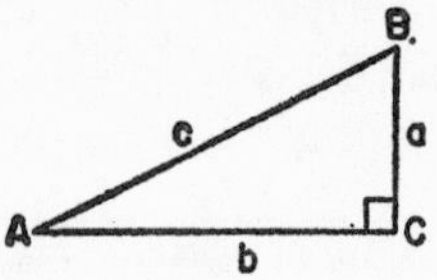

So,

$$\frac{1}{\tan B} = \frac{1}{\frac{a}{b}} = 1 \times \frac{a}{b} = \frac{a}{b} = \tan A$$

Now we have a way to find the tangent of an angle greater than 45°. For example, let's find tan 88°.

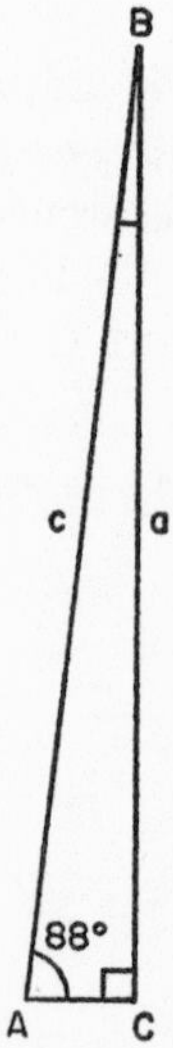

Let 88° be angle A of the triangle. Then angle B is the complement of 88°:

$$B = 90° - A = 90° - 88° = 2°$$

And since $\tan A = \dfrac{1}{\tan B}$, we know that the tangent of 88° is equal to the reciprocal of the tangent (or sine, because the angle is very small) of 2°:

$$\tan 88° = \frac{1}{\tan 2°}$$

To find out how to do it on the slide rule, go right on to page 429.

[*from page 428*]

To find the tangent of 88° on the slide rule:

1. Align the S and A scales.
2. Slide the hairline indicator to 2° on the S scale.
3. Read 3.49 on the A scale under the hairline.

Then, since sin 34.4′ = 0.0100 and sin 5° 44.3′ = 0.100, we can place the decimal point:

$$\sin \text{ (or tan) } 2° = 0.0349$$

So $\dfrac{1}{\tan 2°}$ will be about $\dfrac{1}{3 \times 10^{-2}}$ or 33.

(This is the only reason for taking a reading here—we need it to place the decimal correctly in the final answer.)

4. Shift the left index of the S scale under the hairline.
5. Turn the rule over, and read 28.6 on the B scale under the index hairline.

(This gives us the value of the reciprocal of the tangent of 2°. It's the distance on the A or B scale from sin 2° to the right index of the scale.)

So $\tan 88° = 28.6$

Which of these values is incorrect?

Tan 87° 35′ = 23.7. **page 433**

Tan 84° 30′ = 10.4. **page 437**

Tan 63° 20′ = 2.22. **page 440**

Tan 89° 59′ 15″ = 4,560. **page 442**

[*from page 423*]

YOUR ANSWER: Angle $A = 8° 43'$.

No. And you'll make this kind of mistake time and time again unless you learn to reason out the solution to a problem, rather than make blind substitutions.

Let's make a fresh start.

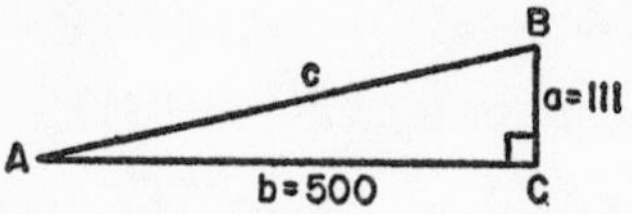

Since tan A can be written $\frac{\tan A}{1}$, we can write the proportion $\frac{\tan A}{1} = \frac{111}{500}$. Then, dividing by 111, we find that

$$\frac{\tan A}{111} = \frac{1}{500}$$

Since 1 is equivalent to the tangent of 45°, we can do it on the slide rule like this:

1. Shift 45° on the T scale over 5.00 on the D scale.
2. Slide the hairline indicator to 1.11 on the D scale.
3. Read angle A on the T scale under the hairline.

The resulting setting will look like this:

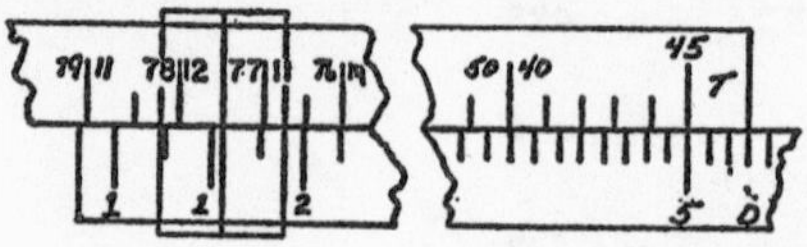

When you've found angle A, return to page 423 to pick the right answer.

[*from page 421*]

YOUR ANSWER: This is incorrect: Tan 6° = 0.0105.

You are right. The answer contains the proper digits, but the decimal point is misplaced. As with the right-hand S scale, the decimal point for values on the T scale appears immediately before the first digit. (Tan 5° 44.5′ = 0.100 and tan 45° = 1.000, remember?) Thus the tangent of 6° is 0.105.

Earlier, we solved the triangle at the right with the S scale. It was necessary first to calculate angle A, then side c, and finally side b ($b = 107$).

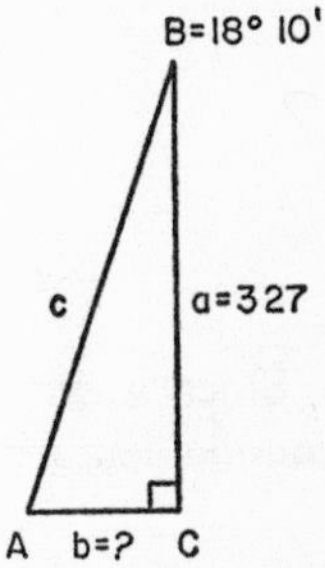

It's much easier with the T scale, because $\frac{b}{a} = \tan B$. So $b = a \times \tan B = 327 \times \tan 18° \, 10'$. On the slide rule, then:

1. Shift the right-hand index of the T scale to 327 on the D scale.
2. Slide the hairline indicator to 18° 10′ on the T scale.
3. Read 107 on the D scale.

There's another advantage to this method besides ease. With the S scale method, we have to calculate angle A and then locate it on the S scale. A turns out to be 71° 50′, which is far to the right of the S scale, and hence difficult to locate accurately. 18° 10′, on the other hand, can be located very accurately on the T scale.

What is side a of the triangle below?

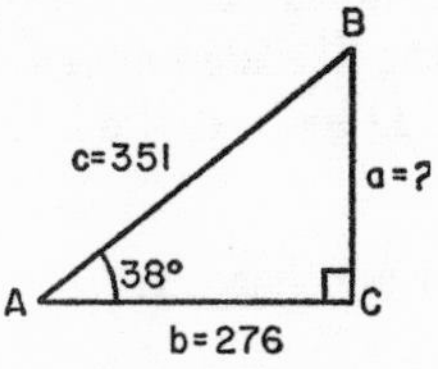

$a = 216$. **page 423** $a = 300$. **page 426** $a = 353$. **page 434**

[*from page 443*]

YOUR ANSWER: Side a is 555 in triangle II.

Let's check it out. Look at the triangle again:

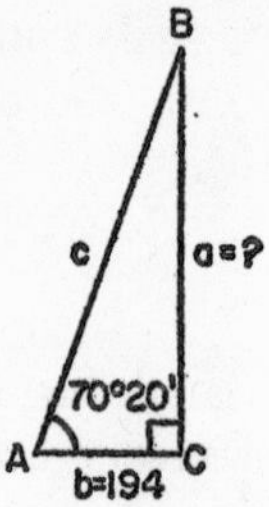

Since angle A is greater than 45°, we'll need to work with the complementary angle, B.

$$B = 90° - A = 90° - 70° 20' = 19° 40'$$

The tangent of an angle of a right triangle is defined as the ratio of the opposite side to the adjacent side, so

$$\frac{b}{a} = \tan B$$

From this we see that $$a = \frac{b}{\tan B} = \frac{194}{\tan 19° 40'}$$

The tangent of 19° 40′ is roughly 0.350, so in approximation form

$$a = \frac{2 \times 10^2}{3.5 \times 10^{-1}} = 0.571 \times 10^3 = 571$$

On the slide rule:

1. Slide the hairline indicator to 1.94 on the D scale.
2. Shift 19° 40′ on the T scale under the hairline.
3. Read 5.43 on the D scale at the index of the T scale.

Then a = 543, not 555.
Return to page 443 for another try.

[*from page 429*]

YOUR ANSWER: This value is incorrect: Tan 87° 35′ = 23.7.

No, it's right.

The complementary angle of 87° 35′ is 90° − 87° 35′, or 2° 25′. Therefore, since

$$\tan A = \frac{1}{\tan B}, \quad \tan 87° \, 35' = \frac{1}{\tan 2° \, 25'}$$

For small angles (angles of less than 5° 44.3′) the sine and tangent are nearly equal.

On the slide rule:

1. Align the S and A scales.
2. Slide the hairline indicator to 2° 25′ on the S scale.
3. Read 4.22 on the A scale under the hairline.

Then, at more than 0.0100, the sine of 34.4′, but less than 0.100, the sine of 5° 44.3′,

$$\sin \text{ (or tan) } 2° \, 25' = 0.0422$$

So $\dfrac{1}{\tan 2° \, 25'}$ will be about $\dfrac{1}{4 \times 10^{-2}}$ or 25.0

4. Shift the left index of the S scale under the hairline.
5. Turn the rule over, and read 23.7 on the B scale under the index hairline.

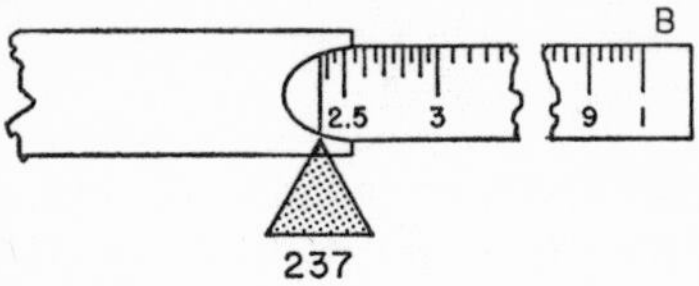

Then sin 87° 35′ = 23.7.

Return to page 429 and try again.

[*from page 431*]

YOUR ANSWER: Side $a = 353$.

No. If side $a = 353$, then side a is longer than the hypotenuse, which just doesn't make sense. Let's start over.

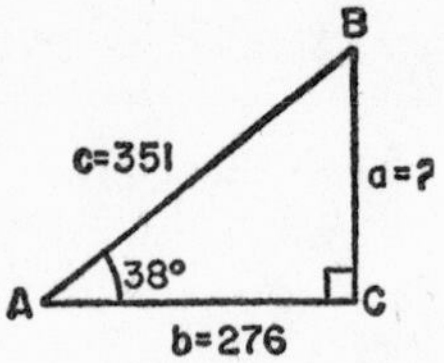

The tangent is defined as the ratio of the opposite side to the adjacent side:

$$\tan A = \frac{a}{b}$$

Therefore, $$a = b \times \tan A = 276 \times \tan 38°$$

(Evidently you *divided* 276 by the tangent of 38°, instead of multiplying.)
In approximation form,

$$\begin{aligned} a &= 3 \times 10^2 \times 8 \times 10^{-1} \\ &= 24 \times 10 \\ &= 240 \end{aligned}$$

It's very simple on the slide rule:

1. Shift the right-hand T-scale index opposite 276 on the D scale.
2. Slide the hairline indicator to 38° on the T scale.
3. Read the significant figures of the answer on the D scale under the hairline.

When you have the complete answer, return to page 431 and make the correct choice.

YOUR ANSWER: Side a is 555 in triangle III.

Right. The first step was to find B:

$$B = 90° - 59° 30' = 30° 30'$$

Then, since

$$\tan B = \frac{b}{a}, \quad a = \frac{b}{\tan B} = \frac{327}{\tan 30° 30'}$$

In approximation form, $a = \dfrac{3 \times 10^2}{6 \times 10^{-1}} = 0.5 \times 10^3 = 500.$

On the slide rule:

1. Slide the hairline indicator to 3.27 on the D scale.
2. Shift 30° 30′ on the T scale under the hairline.
3. Read 5.55 on the D scale at the index of the T scale.

Then $a = 555$.

When we were using the moon for target practice earlier in this chapter, we saw that there is no hard and fast rule for deciding which side of a right triangle with a very small identifying angle should be the hypotenuse.

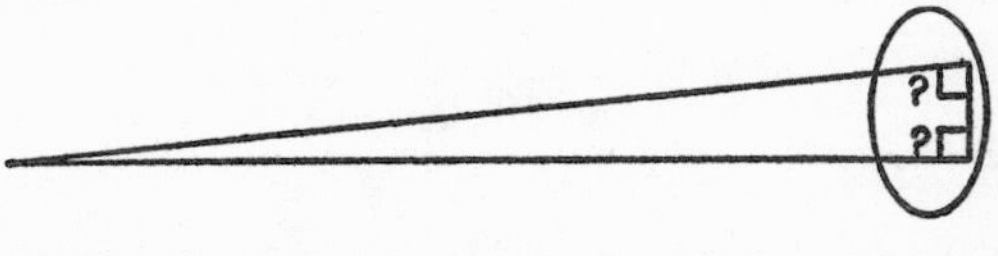

One result of this is that for ordinary slide rule purposes, the sine and tangent of an angle less than 5° 44.3′ can be considered equal. So small angles are no problem.

But how about the tangents of very large angles? We know that if angle A is over 45°, angle B is less than 45°, so we can find the tangent of B. But at the moment that isn't much help, since we haven't yet established any relationship between the tangents of A and B. Let's do that now.

Which of the following expressions is correct? (Hint: Use the definitions of tan A and tan B, as we did when proving trigonometric identities back in Chapter 7.)

Tan $A = \dfrac{1}{\tan B}$. page 428

Tan $A = 1 - \tan B$. page 441

Tan $A = \tan B$. page 439

I'm stuck. page 444

[*from page 440*]

YOUR ANSWER: d is greater than 1,520 feet; he's too far out.

No, he's not. Look at the diagram again:

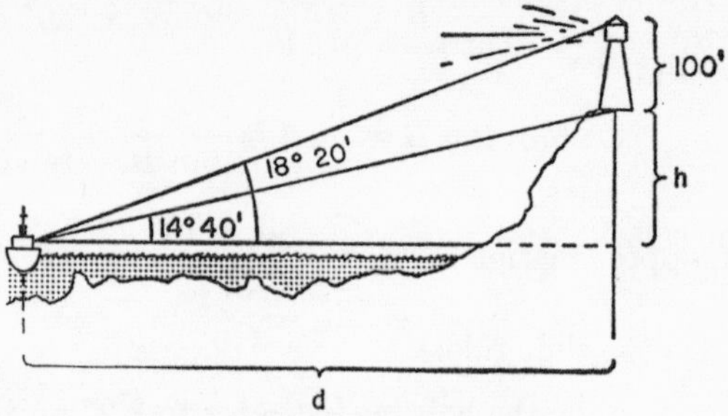

From the sketch we see that

$$\frac{h}{d} = \tan 14° 40', \quad \text{and}$$

$$\frac{h + 100}{d} = \tan 18° 20'$$

Solving each of these two expressions for h, we get

$$h = d(\tan 14° 40') \quad \text{and} \quad h = d(\tan 18° 20') - 100$$

Equating these two expressions for h and solving for d,

$$d(\tan 14° 40') = d(\tan 18° 20') - 100$$

$$100 = d(\tan 18° 20' - \tan 14° 40')$$

$$d = \frac{100}{\tan 18° 20' - \tan 14° 40'}$$

On the slide rule:

1. Align the T and D scales.
2. Slide the hairline indicator to 18° 20′ on the T scale.
3. Read 3.31 on the D scale. Then tan 18° 20′ = 0.331.
4. Slide the hairline indicator to 14° 40′ on the T scale.
5. Read 2.62 on the D scale under the hairline.

Then tan 14° 40′ = 0.262.

So $$d = \frac{100}{0.331 - 0.262} = \frac{100}{0.069}$$

In approximation form, $\frac{10^2}{7 \times 10^{-2}} = \frac{1}{7} \times 10^4 = 0.143 \times 10^4 = 1{,}430.$

So d will be in the neighborhood of 1,430 feet.

Complete the calculation for yourself. Then return to page 440 to choose the correct answer.

[*from page 429*]

YOUR ANSWER: This value is incorrect: Tan 84° 30′ = 10.4.

Sorry, it's right.

The complementary angle of 84° 30′ is 5° 30′, because 84° 30′ + 5° 30′ = 90°. Therefore, since

$$\tan A = \frac{1}{\tan B}, \quad \tan 84^\circ 30' = \frac{1}{\tan 5^\circ 30'}$$

For small angles (angles of less than 5° 44.3′) the sine and tangent are nearly equal.

On the slide rule:

1. Align the S and A scales.
2. Slide the hairline indicator to 5° 30′ on the S scale.
3. Read 9.60 on the A scale under the hairline.

Then, at just slightly less than 0.100, the sine of 5° 44.3′,

$$\sin \text{ (or tan) } 5^\circ 30' = 0.0960$$

So $$\frac{1}{\tan 5^\circ 30'} \text{ will be about } \frac{1}{10 \times 10^{-2}} \text{ or } 10.0.$$

4. Shift the left index of the S scale under the hairline.
5. Turn the rule over, and read 10.4 on the B scale under the index hairline.

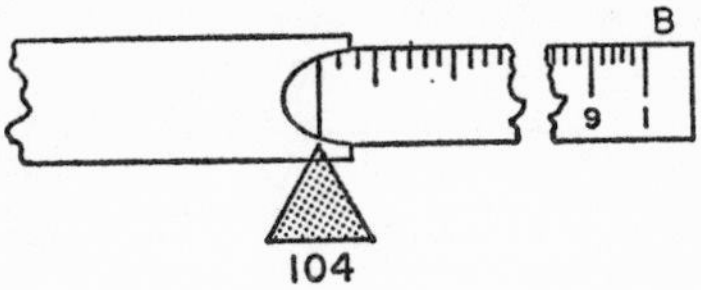

Then sin 84° 30′ = 10.4.

Return to page 429 for another try.

[*from page 423*]

YOUR ANSWER: Angle $A = 12° 50'$.

No. Evidently you performed the operation correctly, and then read the T scale wrong. Just to make sure, let's quickly work the problem again.

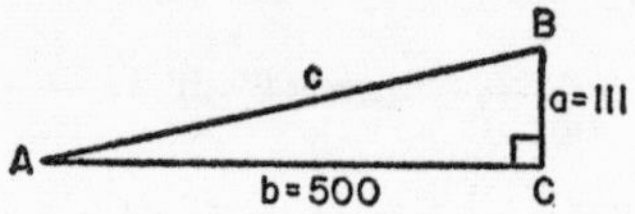

Since tan A can be written $\frac{\tan A}{1}$, we can write the proportion $\frac{\tan A}{1} = \frac{111}{500}$. Then, dividing by 111, we find that $\frac{\tan A}{111} = \frac{1}{500}$.

Since 1 is equivalent to the tangent of 45°, we can do it on the slide rule like this:

1. Shift 45° on the T scale over 5.00 on the D scale.
2. Slide the hairline indicator to 1.11 on the D scale.
3. Read angle A on the T scale under the hairline.

Evidently this is where you went wrong. There are 60 minutes to a degree, so on the S and T scales the distance between degrees is marked off into six major divisions, with each division representing 10 minutes. Thus the midpoint between 12 degrees and 13 degrees on the T scale is read as 12° 30′, *not* 12° 50′.

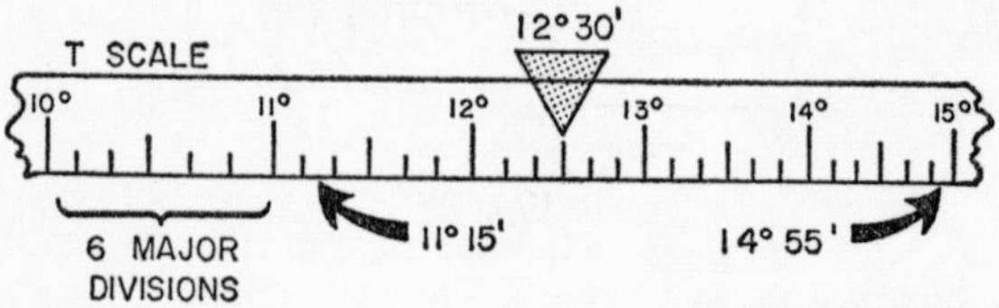

Study the illustration carefully. Then return to page 423 to choose the correct answer.

[from page 435]

YOUR ANSWER: Tan A = tan B.

Well, let's check it.

The tangent of an acute angle of a right triangle is defined as the ratio of the opposite side to the adjacent side. Therefore,

$$\tan A = \frac{a}{b} \quad \text{and} \quad \tan B = \frac{b}{a}$$

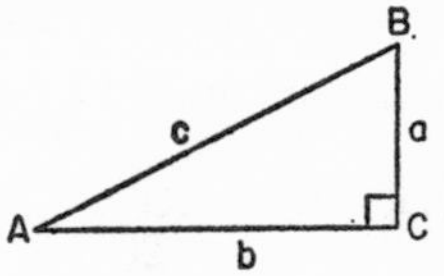

So tan A isn't equal to tan B, because $\frac{a}{b} \neq \frac{b}{a}$. (Remember that we are trying to find an *identity*—a statement that is true regardless of the size of the angles. It's true, for instance, that tan A = tan B if A and B are 45°, but in general the expression tan A = tan B is not true.)

Let's check the other two expressions given.

Since $\tan B = \frac{b}{a}$,

$$1 - \tan B = 1 - \frac{b}{a} = \frac{a - b}{a}$$

So, clearly, $\tan A \neq 1 - \tan B$.

How about the expression $\tan A = \frac{1}{\tan B}$?

$$\frac{1}{\tan B} = \frac{1}{\frac{b}{a}} = 1 \times \frac{a}{b} = \frac{a}{b}$$

Draw your own conclusion. Then return to page 435 to choose the correct expression.

[*from page 429*]

YOUR ANSWER: This value is incorrect: Tan 63° 20′ = 2.22.

Yes, it's wrong. The complementary angle of 63° 20′ is 90° − 63° 20′, or 26° 40′.

So $$\tan 63° 20' = \frac{1}{\tan 26° 40'}$$

On the slide rule:

1. Align the T and D scales.
2. Slide the hairline indicator to 26° 40′ on the T scale.
3. Read 5.02 on the D scale under the hairline.

Then tan 26° 40′ = 0.502. So $\frac{1}{\tan 26° 40'}$ will be about $\frac{1}{5 \times 10^{-1}}$, or 2.0.

4. Shift the left T-scale index under the hairline.
5. Turn the rule over, and read 1.99 on the C scale under the index hairline. Then tan 63° 20′ = 1.99, not 2.22.

To finish up this lesson on the S and T scales, try this problem: The skipper of a coastwise steamer lets out his anchor in the lee of a lighthouse. After all the 200-foot chain is played out, it still hasn't touched bottom. On his chart, the water is only 150 feet deep within 1,520 feet of the lighthouse, though there is a drop-off at that point. Rather than move closer to shore, the captain decides first to make sure that he is within 1,520 feet of the lighthouse. If he is, then he may conclude that the anchor chain is broken. Knowing that the lighthouse is 125 feet high, he uses his sextant to measure the angle from the horizontal to the top and bottom of the tower: to the top it is 18° 20′, and to the bottom, 14° 40′. Is he too far out, or is his anchor chain broken? In other words, is *d* (the distance) greater or less than 1,520 feet?

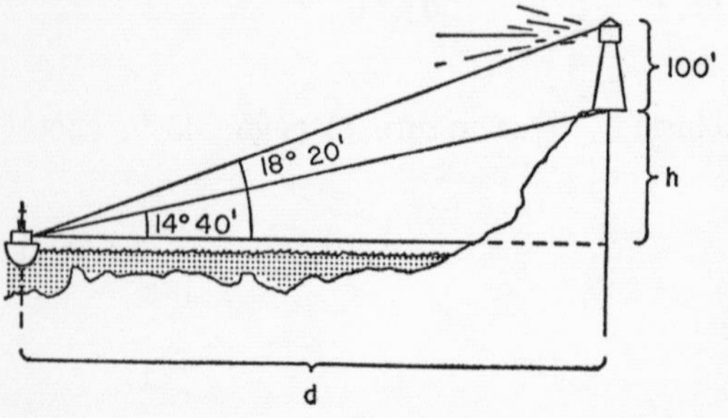

d is greater than 1,520 feet; he's too far out.
page 436

d is less than 1,520 feet; his chain is broken.
page 445

[*from page 435*]

YOUR ANSWER: Tan $A = 1 - \tan B$.

Let's check it out.

The tangent of an acute angle of a right triangle is defined as the ratio of the opposite side to the adjacent side. Therefore,

$$\tan A = \frac{a}{b} \quad \text{and} \quad \tan B = \frac{b}{a}$$

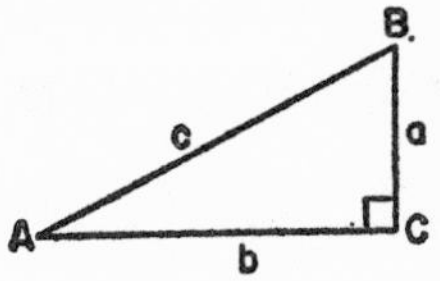

So,

$$1 - \tan B = 1 - \frac{b}{a} = \frac{a - b}{a}$$

And, obviously,

$$\frac{a - b}{a} \neq \frac{a}{b}$$

So,

$$\tan A \neq 1 - \tan B$$

Let's check the other expression given.

Well, clearly $\tan A \neq \tan B$, because $\frac{a}{b} \neq \frac{b}{a}$. (Remember that we are trying to find an *identity*—a statement that is true regardless of the size of the angles. It's true, for instance, that $\tan A = \tan B$ if A and B are 45°, but in general the expression $\tan A = \tan B$ is not true.)

But how about $\tan A = \dfrac{1}{\tan B}$?

$$\frac{1}{\tan B} = \frac{1}{\frac{b}{a}} = 1 \times \frac{a}{b} = \frac{a}{b}$$

Draw your own conclusion; then return to page 435 to choose the correct answer.

[*from page 429*]

YOUR ANSWER: This value is incorrect: Tan 89° 59′ 15″ = 4,560.

No, it's right.

The complement of 89° 59′ 15″ is 45″, because

$$89° \; 59' \; 15'' + 45'' = 90°$$

Therefore, since

$$\tan A = \frac{1}{\tan B}, \qquad \tan 89° \; 59' \; 15'' = \frac{1}{\tan 45''}$$

For small angles (angles of less than 5° 44.3′) the sine and tangent are almost equal.

On the slide rule:

1. Slide the hairline indicator to 45 on the A scale.
2. Shift the seconds gauge mark under the hairline.
3. Read 21.8 on the A scale at the index of the S scale.

Recalling the sine of 1″ as *five zeros five*, we see that the sine (or tangent) of 45″ should be roughly 45 × 0.000005, or 0.000225. Using the A scale reading, we get sin (or tan) 45″ = 0.000218.

So $\dfrac{1}{\tan 45''}$ will be about $\dfrac{1}{2 \times 10^{-4}}$ or 5,000.

4. Turn the rule over, and read 4.56 on the B scale under the index hairline.

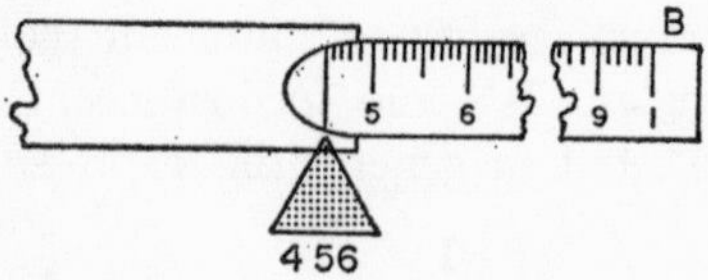

Then tan 89° 59′ 15″ = 4,560.

Return to page 429 for another try.

YOUR ANSWER: Angle $A = 12° 30'$.

Right. There really wasn't much to it. So

$$\frac{\tan A}{1} = \frac{111}{500},$$

$$\frac{\tan A}{111} = \frac{1}{500}$$

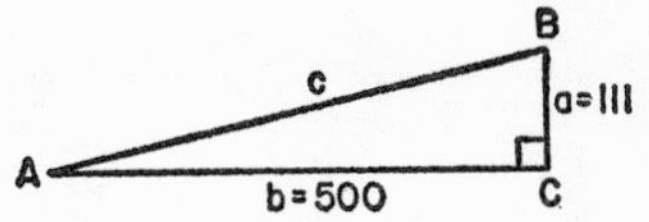

On the slide rule:

1. Shift 45° on the T scale over 5.00 on the D scale.
2. Slide the hairline indicator to 1.11 on the D scale.
3. Read 12° 30′ on the T scale under the hairline.

Suppose you wanted to find side a of the triangle at the right. Well, $a = b \times \tan A$. But in this case angle A is greater than 45°, so we can't read its tangent directly. This really isn't any problem, however; we simply work with the complementary angle, B, which must be less than 45°. $B = 90° - A = 90° - 65° = 25°$.

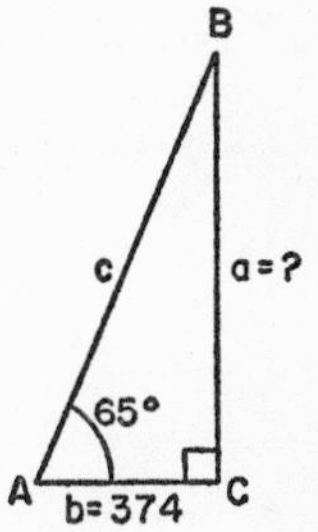

Then $\quad \frac{b}{a} = \tan B, \quad$ so $\quad a = \frac{b}{\tan B} = \frac{374}{\tan 25°} = 804$

In which of the triangles below is side a 555?

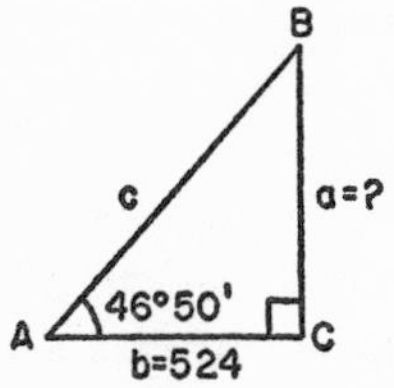

I

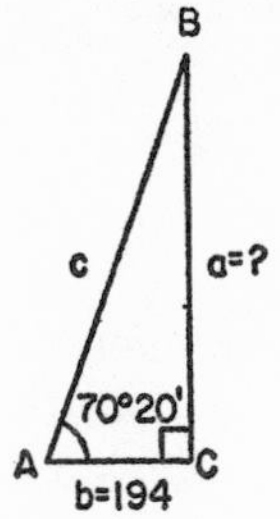

II

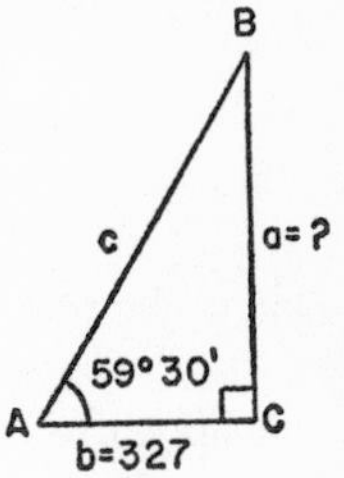

III

Side a is 555 in triangle I. page 425

Side a is 555 in triangle II. page 432

Side a is 555 in triangle III. page 435

[*from page 435*]

YOUR ANSWER: I'm stuck.

The easiest way to discover which of the given expressions is correct is to substitute the definitions of tan A and tan B into each of them.

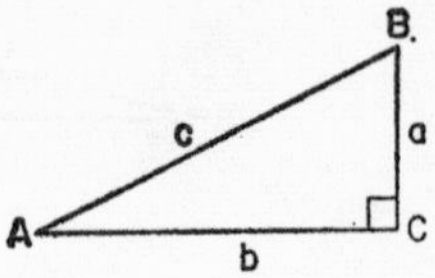

The tangent of an acute angle of a right triangle is defined as the ratio of the opposite side to the adjacent side. Therefore,

$$\tan A = \frac{a}{b} \quad \text{and} \quad \tan B = \frac{b}{a}$$

Clearly, then, the expression $\tan A = \tan B$ can't be true, because $\frac{a}{b} \neq \frac{b}{a}$.

How about the expression $\tan A = 1 - \tan B$? Well,

$$1 - \tan B = 1 - \frac{b}{a} = \frac{a - b}{a}$$

and since $\frac{a-b}{a} \neq \frac{a}{b}$, this expression is also incorrect.

There's only one expression remaining: $\tan A = \frac{1}{\tan B}$. Just to be sure, let's check it out:

$$\frac{1}{\tan B} = \frac{1}{\frac{b}{a}} = 1 \times \frac{a}{b} = \frac{a}{b} = \tan A$$

So this is the one we're looking for.

When you're sure you understand the method we used to check these relationships, return to page 435 to choose the correct answer.

[*from page 440*]

YOUR ANSWER: d is less than 1,520 feet; his chain is broken.

Right. Here's the way it goes:

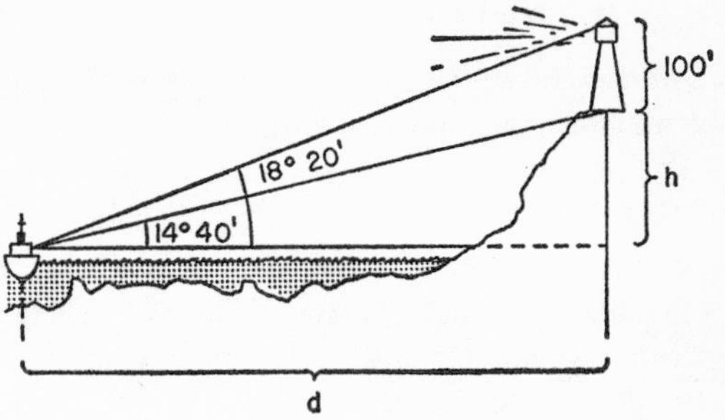

From the diagram,

$$\frac{h}{d} = \tan 14° 40',$$

so that

$$h = d(\tan 14° 40'),$$

and

$$\frac{h + 100}{d} = \tan 18° 20', \quad \text{so} \quad h = d(\tan 18° 20') - 100$$

Equating these two expressions for h and solving for d,

$$d(\tan 14° 40') = d(\tan 18° 20') - 100$$

$$100 = d(\tan 18° 20' - \tan 14° 40')$$

$$d = \frac{100}{\tan 18° 20' - \tan 14° 40'}$$

On the slide rule:

1. Align the T and D scales.
2. Slide the hairline indicator to 18° 20′ on the T scale.
3. Read 3.31 on the D scale.

Then tan 18° 20′ = 0.331.

4. Slide the hairline indicator to 14° 40′ on the T scale.
5. Read 2.62 on the D scale. Then tan 14° 40′ = 0.262.

So
$$d = \frac{100}{0.331 - 0.262} = \frac{100}{0.069}$$

In approximation form, $\dfrac{10^2}{7 \times 10^{-2}} = \dfrac{1}{7} \times 10^4 = 0.143 \times 10^4 = 1{,}430.$

So d should be in the neighborhood of 1,430 feet.

It can be done on the slide rule without reversing the sliding scale. To find out how, go on to page 446.

[*from page 445*]

On the slide rule:

1. Shift the left index of the S scale to 6.90 on the D scale.
2. Reverse the rule (the entire rule, not just the sliding scale) and read 1449 on the C scale under the index hairline.

Then $d = 1{,}449$ feet. So the ship is well within the 1,520-foot limit; the anchor chain must be broken.

This completes the regular instruction portion of this TutorText* on the slide rule. We haven't exhausted all the possible scales, of course. Knowing how the slide rule works, you should be able to think up new scales yourself to simplify certain operations.

Many slide rules have the so-called "folded" scales, CF, DF, and CIF, as well as the C, D, and CI scales. The CF and DF scales begin and end with π, putting the index 1 near the middle of the scale:

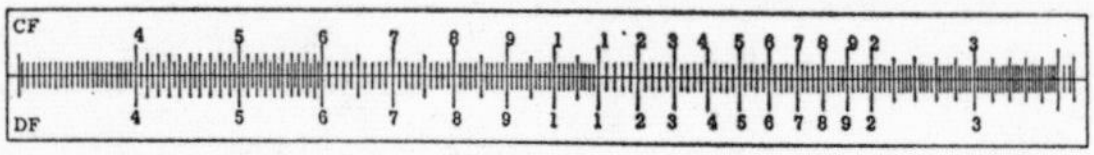

The folded scales may be used independently for multiplication and division, or they may be used in conjunction with the C, D, and CI scales. Often they will save you an extra setting of the rule. For instance, let's say you want to multiply 244 by 431. You suspect that the answer will appear beyond the end of the D scale, but rather than use the CI scale you could proceed by setting the index of the C scale at 244 on the D scale. You cannot get a reading on the D scale, but it will appear on the DF scale without further setting. Taking the powers of 10 into account, you should get 10,500. Note that the index of the CF scale is on 244 of the DF scale at the same time that the index of the C scale is on 244 of the D scale. The answer appears on the DF scale, however, because the index is near the middle and readings may be made on either side.

Please go on to page 447.

*TM

[*from page 446*]

With a little practice you will be able to work complex multiplication and division problems in this manner, jumping back and forth from the regular scales to the folded scales. The CIF scale, of course, is used with the DF scale just as the CI scale is used with the D scale.

Your slide rule may also have *log-log scales* (LL, LL1, LL01, . . .). They are used to work with the logs of logs.

Take a problem of the sort $A^x = B$, where we want to find x. We've seen that, in general, log $(M^n) = n(\log M)$. Therefore,

$$x(\log A) = \log B \quad \text{so that} \quad x = \frac{\log B}{\log A}$$

Using the L scale to find these logs, and setting them on the C and D scales, we can find x by simple division. The settings on the C and D scales actually represent the *logs of the logs* of A and B, of course.

Log-log scales save you the trouble of using the L scale. A diagram of the log-log solution looks like this:

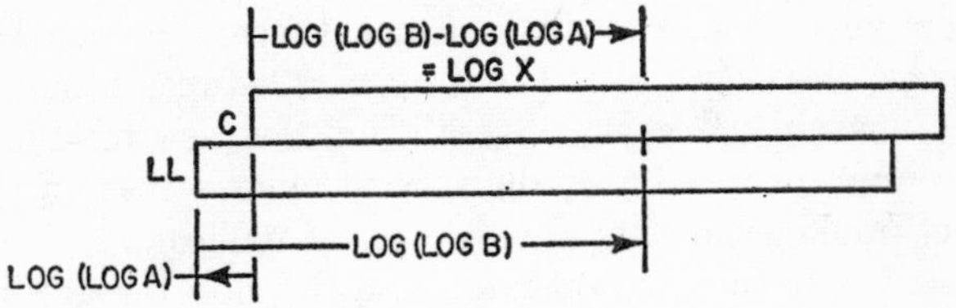

There's a good deal more—but if you ever have to get numerical solutions to equations like $A^x = B$, learning to use the LL scales will be the least of your worries.

For some interesting review problems and practical applications of the slide rule, go on to Chapter 9, page 448.

CHAPTER 9

Review with Applications

In this chapter you'll have an opportunity to review the principles underlying the fundamental slide rule techniques through the medium of problems from several technical fields. Work each of the problems carefully. The practice you get will stand you in good stead. Here's one from civil engineering:

When it's necessary to determine the distance between two points on reasonably level ground with extreme accuracy, the common practice is to measure it directly with a very precisely calibrated steel tape.

Where the ground isn't level, or the distance need not be known with great accuracy, *stadia* methods are employed. One of these employs the surveyor's level and rod. The level is essentially a telescope used to determine relative elevations from readings of the rod.

To determine distance, the instrument operator calculates the *rod intercept,* the length of rod that appears between a pair of horizontal hairlines in the level. If it is found that at a distance of 100 feet, the intercept is 0.3 feet, the surveyor knows that an intercept of 0.6 feet would occur only at a distance of 200 feet.

Suppose you're the level operator, and the view through the telescope looks like this:

If this is the same level for which a distance of 100 feet gave an intercept of 0.3 feet, what must the distance be?

Go to page 452 to check your answer.

[*from page 453*]

Under a force of 140 pounds, the contact circle of a ball bearing 0.625 inch in diameter for which $E = 25{,}000{,}000$ lb/in^2 will be larger than the circle for a ball 0.685 inch in diameter for which $E = 28{,}000{,}000$ lb/in^2.

The obvious way to do the problem is to calculate each diameter and compare. It may surprise you to learn that there's another way.

If the diameter of the contact circle for the 0.625-inch ball is d_1, and d_2 is the corresponding value for the 0.685-inch ball, the formulas for each are:

$$d_1 = 1.76\sqrt[3]{\frac{140 \times 0.625}{25 \times 10^6}}, \quad \text{and} \quad d_2 = 1.76\sqrt[3]{\frac{140 \times 0.685}{28 \times 10^6}}$$

If both of these expressions are cubed, they become a good deal less formidable. In addition, note that $1.76^3 \times 140$ can be factored out of each expression. Consequently, we'll replace the whole factor $1.76^3 \times 140$ by the constant K. Then

$$d_1{}^3 = K \times \frac{0.625}{25 \times 10^6} \quad \text{and} \quad d_2{}^3 = K \times \frac{0.685}{28 \times 10^6}.$$

Solving, we get

$$d_1{}^3 = 25 \times 10^{-9} \qquad\qquad d_2{}^3 = 24.5 \times 10^{-9}$$

It isn't necessary to go any further, since, clearly, the cube root of 25 will be larger than the cube root of 24.5.

The deflection of a spring under a load is given by

$$F = \frac{8PND^3}{Gd^4}$$

If $N = 12$ (the number of coils),
$P = 58$ lb. (the applied force),
$D = 0.625$ in. (the coil diameter),
$G = 11{,}000{,}000$ lb/in^2 (the wire constant),
and $d = 0.125$ in. (the wire diameter),

then the deflection, F, is 0.51 in.

Is this answer correct?

To check your answer, turn to page 456.

[*from page 461*]

The engine's horsepower at 7 miles is 430 hp.
Here's where the L scale is indispensable.

$$H = H_0 \sqrt[5]{\left(\frac{P}{P_0}\right)^7} = 2{,}260 \times \left(\frac{190}{760}\right)^{\frac{7}{5}}$$

With the rule, $\frac{190}{760} = 0.250$, or better yet, $\frac{190}{760} = \frac{1}{4}$.

$$H = 2{,}260 \times \left(\frac{1}{4}\right)^{\frac{7}{5}}$$

From the chapter on logarithms:

$$\log \left(\frac{1}{4}\right)^{\frac{7}{5}} = \frac{7}{5} \log \left(\frac{1}{4}\right) = \frac{7}{5} (\log 1 - \log 4)$$

The log of 1 is zero ($10^0 = 1$, remember?). Shifting the hairline to 4 on the D scale, we read log 4 = 0.398 on the L scale under the hairline. So $\log \left(\frac{1}{4}\right)^{\frac{7}{5}} = 0 - \frac{7}{5}(0.398) = -0.557$.

To find the antilog of −0.557, we must first change −0.557 into a log whose value we can read on the slide rule: the L scale shows only positive logs, as you should recall. Therefore, we must add zero in the form of 1 − 1: (1.000 − 1) − (0.557) = 0.443 − 1.

Setting the hairline to 0.443 on the L scale, read the antilog digits (277) on the D scale. Since the logarithm was 0.443 − 1, the antilog will be $277 \times 10^{-1} = 0.277$.

So $H = 2{,}260 \times 0.277$, or, considering the approximate nature of the data, 625 horsepower.

This seems to be quite a severe drop, and it certainly is. Seven miles is about as high as piston-engined aircraft can fly. In general, the most economical altitude is a good deal lower. Without knowing the limitations on the basic equation, you don't know how accurate your answer is. But this shouldn't cause you to get careless about accurate manipulations of the rule.

Here's a problem to test your proficiency. Do it without resetting:

$$\frac{\sqrt{0.0705} \times \sqrt{19.8} \times 1{,}693}{621 \times \sqrt{234} \times 93.6} = ?$$

The correct solution is on page 458.

[*from page 459*]

At an altitude of 2,160 miles, the escape velocity must be 5.58 miles per second. The equation looked like this:

$$\frac{v_1^2}{\left(6.95\,\frac{\text{mi.}}{\text{sec.}}\right)^2} = \frac{3{,}960\text{ mi.}}{6{,}120\text{ mi.}};$$

6,120 because at a height of 2,160 miles above the earth's surface, the rocket is 2,160 miles + 3,960 miles = 6,120 miles from the center of the earth.

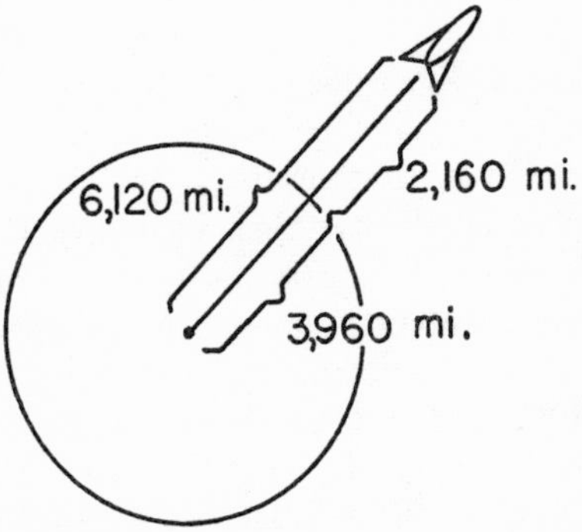

From this equation we see that

$$v_1^2 = \frac{6.95^2 \times 3{,}960}{6{,}120} \times \frac{\text{mi.}^2}{\text{sec.}^2}$$

So

$$v_1 = \frac{6.95 \times \sqrt{3{,}960}}{\sqrt{6{,}120}} \times \frac{\text{mi.}}{\text{sec.}} = \frac{6.95 \times \sqrt{39.6}}{\sqrt{61.2}} \times \frac{\text{mi.}}{\text{sec.}}$$

In approximation form,

$$\frac{7 \times 6}{8} = \frac{42}{8} = 5.25$$

On the slide rule:

1. Slide the hairline indicator to 6.95 on the D scale.
2. Shift 61.2 on the right-hand B scale under the hairline.
3. Slide the hairline to 39.6 on the right-hand B scale.
4. Read 5.58 on the D scale under the hairline.

Then the escape velocity at 2,160 miles above the earth is 5.58 miles per second. For another problem, turn to page 457.

[*from page 448*]

The distance from the level to the rod is 633 feet. Here's the proportion we needed:

$$\frac{d}{100} = \frac{1.9}{0.3} \qquad d = 633 \text{ feet}$$

Here's a problem in proportion that may not be so farfetched in a few years:

On approaching Moon City, you forget to switch on your retro-rockets in time and overshoot the landing pad. By the time you do manage to land, you're in an uninhabited crater far from Mare Imbrium where Moon City is located.

By radio, the Search Director is able to determine that you've landed due north but your distance is uncertain. Distance is critical, for the search parties must carry their own oxygen.

The Search Director asks you to measure the angle of the earth's rays at the meridian in about 2 hours. At the prescribed hour, you radio him that the earth is 42° from the vertical.

The angle at Moon City is 38°. By assuming the rays are parallel, the Director readily finds his distance from you, since he knows that the radius of the moon is 2,160 miles.

Go to page 460 for the correct solution.

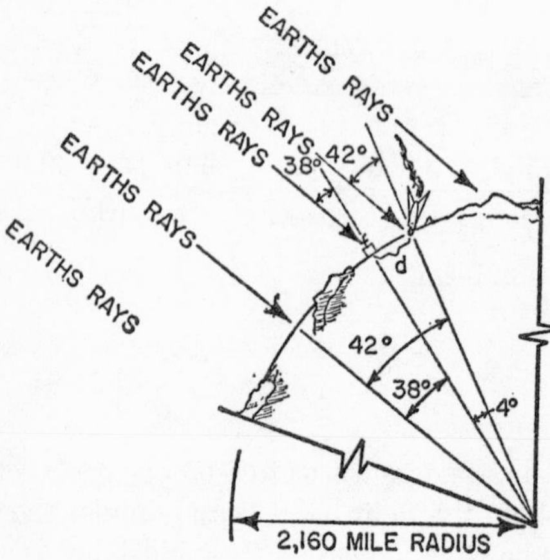

[*from page 464*]

The error might have been as large as 200 miles. Using the data given, the initial proportion becomes:

$$\frac{c}{4{,}950} = \frac{360}{7^\circ\ 12'}, \quad \text{from which} \quad c = 248{,}000$$

This gives rise to a new proportion:

$$\frac{D}{7{,}850} = \frac{248{,}000}{252{,}000}$$

Solving, $D = 7{,}730$, or 7,700 to two figures, a difference of 200 miles—still pretty good!

This has been a purely hypothetical exercise, of course, and in it we assumed that the angle $7^\circ\ 12'$ was accurate. This is reasonable, for it is given to the minute, and is thus probably within $7^\circ\ 11'\ 30''$ and $7^\circ\ 12'\ 30''$.

But how about the distance from Alexandria to Syene? In a number such as 5,000, there is no way of telling how many of the zeros following the 5 are significant. This illustrates the beauty of scientific notation, for this same distance, given as 5.00×10^3, would assure a reader that the actual value is within 4,995 and 5,005 stadia.

In mathemetics, the surfaces of a sphere and a plane are tangent in a point. Unfortunately for ball-bearing engineers, this isn't true in practice; there is a *finite* area in contact. To relate the various perimeters to the contact area, this formula has been devised:

$$d = 1.76\sqrt[3]{\frac{PD}{E}}$$

In this formula, d is the diameter of the contact circle, P is the force in pounds between the ball and its race, D is the diameter of the ball, and E is the *modulus of elasticity*, a measure of the material's resistance to deformation.

If P is 140 lb., will a 0.625-inch diameter ball of steel for which $E = 25{,}000{,}000$ have a larger or smaller contact circle than another ball 0.685 in diameter for which $E = 28{,}000{,}000$?

Turn to page 449 to check your answer.

[*from page 463*]

The bevel corresponding to 23° 30′ is

$$\frac{5\frac{7}{32}}{12}$$

Here's the expression we needed:

$$\tan 23^\circ\, 30' = \frac{x}{12}$$

where x is the value we need to express 23° 30′ in terms of its bevel. Then

$$x = 12 \tan 23^\circ\, 30'$$

The tangent of 23° 30′ is roughly 0.400, so x is about 12(0.4), or 4.8. On the slide rule:

1. Shift the index of the T scale to 12 on the D scale.
2. Slide the hairline indicator to 23° 30′ on the T scale.
3. Read 522 on the D scale.

Then $x = 5.22$, so $\tan 23^\circ\, 30' = \dfrac{5.22}{12}$

But we're not quite through. We have to express 0.22 in terms of some fraction usually indicated on an ordinary ruler. Using thirty-seconds:

$$\frac{y}{32} = 0.22, \quad \text{so} \quad y = 0.22 \times 32 = 7.04,$$

which rounds off to 7.0. So the bevel corresponding to 23° 30′ is

$$\frac{5\frac{7}{32}}{12} \quad \text{or} \quad 5\tfrac{7}{32}\,\overline{\big|\quad 12 \quad}$$

For the next problem, go on to page 455.

[*from page 463*]

Given the job of measuring a property line, your survey crew finds a house in the way. From a point on a hill overlooking the house, you find that you can see points on either side of the house that are known to be on the property line. Setting up a transit on the hill, you measure the distance and elevation of each point, and in addition, the angle between the two transit bearings. Using your measurements, here's what a sketch would look like:

On the face of it, this seems like a fairly straightforward application of the law of cosines. However, note that the distances given are *slant* distances, while the angle 66° 15′ is a *horizontal* angle.

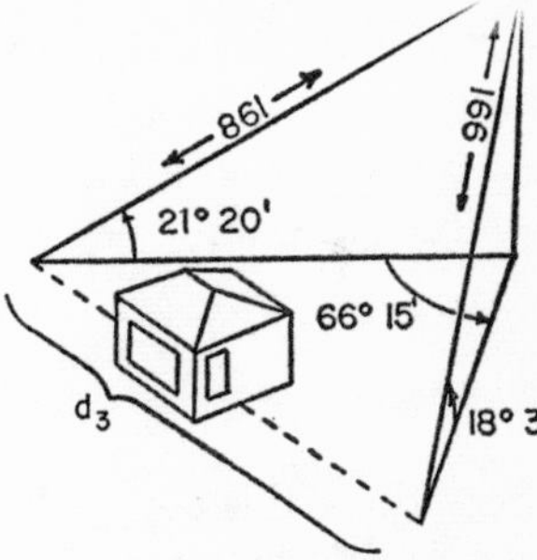

In order to convert slant distances to horizontal, it is necessary to multiply each slant distance by the cosine of the angle of elevation.

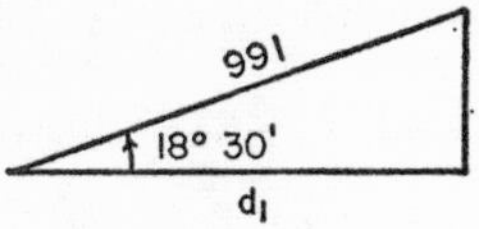

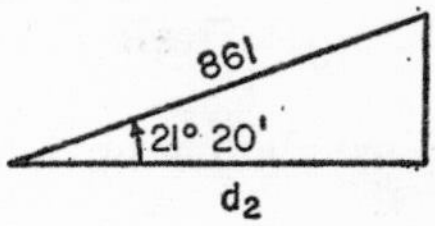

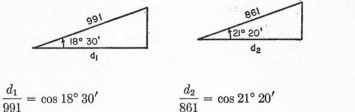

$$\frac{d_1}{991} = \cos 18^\circ\, 30' \qquad \frac{d_2}{861} = \cos 21^\circ\, 20'$$

$$d_1 = 991 \cos 18^\circ\, 30' = 939 \qquad d_2 = 861 \cos 21^\circ\, 20' = 801$$

Here is the triangle, with all the values measured on the horizontal:

If you've forgotten the law of cosines, flip back to page 404 and brush up a bit. (But don't lose your place here.) Then solve this triangle for d_3. Check your answer on page 465.

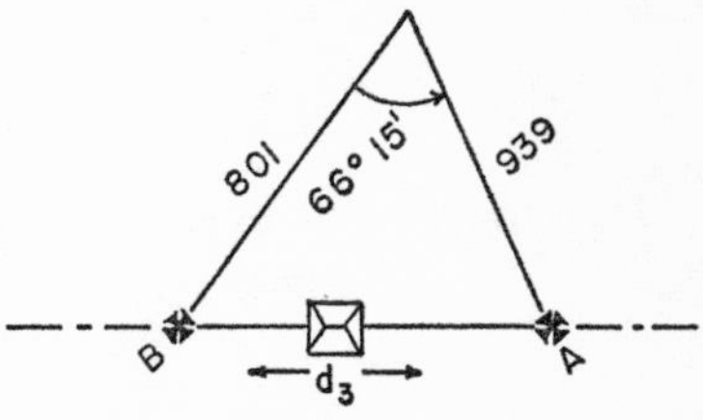

[*from page 449*]

The answer given, $F = 0.51$ inches, is correct.

Here's the formula again, with the given values inserted:

$$F = \frac{8PND^3}{Gd^4} = \frac{8 \times 58 \times 12 \times 0.625^3}{11 \times 10^6 \times 0.125^4} = 0.51 \text{ in.}$$

What approach did you use? There certainly isn't any obvious plan of attack. Using the A and K scales means a "read and reset" type of approach, with all its dangers of observational error. To get around this, you might have rewritten the problem for alternate multiplication and division with the C, D, and CI scales:

$$F = 8 \times \frac{1}{11} \times 58 \times \frac{1}{0.125} \times 0.625 \times \frac{1}{0.125} \times 0.625 \times \frac{1}{0.125} \times 0.625 \times \frac{1}{0.125} = 0.51$$

Sometimes this approach is necessary, as a last resort. In general, however, it's better to try and simplify the problem. Here, note that 0.625 may be written as (5×0.125), $(0.125)^4 = (0.125)(0.125)^3$, and $0.125 = \frac{1}{8}$:

$$F = \frac{8 \times 58 \times 12 \times (5 \times 0.125)^3}{11 \times 10^6 \times 0.125 \times 0.125^3} = \frac{8 \times 58 \times 12 \times 125 \times 0.125^3}{11 \times 10^6 \times \frac{1}{8} \times 0.125^3}$$

Canceling, combining obvious terms, and rewriting, this becomes:

$$F = \frac{8 \times 58 \times 12 \times 125 \times 8}{11 \times 10^6} = \frac{64 \times 58 \times 12 \times 125 \times 10^{-6}}{11} = 0.51$$

It is only on this last expression that the slide rule is used.

Of course not every problem falls apart so readily, but it happens often enough to make looking for short cuts worth while.

Here's a similar problem. Before you use your slide rule, see if you can't simplify it. Remember that the square root of 2 is 1.41.

$$T = \frac{NR^3}{\sqrt{2}\,fL^2} = \frac{564 \times 0.1875^3}{8.00 \times \sqrt{2} \times 0.9375^2} = ?$$

Turn to page 461 to check your answer.

[*from page 451*]

Here's a more down-to-earth problem the steel designer often runs into: how to cut two structural shapes for welding as shown below.

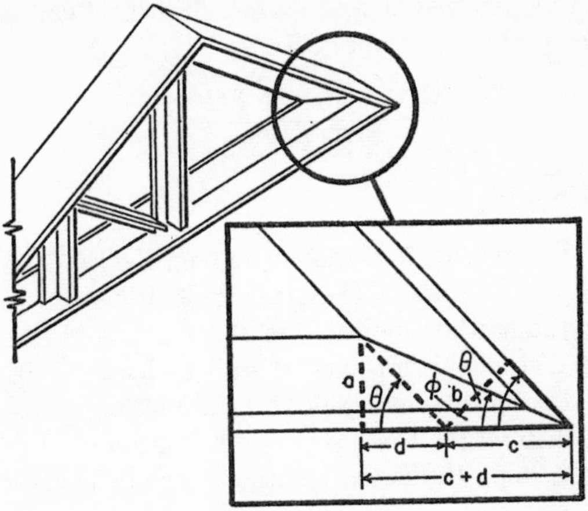

The first thing to notice is that

$$\tan\phi = \frac{a}{c+d}$$

Finding c and d is quite easy if the problem is reduced to solving two right triangles as shown in the right-hand sketch. In the first triangle,

$$\frac{b}{c} = \sin\theta, \quad \text{so that} \quad c = \frac{b}{\sin\theta}$$

In the second triangle: $\dfrac{a}{d} = \tan\theta$, so that

$$d = \frac{a}{\tan\theta} = \frac{a\cos\theta}{\sin\theta}, \quad \text{because} \quad \frac{1}{\tan\theta} = \frac{1}{\dfrac{\sin\theta}{\cos\theta}} = \frac{\cos\theta}{\sin\theta}$$

Combining these values:

$$\tan\phi = \frac{a}{c+d} = \frac{a\sin\theta}{\dfrac{b}{\sin\theta} + \dfrac{a(\cos\theta)}{\sin\theta}} = \frac{a(\sin\theta)}{b + a(\cos\theta)}$$

If $\theta = 42.5°$, $a = 8.03$, $b = 6.53$, find ϕ.
The correct solution is on page 462.

[*from page 450*]

$\dfrac{\sqrt{0.0705} \times \sqrt{19.8} \times 1{,}693}{621 \times \sqrt{234} \times 93.6} = 0.00225$. You should have been able to arrive at this answer without re-indexing. Rearranged for the slide rule, the problem becomes

$$\frac{\sqrt{7.05} \times \sqrt{19.8} \times 1.693}{6.21 \times \sqrt{2.34} \times 9.36} \times 10^{-2}$$

On the slide rule,

1. Slide the hairline indicator to 7.05 on the left-hand A scale.
2. Shift 6.21 on the C scale under the hairline.
3. Slide the hairline indicator to 19.8 on the right-hand B scale.
4. Shift 2.34 on the left-hand B scale under the hairline.
5. Slide the hairline indicator to 1.693 on the C scale.
6. Shift 9.36 on the C scale under the hairline.
7. Read 2.25 on the D scale at the index of the C scale.

If you made an approximation, as you should have, you didn't have any trouble placing the decimal correctly: the answer is 0.00225.

Please go on to page 459.

[*from page 458*]

If a cannon shell were fired straight up at the impractically high velocity of 6.95 miles per second, it would never return to earth but would continue out into space. This is because 6.95 miles per second is the *escape velocity* of an object from the earth, the velocity at which an object can overcome the effects of gravity.

As you may have learned, this force of gravity is lower at great heights. Consequently, a rocket which achieves its maximum velocity at an altitude of several hundred or thousand miles need not achieve a speed of 6.95 miles per second in order to escape the earth's pull.

Here is an equation which relates the escape velocity (v_1) at any distance (r_1) from the center of the earth to the escape velocity at the earth's surface:

$$\frac{v_1^2}{v_2^2} = \frac{r_1}{r_2}$$

In this equation, v_2 is 6.95 miles per second, and r_2, the radius of the earth, is 3,960 miles.

If the space rocket is to achieve its maximum velocity at an altitude of 2,160 miles, what must the velocity be to insure that it won't fall back to earth?

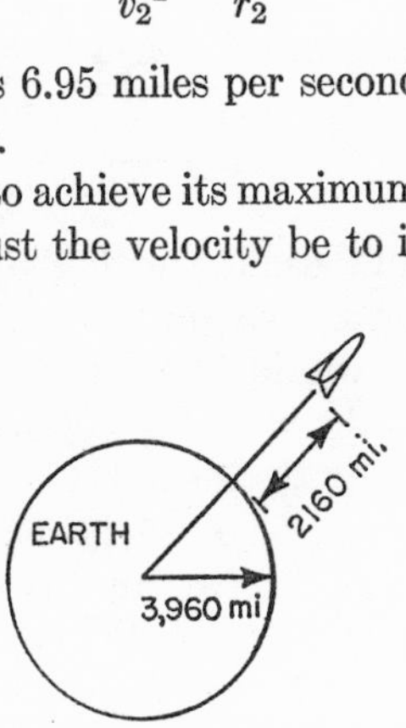

Turn to page 451 to check your solution.

[*from page 452*]

The distance from the point of landing to Moon City is 151 miles. Here's the way we get it:

$$\frac{d}{2{,}160} = \sin 4°, \quad \text{so} \quad d = 2{,}160 \times \sin 4° = 151 \text{ miles}$$

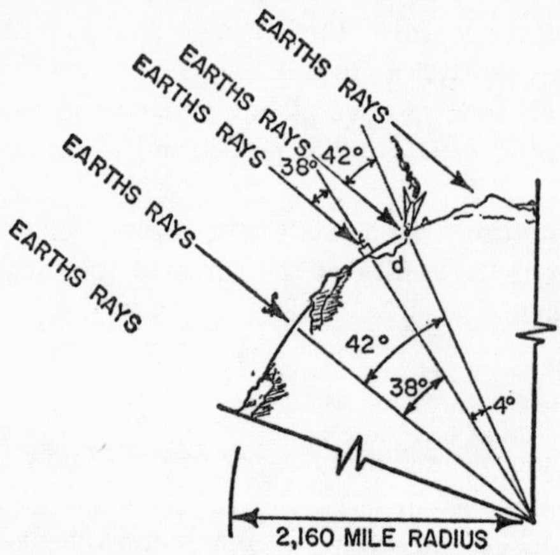

In nearly every volume dealing with the history of science, the story is told of Eratosthenes, who in 200 B.C. measured the diameter of the earth accurately to within 50 miles! To arrive at this measurement, Eratosthenes used the following approach:

He found that at noon on the longest day of the year, the sun was directly overhead at Syene, 5,000 *stadia* north of Alexandria. At the same instant in Alexandria, the sun was 7° 12′ from the vertical. He used this information to calculate the circumference of the earth, from which, in turn, he calculated the diameter.

What is the circumference of the earth, as calculated from the data above?

Go to page 464 for the correct answer.

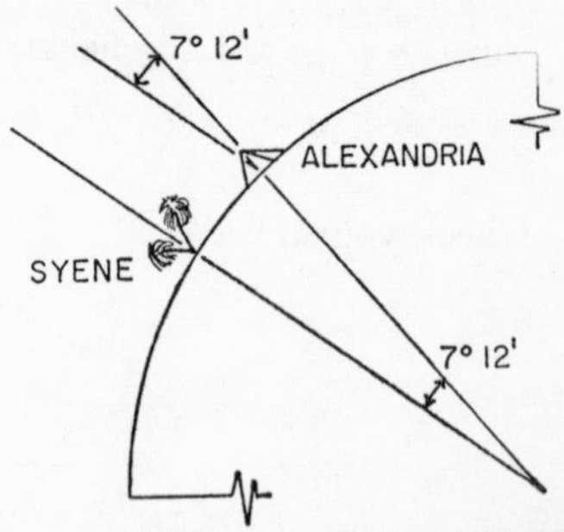

[*from page 456*]

$T = 0.376.$

Did you find the answer without using the slide rule at all?

Here are the short cuts you should have found:

$$564 = 400 \times 1.41 = 400\sqrt{2}$$

$$0.9375^2 = (5 \times 0.1875)^2 = 25 \times 0.1875^2$$

$$0.1875^3 = 0.1875 \times 0.1875^2$$

Using these short cuts, the problem becomes:

$$T = \frac{564 \times (0.1875)^3}{8.00 \times \sqrt{2} \times (0.9375)^2} = \frac{400\sqrt{2} \times (0.1875)(0.1875)^2}{8.00\sqrt{2} \times 25 \times (0.1875)^2}$$

Canceling common terms, this finally reduces to:

$T = 2 \times 0.1875$, or 0.375 to three figures.

Perhaps you've noticed that slide rule accuracy has been more than adequate in this chapter. The reason for this is that in a great many instances, the formulas encountered in practice are empirical, that is, they are derived from experiment and observation rather than purely mathematical considerations. As such, any of the values found in such formulas are *average* values, and even three figures of accuracy are unjustified.

An example of such a formula is:

$$H = H_0 \sqrt[5]{\left(\frac{P}{P_0}\right)^7}$$

This formula attempts to express the horsepower (H) of an aircraft engine as a function of the air pressure (P) at various altitudes.

A certain engine is nominally rated at about 2,260 hp. (H_0) at sea level where the standard pressure is 760 mm. (P_0). What is the horsepower at 7 miles above sea level, where air pressure (P) is 190 mm.?

Check your answer on page 450.

[*from page 457*]

If $\theta = 42.5°$, $a = 8.03$, and $b = 6.53$, then $\phi = 23° 30'$. Here's the way it goes:

From the formula $\tan \phi = \dfrac{a \sin \theta}{b + a \cos \theta}$ we see that

$$\tan \phi = \frac{8.03 \sin 42.5°}{6.53 + 8.03 \cos 42.5°} = \frac{8.03 \sin 42.5°}{6.53 + 8.03 \sin 47.5°}$$

[The cosine of an angle is equal to the sine of the complementary angle. Therefore, $\cos 42.5° = \sin (90° - 42.5°) = \sin 47.5°$.] By the usual approximation methods, $\tan \phi$ will be about 0.400, so ϕ will be roughly 23°. Unfortunately, there isn't any short cut on the slide rule:

1. Shift the right-hand index of the S scale to 8.03 on the A scale.
2. Slide the hairline to 47° 30′ on the S scale.
3. Read 5.92 on the A scale. Then $8.03 \sin 47.5° = 5.92$, and

$$\tan \phi = \frac{8.03 \sin 42.5°}{6.53 + 5.92} = \frac{8.03 \sin 42.5°}{12.45}$$

4. With the S-scale index still at 8.03 on the A scale, slide the hairline indicator to 42° 30′ on the S scale.
5. Reverse the sliding scale, and shift 12.45 on the B scale under the hairline.
6. Read 434 on the A scale at the index of the S scale. Then $\tan \phi = 0.434$.
7. Slide 434 on the C scale over the right index of the D scale.
8. Reverse the sliding scale and read 23° 30′ under the index hairline on the back.

You may have done the last part of the problem (steps 7 and 8 above) like this:

7. Reverse the sliding scale and align the D and T scales.
8. Slide the hairline indicator to 434 on the D scale.
9. Read 23° 30′ on the T scale under the hairline.

Please go on to page 463.

[*from page 462*]

In practice, angles are often specified in *bevels* rather than degrees. The bevel of an angle is its tangent expressed as a fraction of 12.

For example, tan 42° 30′ = 0.667. As a bevel:

$$0.667 = \frac{8}{12}$$

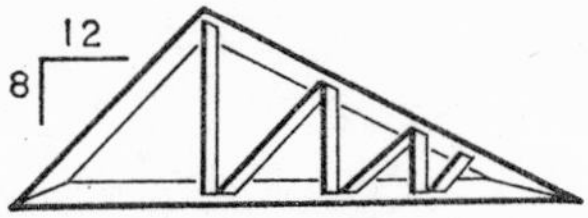

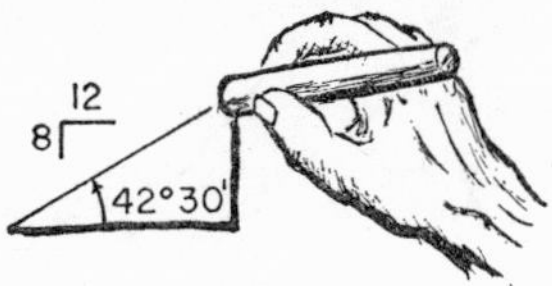

This notation makes such an angle easy to lay out. The fabricator just draws a line 12 inches *over*, and 8 *up*.

Usually bevels don't come out to even numbers. When they do not, the remainder is expressed as though it were a fraction of an inch. The fractions used are halves, fourths, sixteenths, and so on—the fractions into which an inch is ordinarily divided on a ruler.

The tangent of 30° is 0.578. As a bevel:

$$0.578 = \frac{6.94}{12} = \frac{6\frac{15}{16}}{12}$$

What is the bevel corresponding to 23° 30′?

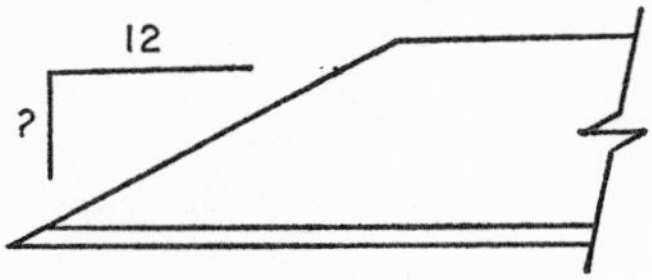

Turn to page 454 to check your answer.

[*from page 460*]

The circumference is given by the proportion

$$\frac{c}{5{,}000} = \frac{360^\circ}{7^\circ\ 12'}$$

from which we see that

$$c = 250{,}000 \text{ stadia}$$

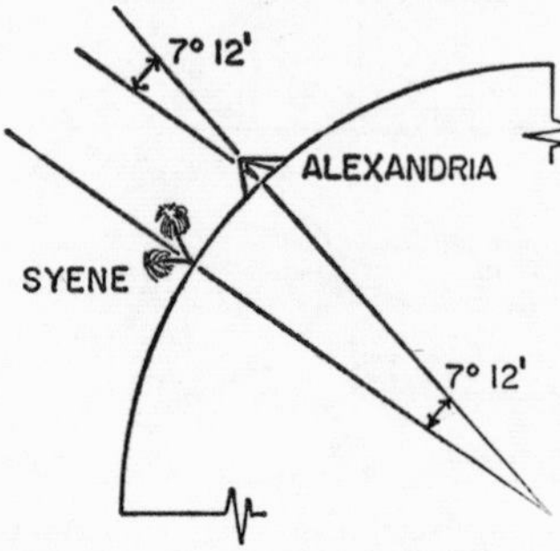

Before marveling at his accuracy, let's take a closer look at some of Eratosthenes' figures.

It turns out that in order to have a figure divisible by 60, he upped the circumference to 252,000, and it is *this* figure which when converted to miles becomes 7,850, just 50 miles short of the actual value of 7,900 miles.

Suppose he hadn't corrected the circumference—further, suppose the distance from Syene to Alexandria was known only to two figures, as is not at all unlikely.

Taking this into consideration, what might his error have been?

Go to page 453 for the answer.

[from page 455]

Side d_3 = 959 feet. We used the law of cosines, which says that in any triangle, the square of any side is equal to the sum of the squares of the other two sides minus twice the product of those sides and the cosine of their included angle. In this case, then,

$$d_3{}^2 = 801^2 + 939^2 - 2(801)(939)(\cos 66° \, 15')$$

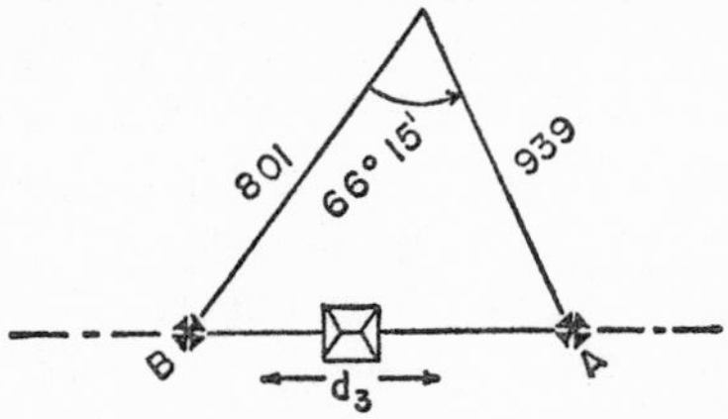

This calculation didn't give you any trouble if you remembered that the cosine of an angle is equal to the sine of the complementary angle, so that

$$\cos 66° \, 15' = \sin (90° - 66° \, 15') = \sin 23° \, 45'$$

On the slide rule:

1. Slide the hairline indicator to 801 on the D scale.
2. Read 642 on the A scale. Then 801^2 = 642,000.
3. Slide the hairline indicator to 939 on the D scale.
4. Read 882 on the A scale. Then 939^2 = 882,000.
5. By inspection, $2 \times 801 = 1{,}602$. Therefore, index the S scale at 1,602 on the left-hand A scale.
6. Slide the hairline indicator to 23° 45′ on the S scale.
7. Reverse the sliding scale and shift the right-hand index of the B scale under the hairline.
8. Slide the hairline to 939 on the B scale.
9. Read 604 on the A scale under the hairline. Then $2(801)(939)(\cos 66° \, 15') = 604{,}000$.

So, $d_3{}^2 = 642{,}000 + 882{,}000 - 604{,}000 = 920{,}000$, and

$$d_3 = \sqrt{920{,}000} = \sqrt{92} \times 10^2$$

Please go on to page 466.

[*from page 465*]

On the rule:

1. Slide the hairline to 92 on the right-hand A scale.
2. Read 959 on the D scale under the hairline.

Then $d_3 = 9.59 \times 10^2$ ft. $=$ 959 ft.

With this TutorText*, you have acquired considerable proficiency in the manipulation of the slide rule, and, in addition, you've made the acquaintance of logarithms, scientific notation, and basic trigonometry. The unique TutorText* method has helped you develop these notions as logical outgrowths of knowledge you already possessed; you've made them your own.

Use your new knowledge at every opportunity. You'll find it an asset in almost any field of business or scientific endeavor, and a source of personal satisfaction as well.

*TM

Index

TUTORTEXTS

ADVENTURES IN ALGEBRA
by Norman A. Crowder and Grace C. Martin

THE ARITHMETIC OF COMPUTERS
by Norman A. Crowder

THE ELEMENTS OF BRIDGE
by Charles H. Goren

INTRODUCTION TO ELECTRONICS
by Robert J. Hughes and Peter Pipe

PRACTICAL LAW: A COURSE IN EVERYDAY CONTRACTS
by Warren Lehman

THE SLIDE RULE
by Robert Saffold and Ann Smalley

TRIGONOMETRY: A PRACTICAL COURSE
by Norman A. Crowder and Grace C. Martin

D1